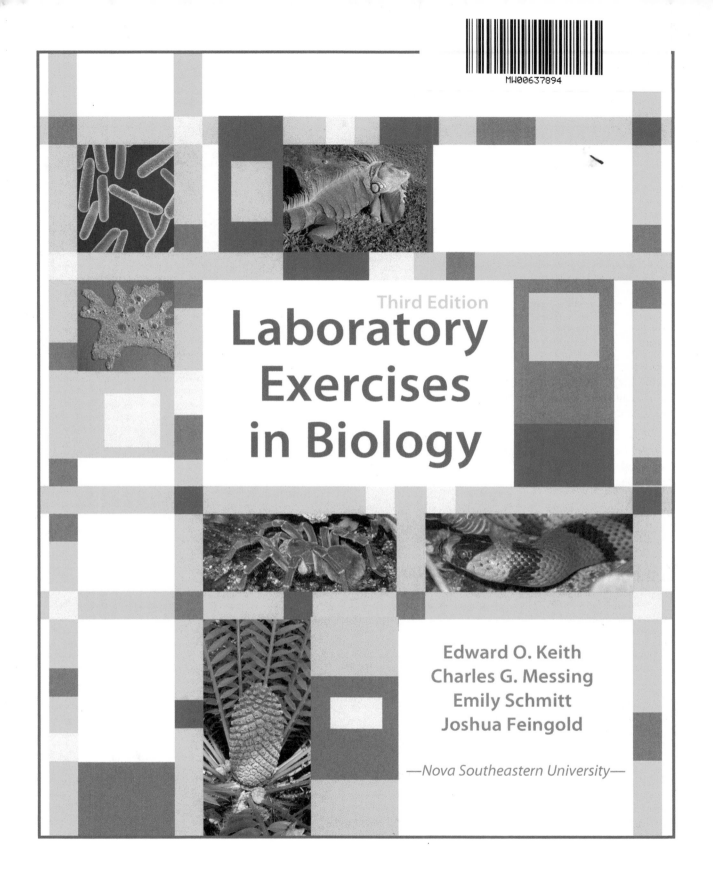

Third Edition

Laboratory Exercises in Biology

Edward O. Keith
Charles G. Messing
Emily Schmitt
Joshua Feingold

—*Nova Southeastern University*—

Kendall Hunt
publishing company

Front cover:
Iguana image courtesy of Joshua Feingold
Snake image courtesy of Charles G. Messing
Tarantula image courtesy of Charles G. Messing

Rear Cover:
Butterfly image courtesy of Charles G. Messing
Cactus tree image courtesy of Joshua Feingold
Okapi image courtesy of Charles G. Messing

All other cover images © Shutterstock, Inc.

Kendall Hunt
publishing company

www.kendallhunt.com
Send all inquiries to:
4050 Westmark Drive
Dubuque, IA 52004-1840

Copyright © 2010, 2011, 2012 by Edward Keith, Charles G. Messing, Emily Schmitt and Joshua Feingold

ISBN 978-1-4652-0667-1

Printed in the United States of America
10 9 8 7 6 5 4 3 2

CONTENTS

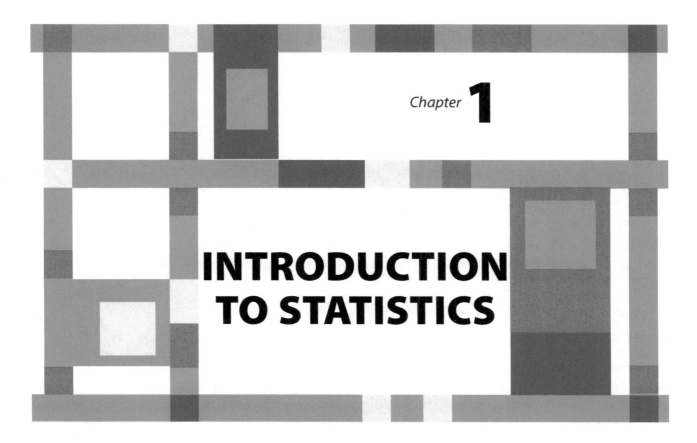

Chapter **1**

INTRODUCTION TO STATISTICS

Introduction

Statistics is a mathematical science concerned with collecting, analyzing, explaining, and presenting data of all sorts. It is a tool for planning how data will be collected and for organizing and summarizing it. Statistics allows us to make inferences about the data and communicate our research findings clearly and meaningfully to others. The simplest types of statistics are **descriptive statistics** that involve organizing, summarizing, and presenting the data. **Inferential statistics** involves estimating parameters from sample variables and comparing different samples.

The population is the set of all measurements of interest and parameters such as the mean (average), standard deviation, etc., describe it. However, because it is rarely feasible to measure every component or individual in the population and actually determine the characters or parameters of the entire population, we usually take measurements from an accessible sample, or subset, of the population. To describe the sample, we use variables such as averages and standard deviation. We then use these variables to estimate, or infer, the characteristics of the entire population.

You can make different types of measurements that result in different types of data. There are four measurement scales:

1. **Nominal scale:** a name is assigned to each observation,

    e.g., blood type, race.

2. **Ordinal scale:** each observation is ranked in graded order,

    e.g., +, ++, +++, ++++ proteinuria.

3. **Interval scale:** each observation is scaled by numbers which are the same distance apart, but which have no true zero (absence) point,

    e.g., temperature in degrees Centigrade (°C) or Fahrenheit (°F).

1

4. **Ratio scale:** each observation is scaled by numbers the same distance apart and which have a true zero point,

   e.g., blood glucose concentration

There are also two types of data: discrete and continuous. With **discrete data,** each observation is assigned an integer value based on a numerical count, e.g., the number of children in a classroom. With **continuous data,** each observation can be assigned a value which can theoretically be subdivided into smaller units, e.g., height, weight.

The relationship between two sets of measurements is determined by which one is the dependent variable and which one is the independent variable. **Independent variables** are those that are assumed to affect the other, dependent variable. **Dependent variables** are those that the investigator can manipulate or which arise from the environment. In most equations, x is the independent variable and y is the dependent variable.

Dependent variables are usually the variables of highest interest, or the point of the study. We usually test hypotheses or make estimates about the dependent variable. The number of variables determines the category of statistical methods to be used. For situations with one dependent variable without any independent variables, we use **bivariate analysis**. In cases with one dependent variable and many independent variables, we use **multivariate analyses**.

The raw data must be organized and summarized so that the important features may be grasped at a glance. There are a variety of pictorial summaries, or graphs, which can be used. In a **frequency distribution**, the data are grouped into equal intervals, and the frequency of each group is plotted in a **histogram**. Alternatively, the data can then be tabulated, creating a frequency table. **Symmetrical distributions** occur when the frequencies are equal, or near equal, on either side of a center point. **Skewed distributions** are not symmetrical. It is also possible to plot the **relative frequencies**, or the proportion of each frequency, versus the total number of observations. Relative frequencies are better used to compare two sets of data, especially when the total numbers of observations are different. **Cumulative frequencies** are also used. In this case, the sum of all previous frequencies is plotted in each interval.

Other popular ways to present data are circle charts and bar charts. **Circle charts** (pie charts) depict relative frequencies as a portion of a circle representing the total number of observations. **Bar charts** are similar to histograms except that the horizontal scale (x-axis) consists of distinct categories (nominal or ordinal data) rather than continuous numerical intervals.

Often, we need a numerical summary of the data. As already mentioned, we can use frequency tables to summarize frequency distributions. However, most numerical summaries include **measures of central tendency**, such as the mean, median, and mode, and **measures of dispersion** such as the range, variance, and standard deviation. These types of numerical summaries comprise what is usually thought of as "statistics."

The mean is the most commonly used measure of central tendency. The **mean** is the arithmetic average of a set of data values. It is equal to the sum of the values divided by the number of values:

$$\frac{\sum_{i=1}^{N} x_i}{N}$$

One of the pitfalls of the mean is that data that fall extremely far from the mean (outliers), such as a professional basketball player relative to a roomful of high school students, can cause the mean to give a misleading indication of the center of the distribution. If this occurs, we use the median as the measure of central tendency. The **median** is the "middle" value when the data are arranged in numerical order. For an odd number of values, it is the middlemost value. For an even number of values, it is the average of the two middlemost values. The value of using the median is that it is unaffected by the extreme data values and is preferred over the mean when the possibility of extreme values is high. The median divides the data into two halves, with 50% of the values lying below and 50% above. Thus, the median marks the 50th percentile. We can likewise divide the data into quartiles (e.g., 25%, 50%, and 75%), or even **percentiles** (e.g., 10%, 20%, 30%, ... 100%).

When both the mean and the median do not provide the best measure of central tendency, we can use the **mode**, which is the most commonly occurring value in the data set. The mode works well for nominal scale data. For example, the manager of a pizza parlor wants to know which pizza is most popular with her customers. She counts the number of each type of pizza sold for one week. The mode is the type of pizza with the highest number of sales, and this pizza is the most popular.

Once the measures of central tendence have been determined, it is often useful to calculate some **measures of dispersion** that reflect how the data vary. For example, if the mean weight of professional wrestlers in a league is 114 kg, are the maximum and minimum weights 112 and 118 kg, or 85 and 200 kg? The **range** is the difference between the largest and smallest values in the sample and is the simplest measure of dispersion. The variance is the average of the magnitude of all deviations from the mean in the sample. The deviation is the distance between any measurement in the sample and the sample mean. The larger the **deviation**, the more dispersed the data are. The **variance (s^2)** is the sum of the squared deviations divided by the number of samples. The **standard deviation (s)** is the square root of the variance.

$$s^2 = \frac{1}{n} \sum_{i=1}^{n} \left(\overline{x} - x_i \right)^2$$

$$s = \sqrt{s^2}$$

Other measures of dispersion include the standard error of the mean and the coefficient of variation. The **standard error of the mean** represents the standard deviation of the average of multiple means, and it is calculated by dividing the standard deviation by the square root of the number of observations. The **coefficient of variation** is equal to the standard deviation divided by the mean, multiplied by 100%.

$$\text{SEM} = s/\sqrt{n}$$

The following symbols are used to distinguish population parameters from sample variables:

Statistic	Sample variable	Population variable
Mean	$\overline{x}$	μ
Standard deviation	s	σ
Variance	s^2	σ^2

Measures of dispersion attempt to quantify the distribution of the data around the measures of central tendency. There are two major types of distributions. **Empirical distributions** are derived from the data, and apply only to the sample itself. **Frequency distributions** and relative frequency distributions are examples of empirical distributions. **Theoretical distributions**, on the other hand, describe the entire population. Thus, they are rarely obtainable in practice and so must be approximated by empirical distributions. The most commonly used theoretical distribution is the normal distribution, which is a continuous theoretical frequency distribution which represents the theoretical (and empirical) distribution of most naturally occurring phenomena, i.e., height, weight, blood pressure, cholesterol, etc.

The **normal distribution** has the following characteristics. It is "bell-shaped" and symmetrical about its mean (μ). The mean, median, and mode are all equal to each other. Its center is the mean, μ, and its dispersion is determined by its standard deviation, σ. For small values of σ, the curve is tall and thin. For large values of σ, the curve is short and fat. In addition, 68.27% of the values lie within ± 1 S.D. of the mean, 95.45% of the values lie within ± 2 S.D. of the mean, and 99.73% of the values lie within ± 3 S.D. of the mean.

Another way to state this is to say that from the normal distribution, 50% of the values lie within ± 0.647 S.D. of the mean, 95% of the values lie within ± 1.96 S.D. of the mean, and 99% of the values lie within ± 2.57

S.D. of the mean. These properties of the normal distribution provide the foundation for performing most statistical tests, i.e., *t*-tests and other "tests of hypothesis."

Once the sample has been characterized, the next step is to use the sample's variables to estimate the population parameters. This is the realm of statistical inference. There are two major types of statistical inference, **estimation** and **hypothesis** testing. The most common form of estimation is the confidence interval. For multiple sample estimates of a population parameter, the confidence interval is the frequency with which the parameter will actually lie within the interval; i.e., for a 95% confidence interval around the sample mean, the population mean will lie within this interval 95% of the time. Another way to say this is that for a given confidence interval around a sample variable, we are confident that the population parameter lies within that interval by the same percentage, or for a 95% confidence interval around a sample mean, we are 95% confident that the population mean lies within this interval.

How the **confidence interval** is calculated depends on what is known about the population. When certain population parameters are known, the calculation of confidence intervals uses the confidence coefficient, Z, from the standard normal distribution. The confidence interval around the true population mean (μ) when population standard deviation (σ) is known is:

$$\mu \pm z\left(\sigma / \sqrt{N}\right)$$

Usually, however, we don't know any of the population parameters and we must construct confidence intervals using sample statistics. In this case, we use the confidence coefficient, t, derived from the *t*-distribution, whose value varies with the sample size:

$$\overline{x} \pm t\left(s / \sqrt{N}\right)$$

Sometimes we want to draw a confidence interval on the *difference* between two population means. Again, the formula we use depends in whether or not we know anything about the population parameters. A confidence interval on the true difference in means when the population standard deviations are known is:

$$\left(\mu_1 - \mu_2\right) \pm z\sqrt{\frac{\sigma_1^2}{N_1} + \frac{\sigma_2^2}{N_2}}$$

A confidence interval on the true difference in means when only the sample standard deviations are known is:

$$\left(\overline{x}_1 - \overline{x}_2\right) \pm t\left(Sp\sqrt{\frac{1}{N_1} + \frac{1}{N_2}}\right)$$

This estimate must include some information about the sample standard deviations, Sp:

$$Sp = \sqrt{\frac{\left(N_1 - 1\right)S_1^2 + \left(N_2 - 1\right)S_2^2}{N_1 + N_2 - 2}}$$

A confidence interval on the true mean difference (D) in a paired or matched study is:

$$\overline{d} \pm t\left(S_d / \sqrt{N}\right)$$

where d and S_d are the average and standard deviation of the sample differences, respectively.

One of the most powerful statistical tools is **hypothesis testing**. Here, population parameters, or most commonly sample variables, are used to make predictions or divine relationships. There are four steps in hypothesis testing: (1) we hypothesize that a population parameter of interest has a certain value, (2) we take a sample from the population and calculate the corresponding sample statistic (variable), (3) we make a decision about the parameter based on the discrepancy between the hypothesized value of the parameter and the computed value of the sample statistic, and (4) we either "reject" or "accept" the hypothesized value using the following criteria. If the discrepancy is "large," we conclude that our initial estimate (hypothesis) was wrong. If the discrepancy is "small," we conclude that our initial estimate (hypothesis) was accurate. However, since we are never absolutely sure of the value of the population parameter, we can only have some specified level of confidence in our estimate.

In statistics, there are two types of hypotheses. The **null hypothesis** (H_0) which is generally based on there being no difference, i.e., that a given treatment has no effect, that the two sample means are not different, etc. The null hypothesis can be seen as the "Devil's advocate" approach. The **alternate hypothesis** (H_a) is generally the research hypothesis, i.e., what the investigator thinks is happening. Generally, one phrases the null hypothesis so that if the predicted (desired) outcome eventuates, one can then "reject the null hypothesis" and "accept the alternate hypothesis."

If the null hypothesis is such that the means are not different, one uses a "two-tailed" statistical test. If the null hypothesis is such that one mean is greater (or lesser) than another, i.e., there may be some direction to the relationship, one uses a "one-tailed" statistical test. It is important to note that one generally states these hypotheses before one designs the study or collects the data. It is considered "bad form" to do the reverse.

To determine whether to accept or reject the null hypothesis, one must calculate a **test statistic**, which is a measure of the magnitude of the disparity between the hypothesized value of a population parameter and the corresponding sample variable, i.e., how "large" or "small" the difference is. The discrepancy between the two has at least two explanations: one is that the values are different because of random sampling error; the alternative is that there is a meaningful "real" difference between the two values. The larger the value of the test statistic, the more likely it is that the second explanation is correct, and that one can correctly reject the null hypothesis.

The cutoff value of the test statistic depends on the level of significance, which is the probability of rejecting the null hypothesis when it is in fact true. The choice of **level of significance** is arbitrary, but the most common choices are 0.05 and 0.01. This means that there is a 5% or a 1% likelihood of incorrectly rejecting the null hypothesis. This also means that 95% (or 99%) of the time, the differences we are observing are real. Sometimes we specify a level of significance that we are going to use for our experiment. This is the **alpha level**, and it refers to a predefined level of significance. A **p value** is the probability of obtaining the particular value of the test statistic given that H_0 is true.

The **student's t-test** represents the simplest form of test statistic. This test is based on the student's t distribution, which was developed by William Gossett in 1908. The minimal value of t required to determine a specified degree of confidence is found in a **t-table**. We can use t-tests to answer three general questions:

(1) Is the sample mean equal to a known population mean?

$$H_0 : x = \mu$$
$$H_a : x \neq \mu$$

OR

$$H_a : x > \mu$$

or

$$H_a : x < \mu$$

test statistic:

$$T : = \frac{\overline{X}}{s / \sqrt{N}}$$

for $x = \mu$, check t-table for $\alpha/2$ with 1 degree of freedom

for $x > \mu$, check the t-table for α with 1 degree of freedom

If $T > t$, then we can reject H_0. (in other words, the sample mean is not equal to the population mean).

(2) Are the means of two independent random samples equal?

$$H_0 : x_1 = x_2$$

$$H_a : x_1 \neq x_2$$

OR

$$H_a : x > \mu$$

test statistic:

$$T = \frac{(x_1 - x_2)}{Sp\sqrt{\dfrac{1}{N_1} + \dfrac{1}{N_2}}}$$

$$Sp = \sqrt{\frac{S_1^2(n_1 - 1) + S_2^2(n_2 - 1)}{n_1 + n_2 - 2}}$$

For $x_1 = x_2$, check t-table for $\alpha/2$ with $(n_1 + n_2) - 2$ degrees of freedom.

For $x_1 >$ or $x_2 <$, check the t-table for α with $(n_1 + n_2)$ degrees of freedom.

If $T > t$, then we can reject the null hypothesis, i.e., the sample means are different or one sample mean is greater (or lesser) than the other.

(3) Are the means of two paired samples equal?

$$H_0 : \bar{D} = 0$$

$$H_a : \bar{D} \neq 0$$

$$H_a : \bar{D} > 0$$

$$H_a : \bar{D} < 0$$

test statistic:

$$T = \bar{D} / S_d \sqrt{N}$$

where $\quad \bar{D} = \dfrac{\sum\left(x_i^1 - x_i^2\right)}{N}$

S_d = the standard deviation of the differences

$$S_d = \frac{\sqrt{\dfrac{\sum d^2 - \left(\sum d\right)^2 / N}{n - 1}}}{n}$$

Check t-table (as above).

If $T > t$, then reject H_0.

There are several critical assumptions of t-tests, that, if violated, render the t-test invalid. In order to do t-tests, one must be able to assume that the sample data are normally distributed (see above) and that the variances in both populations are equal (this applies to the unpaired t-test only). There is a commonly encountered fallacious use of paired t-test. The unpaired t-test calculations generally result in lower values of T than do the paired t-test calculations, i.e., it is harder to demonstrate significance for the unpaired test. Thus, researchers often try to link or pair the observations to ensure the calculation of a significant difference. Often this is done with little or no supporting evidence or substantiation of the fact that the observations are in fact paired in any real way.

One can test for the differences between means of more than two samples using **analysis of variance** (ANOVA). To do this, the total variability in the measurement set is subdivided into the variance within each group and the variance between each group. If the treatment groups are all alike, the ratio of between group variance to within group variance will be close to unity (1.0). If there are real differences between the groups, the ratio will be greater than one, and if it is significantly "large," we can reject the null hypothesis that the means are all equal:

$$H_0: x_1 = x_2 = x_3 = x_n \qquad \text{for } n \text{ number of groups}$$

To reject H_0, the ratio must be greater than the value of F, which is obtained from an F-table, which is similar to a t-table, but with more degrees of freedom, i.e., the number of samples and the number of observations in each sample. There is one caution in the use of ANOVA, and that it that if we reject H_0, we only know that one pair of means is not equal but we do not know for sure which pair is different. Other tests are used to determine which pair of means is different.

The direction and magnitude of the relationship between two variables can be determined with the use of a **correlation statistic**. The use of **regression** enables us to predict the value of one variable (dependent) from the value of another variable (independent). To begin, one usually plots the data in a **scatter diagram**, i.e., one variable versus the other. We usually plot the independent variable on the x-axis and the dependent variable on the y-axis. A positive linear relationship occurs when the values of both variables increase concurrently. A negative linear relationship occurs when the values of both variables decrease concurrently. If the values of the variables seem to make a curve, the relationship is curvilinear.

We can express the magnitude of the relationship between the variables with the **correlation coefficient**, r, which is known as Pearson's product moment correlation coefficient. The correlation coefficient varies in value from -1 to $+1$ and is calculated:

$$r = \frac{S_{xy}}{\sqrt{S_{xx}S_{yy}}}$$

$$S_{xx} = \sum x^2 - \frac{\left(\sum x\right)^2}{n}; \quad S_{yy} = \sum y^2 - \frac{\left(\sum x\right)^2}{n}; \quad S_{xy} = \sum xy - \frac{\sum x \sum y}{n}$$

One can determine if the relationship is significant by calculating a T value for the correlation coefficient, and comparing it to the value obtained from a t-table:

$$T = r\sqrt{\frac{n-2}{1-r^2}}$$

By squaring the correlation coefficient (r^2), one determines how much of the variation of one variable is explained by variation of the other.

There are two important limitations of the correlation coefficient. First of all, it is not a ratio scale, i.e., a correlation coefficient of 0.5 does not imply that the relationship is halfway between no relationship and a perfectly positive relationship. The second is easier to say, but much more easily overlooked. This is, that correlation does not equal causation. A significant correlation can be made between a large number of interesting variables, but this does not mean that there is any causal link between them. An astute student of science can find many examples of the violation of this caveat.

We can "fit" the data to a straight line by regression analysis. The equation for a straight line is $y = ax + b$. We can calculate a and b:

$$a = \frac{S_{xy}}{S_{xx}} \qquad b = \bar{y} - a\bar{x}$$

We can also determine the significance of the regression:

$$H_0 : a = 0$$

$$T = \frac{\text{Slope}}{\text{Std error of slope}}$$

$$T = \frac{a}{S_{yx} \sqrt{Sxx}}$$

$$Syx = \frac{S_{yy} - aS_{xy}}{n - 2}$$

To determine the significance, compare T to the t-table.

In contrast to the statistical tests discussed so far, which require many assumptions about the nature of the population from which the sample(s) was drawn (i.e., normally distributed, etc.), **nonparametric statistics** require few or no assumptions. Thus, nonparametric statistics are more generalized that parametric statistics. In addition, nonparametric statistics require only nominal or ordinal scale measurements and are especially useful when the data consist of ranked or enumerated observations. In general, nonparametric statistics are easier to calculate for small sample sizes and thus yield rapid results.

There are also certain disadvantages in the use of nonparametric statistics. For large data sets, it can be difficult to rank the data, and thus hard to calculate these statistics. In addition, there is no good way to calculate confidence intervals. Nonparametric statistics are not easy to use when the experiment has a complicated design, i.e., more than three treatment groups or multiple crossover experiments. However, even if all necessary assumptions for "normal" parametric statistics hold, it is often useful to calculate the nonparametric statistics as well, because they can confirm or expand the conclusions generated.

One simple nonparametric test is the **chi square test**. This test is used when the observations consist of a number of individuals, which fall into two or more discreet categories, *and* when one can predict what the distribution "should" be based on the rules of probability, or some other reason. In essence, the chi square test statistic is a measure of the difference between the observed distribution and the predicted distribution.

Generally, the data are displayed in a **contingency table**, which gives the observed frequency of each observation for each category. The categories should be mutually exclusive. The null hypothesis (H_0) is that there is no difference in frequency between what is observed and what is expected. The test statistic is calculated:

$$\chi^2 = \sum \left(\frac{(O - E)^2}{E} \right)$$

OR when df = 1

$$\chi^2 = \sum \left(\frac{(|O - E| - 0.5)^2}{E} \right)$$

The critical value of χ^2 is found in a χ^2 table, with $(r - 1)(c - 1)$ degrees of freedom (r = # rows in the contingency table, c = # columns in the contingency table). If the calculated χ^2 is greater than the critical value, one can reject the hypothesis.

There is an interesting relationship between the χ^2 distribution and the Student's t distribution. The critical value of χ^2 for 1 d.f. at the 95% confidence level is 3.84. This is equal to 1.96 (critical t for infinite d.f. at 95% confidence level) squared. The critical value of χ^2 for 1 d.f. at the 99% confidence level is 6.64, which is 2.57 (critical t for infinite d.f. at 99% confidence) squared.

Other types of nonparametric tests include the **Sign test** and the **Wilcoxon signed rank test**. These are analogs of the paired t-test and are used when the two samples consist of matched pairs of observations. The **Median test** and **Wilcoxon ranked sum test** are analogs of the unpaired t-test, and are used when the two samples are independent random samples from the same population. The **Cochran Q-test, Kruskal-Wallis one-way analysis of variance**, and **Friedman two-way analysis of variance** are analogs of ANOVA, used to compare more than two groups. All of these tests yield precise values of p, which are usually reported as determined in published papers. This is why you sometimes see things like $p = 0.24$ or $p = 0.62$. In addition, there are **nonparametric correlation coefficients,** including the **correlation ratio** that is used when there is a curvilinear relationship between two variables; and **Spearman's rank order correlation coefficient** and **Kendall's Tau** for rank data. For multiple ranked variables, one can use the **coefficient of concordance**.

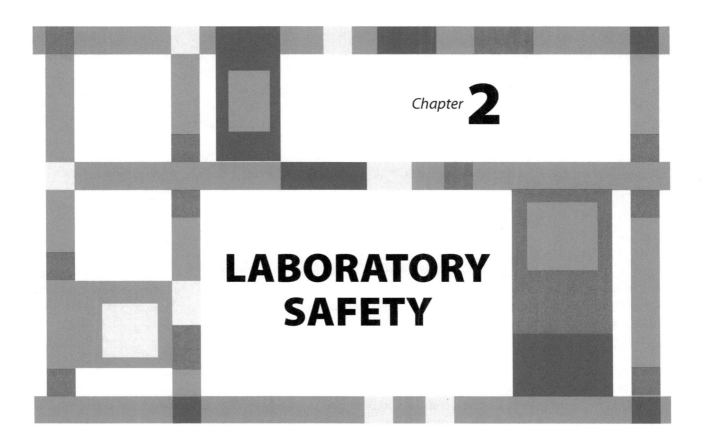

Chapter **2**

LABORATORY SAFETY

Introduction

The biology laboratory has many potential hazards for students working there. Unlike most professional settings, the teaching laboratory contains a relatively large number of people working in a relatively small space. Many of these individuals do not have extensive knowledge of the hazards around them. You can protect yourself from these hazards by following the appropriate experimental procedures, being aware of the dangers of the chemicals you use, and taking commonsense safety precautions. This exercise is designed to introduce you to the basic safety rules and procedures, what you should do if an accident occurs, and how to avoid accidents in the first place. At the end of this exercise there is a laboratory safety contract that you must sign prior to beginning work in this laboratory. Note that there are separate copies of the safety contract for both Biology I (BIOL 1500) and Biology II (BIOL 1510).

Basic Safety Rules

To Protect Yourself

1. Wear approved eye protection at all times in the laboratory.

This is strongly suggested. Everyone in the laboratory should wear proper eye protection glasses or goggles. Your eye protection should protect both the front and sides of your eyes, meet the standards set by the Occupational Safety and Health Administration (OSHA), and fit over your prescription glasses if you wear them. Contact lenses present special hazards to your eyes because they can concentrate chemicals and vapors next to your eyes, trap foreign particles next to your eyes, and interfere with the effectiveness of the eyewash fountains. If possible, do not wear contact lenses in the laboratory. Rather, wear your eye glasses.

2. **Wear sensible clothing, low or no heel shoes, and tie back long hair.**

Sensible clothing is clothing that you don't mind becoming stained, wet, or torn. It is generally a good idea to wear old, worn clothing that can be discarded if need be. It should not be too loose, especially in the sleeves, and it should cover as much of your body, arms, and legs as possible. Shoes should be sturdy and should cover your entire foot. Open-toed shoes or sandals, or shoes with high heels are not permitted in the laboratory. Be aware that cloth shoes such as tennis shoes present a hazard because they can absorb spilled liquids and hold the liquids next to your skin. Long hair can dangle into beakers and apparatuses, becoming contaminated, so always tie back long hair. Do not wear caps or hats in the laboratory. Hair spray makes the hair more flammable. You should remove all neckties, scarves, and jewelry. It is a good idea to wear a laboratory coat and/or apron.

3. **Place your personal belongings away from your working area, and keep the laboratory clean.**

Book bags, binders, purses, etc., should not be placed on the bench next to where you are working. They can become contaminated or wet from the experiments. It is best to place them in the front of the laboratory or in an empty drawer or cupboard, if available. Better yet, do not bring them into the laboratory. Bring only what you need to conduct the actual experiment. While you are working in the laboratory, be vigilant about keeping your work area clean. This will minimize the chances for spills and careless accidents due to sloppiness.

4. **Avoid contamination when you are in the laboratory.**

There are three ways that chemicals and contaminants can enter the body: (1) Inhalation. The act of breathing can bring vapors, smoke, and particles into your lungs. (2) Ingestion. Never put anything into your mouth while in the laboratory; this includes chemicals, liquids, and pipettes, but also extends to your fingers. Do not bring food or drink into the laboratory. Smoking is prohibited on the campus of Nova Southeastern University. Never pipette by mouth. (3) Absorption. Once in contact with your skin, many chemicals can enter the body easily. Some chemicals will actually damage your skin. You can avoid this route of contamination by maintaining a clean working surface, cleaning up spills immediately, and placing wet equipment in paper towels. Wash your hands frequently while in the laboratory, and wear gloves as much as possible.

Working in the Laboratory

5. **Perform only the experiment provided by the instructor.**

Do not attempt unauthorized or modified experiments: Do only the procedure outlined in the directions. Never work alone in the laboratory.

6. **Know where the safety equipment is located and how to use it.**

Safety equipment includes first-aid kits, fire extinguishers, safety showers, eyewash fountains, fire blankets, fire alarms, telephones (campus safety x28999), spill control stations, and emergency electricity and gas shut-off valves. Pay attention when the instructor reviews these with you. Be sure to know where the appropriate laboratory room exits are located and which path to take in the event of a fire. You will need this information to complete the laboratory safety quiz at the end of this section.

7. **Use the fume hood when necessary or directed to do so.**

Experiments using toxic and/or irritating substances MUST be performed under the fume hood. Be certain that the fume hood is turned on. Place only your hands and arms in the fume hood, and lower the glass cover to protect your upper body and head. It is your responsibility to know the hazardous properties of all substances used in an experiment. You can find this information in the **Material Safety Data Sheet (MSDS)** for each compound used in the laboratory. These are kept in a binder in the preparation room.

8. **Dispose of waste and excess reagents appropriately.**

Everyone is responsible for disposing of his or her waste and excess materials in an appropriate fashion. You will be told where to dispose of such materials for each laboratory session. Place waste materials in the proper container (e.g., there are separate containers for glass, biohazards, and more usual trash). Do not put paper or other materials in the boxes used for broken and disposable glassware or biohazards.

Handling Equipment

9. **Only use equipment that is in good condition. You can detect damaged equipment by watching for:**

    a. glassware with chipped or broken rims

    b. glassware with linear or star-shaped cracks

    c. glassware with severely scratched bases

    d. burettes, pipettes, or funnels with chipped tips

    e. glassware with sharp edges

    f. clamps, rings, or other supports that don't work

10. **Assemble the experimental apparatus carefully.**

Keep your work area uncluttered of extra equipment or chemicals. It is generally a good idea to wash all of your glassware before you start to work. Be careful, though, because wet glassware is slippery and hard to hold onto. When using a ring stand, assemble the apparatus over the base, not to one side.

11. **Avoid touching hot objects.**

Burns are the most common injury in the laboratory. Be careful when handling hot objects. Use appropriate clamps or pads. Hot glassware stays hot for a long time. Thus, allow objects to cool for an extended period before attempting to pick them up with your bare hands.

Handling Chemicals

12. **Handle chemicals with caution by:**

    a. reading labels carefully

    b. using only the amount needed

    c. leaving chemicals in their proper places

    d. cleaning up spills immediately and appropriately

    e. labeling all containers to identify their contents

Be sure that you select the specified reagents and solutions. Different chemicals can have similar names. Use the specified amount of each material. Take only as much as you will need into a separate container. Do not pipette directly from the stock container. Never return excess materials to their original containers. If you are not sure how much you will need, be conservative; you can always return for more.

Know the hazards associated with the chemicals you are using. In addition to the MSDS discussed above, the National Fire Protection Agency (NFPA) has developed a diamond-shaped symbol used to label chemicals and rate their degree of hazard. The NFPA symbol has a red segment at the top that indicates flammability. The blue segment on the left shows the toxicity hazard. The yellow segment on the right indicates reactivity. The bottom segment is white and is used to designate specific hazards, such as radioactivity. Within each segment there is a number, which rates the degree of hazard:

$$4 = \text{extreme hazard} \qquad 3 = \text{severe hazard} \qquad 2 = \text{moderate hazard}$$

$$1 = \text{slight hazard} \qquad 0 = \text{no hazard}$$

When you obtain chemicals from the stock, make sure to label the container, even if you are going to use it immediately. Do not trust your memory to keep track, especially since you might have to dispose of it later. The only way to identify a spill is by looking at the label on its container. If there is no label, it is impossible to know for sure what the chemical is. This makes cleaning up spills much more difficult and potentially dangerous.

13. **Use a pipette aid when pipetting liquids.**

NEVER PIPETTE BY MOUTH. Be sure you know the difference between a "to deliver" and a "blow-out" pipette. Familiarize yourself with the use of the micropipettes, including the capillary tubes and Pipetman or other types of micropipetters.

14. **Heat liquids cautiously.**

Heat liquids in a test tube by placing them in a beaker of boiling water. You will not need to heat liquids to a temperature greater than 100°C. Never heat liquids in a graduated cylinder or other volumetric glassware. Use water baths if instructed to do so. Remember to use care in removing tubes or containers of hot liquids from water baths.

If an Accident Occurs

1. If you hurt yourself in any way (or think you may have), no matter how slightly, you MUST tell the instructor immediately. Failure to promptly notify the instructor of ANY injury will result in expulsion from the laboratory.

2. If you burn yourself, flush the area of the burn with cold water for at least 20 minutes. Notify the instructor immediately.

3. If you get something in your eyes, immediately flush them at the eyewash station. This should never happen since you are wearing eye protection; but if it does alert someone close to you and proceed to the eyewash fountain. If you get a chemical on your face, but not in your eyes, DO NOT REMOVE EYE PROTECTION. Proceed immediately to the eyewash station and flush your face completely. Then use paper towels to dry off. Then remove the eye protection.

4. If a small amount of chemical comes into contact with your skin, immediately wash your hands with soap and water. Remove any jewelry that might inhibit total cleansing. If you are covered with a large amount of chemicals, use the safety shower.

5. If your clothing becomes contaminated, remove it immediately. Do not be shy; seconds can be important. Then wash the affected areas of your body. Discard all clothing that is contaminated.

6. Open flames will rarely be used in the biology laboratory, so the chance that something will catch on fire is minimal. However, it is imperative that you know what to do in case of a fire in the laboratory. If your clothing catches on fire, use the STOP-DROP-ROLL-YELL technique to put out the flames. STOP what you are doing, DROP to the floor, and ROLL to smother the flames. YELL to alert others to the situation so that they may come and assist you. Never run if some part of your clothing catches on fire. Running just fans the flames. Do not use the safety shower to put out a fire on your clothing. The safety shower is for chemical spills only. There should also be a fire blanket in the laboratory. If you see someone on fire, quickly grab the fire blanket and use it to extinguish the flames. Once the individual affected by the fire is safe, try to put out the fire using the fire extinguisher. Direct the spray from the extinguisher at the base of the flames. Try to turn off the supply of gas to the fire area, should that be the problem. If the fire cannot be extinguished quickly, evacuate the laboratory and pull the fire alarm. Of you use an extinguisher, label it as used so that it can be replaced.

7. If you should injure yourself, tell the instructor immediately. Then proceed with first aid. Wash minor cuts with cold water, removing any foreign material. Apply a bandage from the first-aid kit. Only the instructor is authorized to open the first-aid kit. You will be expelled from the laboratory if you open the first-aid kit without notifying the instructor first. For major cuts and severe bleeding, fast action is essential. Have someone notify Public Safety (x28999 or 954-262-8999) for an ambulance. Apply direct pressure to the open wound with a clean compress or cloth to control bleeding.

LABORATORY SAFETY QUIZ

Name_____ **Date**_____

1. What part of the body requires special protection in the laboratory? Briefly describe what you should do to protect this part of your body.

   Eyes require special protection. Eye wear or goggles are to be used.

2. In your laboratory, where is the nearest:

   a. fire extinguisher? *by door*   d. fire alarm?

   b. safety shower *back of class room*   e. telephone?

   c. eyewash fountain? *"   "*   f. fire blanket?

3. What should you do to avoid becoming contaminated in the laboratory?

4. What does MSDS mean? Why should you be interested?

   Material Safety Data Sheets

5. How do you dispose of waste or excess materials in the laboratory?

6. How can defective glassware be identified?

7. What does the right-sided segment of the NFPA symbol mean?

8. How should you heat liquids to temperatures below 100°C?

9. What should you do **first** if you injure yourself in the laboratory?

10. What should you do **immediately** if your clothing catches on fire in the laboratory?

BIOLOGY 1510 LABORATORY SAFETY CONTRACT

Name_____ **Date**_____

In order for you to work in the biology laboratory, you must read and sign the following safety contract. Failure to do so, or failure to adhere to the terms of this contract, will result in your expulsion from the laboratory.

When I am in the laboratory, I will:

1. wear approved eye protection at all times.

2. wear sensible clothing, closed toe shoes, and tie back long hair.

3. avoid absorbing chemicals into my body by:
   a. never pipetting anything by mouth.
   b. not eating in the laboratory.
   c. washing my hands often.
   d. washing skin and clothing that comes into contact with chemicals.

4. perform only the experiment provided by the instructor.

5. know where the safety equipment is and how to use it.

6. never work alone.

7. use the fume hood when appropriate or so directed.

8. dispose of waste in an appropriate manner.

9. use equipment that is in good condition.

10. assemble apparatus carefully.

11. avoid touching hot objects.

12. keep the laboratory clean.

13. handle chemicals with caution by:
    a. reading labels carefully.
    b. using only the amount needed.
    c. leaving chemicals in their proper places.
    d. cleaning up spills immediately.
    e. labeling all containers to identify their contents.

14. thoroughly wash my hands and face after each laboratory session.

15. notify the instructor if I injure myself.

I have carefully read and understand all of the safety ruled above. I recognize that it is my responsibility to observe all these precautions whenever I am in the biology laboratory.

_____   _____

Signature   Date

_____   _____

Signature of Instructor   Date

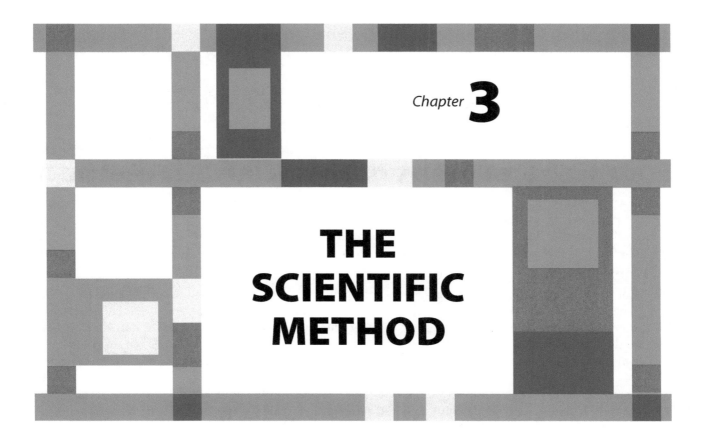

Chapter **3**

THE SCIENTIFIC METHOD

Overview

In this lab, you will learn the basic process of doing scientific research. Briefly, you will develop a research hypothesis, design an experiment to test it, conduct the experiment, record the data, and make conclusions based on the data.

Background

Most people think of science as a collection of facts about the natural world that they have to memorize in order to pass an exam. Others think of science as a bunch of theories about how the world works, many times seemingly unrelated to how we perceive the world, and having to be memorized and regurgitated to pass an exam. In fact, science is a process that involves collecting information, making some assumptions about the information, and then testing these assumptions by means of experiments or more observations.

This process is called the *scientific method*, and it is based on several fundamental ideas:

1. The principle of "parsimony" that says that the simplest explanation for how things work is usually the best;

2. The principle of "similarity of causation" that says that two experiments conducted in exactly the same way will have the same results. A corollary to this principle is that we need a standard way of making measurements that will allow us to compare results.

3. The principle of "uniformity" that says in simple terms that what we learn today will be true tomorrow, or that what caused a certain experimental result today will cause the same result if we repeat the experiment tomorrow.

4. The principle of "objectivity" that says that we should avoid letting our prior knowledge, prejudices, and biases influence how we collect and analyze the data.

5. The principle of "flexibility" that says that we have to be able to change our minds about long-held and/or well supported ideas and theories once new data become available that challenge or falsify what we think we know about how things work in the universe.

The scientific method is used in almost all experiments in scientific research, regardless of the field of investigation. This widespread use allows scientists to understand and criticize research from other fields besides their own specialty.

Four General Steps of the Scientific Method

1. Start by making observations and asking questions pertaining to those observations about some process or phenomenon of interest. This can include reading as much as you can about the process of interest in the scientific literature trying to determine if there are any gaps in knowledge or understanding. On the basis of this preliminary research, formulate a specific question upon which to focus your further investigation.

2. Formulate a hypothesis or a possible answer to your question that takes into account everything you have learned so far. Usually a hypothesis is a limited statement regarding the cause and effect in a specific situation, which can be tested by experimentation and observation or by statistical analysis of the data obtained. The outcome of the hypothesis should be currently unknown, so that the results can provide useful data regarding the validity of the hypothesis. Your hypothesis must be testable and falsifiable: in other words (1) a good hypothesis suggests an experiment that can be conducted to determine if it is correct or not, and (2) it must be possible for your hypothesis to be wrong. It is important to note that the scientific method rarely proves the hypothesis to be true, in most cases the test of the hypothesis fails to disprove it.

   Generally, hypotheses are constructed in pairs. The null hypothesis (H_0) is a statement that the scientist is trying to disprove and is usually formulated as a negative statement, e.g. "the experimental treatment will have no effect" or "there is no difference between these two experimental conditions." The alternative hypothesis (H_a) is a statement of what the scientist is trying to demonstrate, and is usually formulated in the positive, e.g. "the treatment did have an effect" or "there is a difference between groups of experimental subjects." The null hypothesis may also be thought of as "There is no effect of x (independent variable) on y (dependent variable)."

3. Design an experiment to test the hypothesis. This usually starts with the identification of all of the variables that might influence the outcome of the experiment, and then constructing an experiment that will keep all of these variables constant except the variable of interest that was in the hypothesis. Generally speaking, there are two kinds of variables, independent variables and dependent variables. Independent variables can include factors that cannot be controlled by the scientist conducting the experiment and care should be taken to ensure that these do not change during the experiment. These can include such factors as the temperature of the room, the time of day, the weather, etc. Independent variables are usually plotted on the x-axis of a graph. However, the most important independent variable is the one that will be changed by the scientist in order to test the hypothesis.

   Dependent variables, on the other hand, are those factors that are determined by the independent variables. Their value or magnitude thus "depend" upon the independent variable, and dependent variables are usually plotted on the y-axis of a graph. Dependent variables are what the scientist usually measures as the outcome of the experiment and in well designed experiments these variables are usually different between experimental treatments or groups.

4. Analyze the results of the experiment or test. Normally a scientist will display the results of their experiment in a table or graph, and often they will use statistics to reinforce the importance and significance of their results. The goal of the analysis is to determine if the results of the experiment (i.e. the data) support or falsify the null hypothesis. In most well designed scientific experiments testing well formulated hypotheses, the result of the experiment enable the scientist to reject the null hypothesis. This

usually also enables the scientist to accept the alternate hypothesis, however it is important to note that this does not mean that the results prove the alternate hypothesis. In fact, rejection of the null hypothesis can allow the scientist to accept almost any alternate hypothesis.

This leads to the final step in the scientific method, which is to do it all again. Because the results of a well designed experiment lead the scientist to reject the null hypothesis, before they can accept the alternate hypothesis they need to reformulate the alternate hypothesis as a null hypothesis, design a new experiment to test the new null hypothesis, conduct the experiment, collect and analyze the data, and then see if the new results allow them to accept or reject the new null hypothesis. Thus, science can be seen as a never-ending process of formulating, testing, and rejecting (or not) null hypotheses, without ever actually proving anything to be true.

Procedure for Today's Experiment

In today's experiment you are going to be working in small groups examining the factors that affect a person's heart rate. You will start by discussing what determines how fast someone's heart beats. This might include the gender of the person, whether or not the person exercises regularly, whether one inhales or exhales before starting, etc. Each group should try to come up with some unique ideas about these factors that can be tested in the laboratory fairly quickly and easily. Your hypotheses should be focused, testable, falsifiable, and not have an obvious answer.

Then the entire group will discuss the various ideas from each group. After this discussion, five factors or questions will be selected, and formal null and alternative hypotheses will be postulated. Remember also that your null hypotheses should be formulated in the negative (or no difference) while your alternate hypotheses should be formulated in the positive.

During this discussion, the precise methodology for conducting the experiment will be determined. Once this has been established, then each group will test each hypothesis for each member of their group, and record their data on the Lab Report Form that can be found at the end of this chapter.

Each person should have his heart rate determined as shown in Figures 3-1 and 3-2. Use the electronic digital timer to record the number of times the subject's heart beats in 15 seconds, and then multiply by 4 to get the heart rate in beats/minute. Each person should perform whatever action or undergo whatever distraction necessary to test each hypothesis. Enter each person's data in the report form.

Enter your group's data into Data Table 1 on the next page. Then enter your group's data into the electronic spreadsheet that will be provided and use the data from all groups in your laboratory session to answer the questions on the Lab Report form and then generate the required tables and figures as indicated on the Lab Report form.

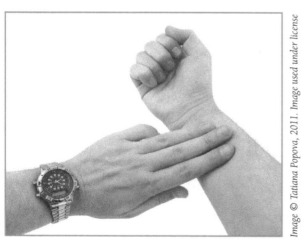

Image © Tatiana Popova, 2011. Image used under license of Shutterstock Inc.

FIGURE 3-1 Monitoring the pulse rate using the radial artery in the wrist.

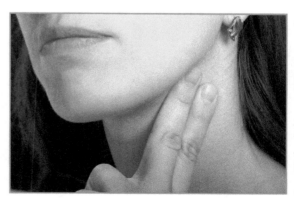

Image © Ilya Andriyanov, 2011. Image used under license of Shutterstock Inc.

FIGURE 3-2 Monitoring the pulse rate using the carotid artery in the neck.

Laboratory Two—The Scientific Method

Subject	Hypothesis One Test Data		Hypothesis Two Test Data		Hypothesis Three Test Data		Hypothesis Four Test Data		Hypothesis Five Test Data	
	Control	Data	Control	Data	Control	Data	Control	Data	Control	Data
#1										
#2										
#3										
#4										
#5										

LABORATORY REPORT FORM
Lab 2

Name_____ Date_____

The Scientific Method

All answers to the following questions are to be **written** in the spaces below and turned in at the **beginning of the next lab meeting**. You must also include printouts of the figure and two tables that you will be creating (see below). Make sure to write your name and date on every page of the worksheet and the pages containing the tables and figure.

Students should work individually to answer the following questions and in creating the figure.

1. In the experiment, what were the different questions or hypotheses examined by the class with respect to factors that affect heart rate?

   Factors discussed by class that may affect heart rate included: age (younger vs. older), gender (male vs. female) activity/fitness level (athlete?), caffeine intake, & smoker vs. non-smoker.

2. State a null and alternative hypothesis formulated during the laboratory session.

   H_0 Activity has no influence on heart rate

   H_a Heart rate will be increased by increasing activity

3. For the hypothesis, which of the variables was the independent variable, the one that was varied to invoke a response?

Jumping Jacks for 30 sec.

4. For the hypothesis, which of the variables was the dependent variable, the one that was the effect?

5. Describe two other variables that were or should have been controlled and how they might have been controlled?

6. Change the title of the table of the class data (that was distributed) to be a meaningful one that reflects the data collected (e.g., don't just write Table 1: Heart Rate). Print this table and include it with this form.

How gender and fitness level affect HR

7. Create a second table that illustrates average of the heart rate for each group for each variable. For instance, imagine that the hypothesis was that there no difference in heart rate between males and females. The new Table 1 will list the students in random order and each student's averaged heart rates. You should then take those data and get an overall average of all the males in the class and an overall average of all the females. Imagine the second question was whether athletes have slower heart rates than nonathletic. Using the same data from Table 1, get an overall average of all the athletes and nonathletes. Do this for all hypotheses tested and put in a new Table 2. Give this table a meaningful title, print it, and include it with this report form.

8. Express the class data from Table 2 in figure form. You will have to use Microsoft Excel or another graphing program to make this figure. The y-axis of the figure will be average heart rates and the x-axis will have different descriptive titles depending upon each hypothesis being tested. Examples of each table and figure will be posted on the class web page. Make sure you label the axes properly and give the figure a meaningful title. Print this figure and include it with this report form.

9. Examine the data in the tables and figure. Return to the hypotheses you formulated in question 2 and compare each of the hypotheses to the experimental results. Would you be more likely to accept or reject each of the null hypotheses? Why? Cite the data (using the tables and figure) used in making your decisions.

10. As you conducted this experiment and analyzed the results, additional questions probably came into your mind. Based on your data, what are two additional questions that you could test if another related experiment were to be done? These questions should directly follow one or more of the five that you tested in the initial experiment. Also, what would be your null hypothesis for each of the two experiments. (EXAMPLE: Suppose you initially asked if having athletic training gave you faster heart rates than if you had no training. If you found that those having athletic training have significantly faster heart rates than those without athletic training, your next question may be if there are differences among athletes who play different sports).

11. What sources of error do you think existed in this exercise? In other words, what differences exist in how individual groups performed the experiment that could have led to variability in the data?

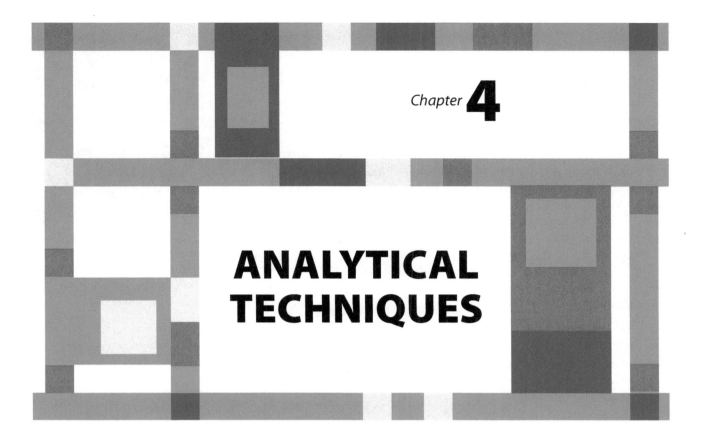

Chapter 4

ANALYTICAL TECHNIQUES

Overview

In this lab, you will learn how to use various kinds of scientific equipment and how to analyze data using basic statistical techniques. You will also learn how to use a spectrophotometer to determine the concentration of glucose in a blood sample from a patient with diabetes.

Background

This laboratory exercise is divided into four parts:

1. Determining the number of beads of different colors in a container by taking a sample of beads from the container, weighing them, and estimating their total number

2. Using a spectrophotometer to determine the wavelength of light that a solution containing glucose and a chromogen will absorb maximally

3. Generating a set of tubes with a known concentration of glucose, adding some chemicals (chromogen) to the tubes to generate a colored solution, and then using a spectrophotometer to measure the absorbance of tubes in order to construct a standard curve

4. Using the standard curve to determine the concentration of glucose in the plasma of a patient with diabetes

Statistical Sampling

Because it can be difficult, expensive or impossible to measure every component or individual in the population in order to actually determine the characters or parameters of the entire population, we usually take measurements from an accessible sample, or subset, of the population. To describe the sample, we use variables such as averages and standard deviations. We then use these variables to estimate, or infer, the characteristics of the entire population.

The first exercise is intended to demonstrtae the effect of sample size on the estimates of certain parameters of a population. You will be filling a container with a known number of beads of six different colors, with the same number of beads of each color (Figure 4-1). The container will represent the population of beads. You will then take three samples of beads of 10, 15, and 20 beads. You will use the weight of the samples, and the composition by color of the samples, to estimate the total number of beads in the container (which you already know) and the number of beads of each color (which you also already know). You will then compare the estimates derived from each sample, i.e., the **sample variables**, to the known **population parameters**.

FIGURE 4-1 Filling the beaker with beads to create a population of beads from which you will take samples in order to estimate the parameters of the bead population.

There are two important features of your estimates. The first is the **accuracy**, which is how close your estimates based on the sample (i.e., sample variables) are to the real or true value of the population (i.e., population parameters). The second is the **precision**, which is how close your sample estimates are to each other, i.e., how reproducible the data are. Obviously it is possible to have very precise estimates that are not very accurate!

The Importance of the Blood Glucose Level

The human body uses a monosaccharide (sugar) called glucose for energy. In order for most tissues in the body to absorb glucose, the hormone *insulin* must be released from the pancreas. When you eat a meal, the digestive tract digests the food into its monomeric constituents (monosaccharides, amino acids, and fatty acids) and these are absorbed into the body across the intestinal wall. Thus, after you eat a meal, your blood glucose concentration increases. In response to this increase in blood glucose, the pancreas releases insulin, which stimulates glucose uptake by the cells in the body, and the concentration of glucose in the blood goes down.

In persons with the most common type of diabetes, i.e., insulin-dependent diabetes, the pancreas stops producing insulin. This removes the stimulus for the cells in the body to take up glucose, and so blood glucose concentration remains elevated for prolonged periods. This has two important consequences: (1) the cells do not have enough energy to maintain their normal activity because they cannot absorb glucose, and (2) the high glucose levels in the blood cause other problems, such as atherosclerosis ("hardening of the arteries"), cataracts, and kidney failure.

This means that people with diabetes have to monitor their blood glucose levels continuously. Current criteria for the diagnosis of diabetes mellitus include two fasting plasma glucose levels of 126 mg/dL or higher, or two "**random**" glucose readings of 200 mg/dL or higher. Currently there are very efficient and almost painless ways to do this, but in the past this required drawing a blood sample. Then the blood had to be spun in a centrifuge to remove the red blood cells, and the remaining fluid, the plasma, was used to measure the blood glucose concentration. The problem is that the glucose molecule is clear when dissolved in watery solutions such as plasma, and so chemicals (i.e., the chromogen) have to be added to the solution to cause a color to appear, that is, where the depth or intensity of the color is directly proportional to the concentration of the glucose.

The Spectrophotometer

We use a spectrophotometer to measure the depth or intensity of the color that is produced by the chemical reaction. Inside the spectrophotometer, a light bulb produces white light, which is then passed through a prism or diffraction grating to split the white light into different colors. Each color corresponds to a particular wavelength of light. This is important because colored solutions do not absorb all wavelengths of light, and we have to determine the precise wavelength of light they do absorb. The spectrophotometer then allows the individual wavelengths of light to pass through the sample, and the wavelengths of light that are not absorbed go through the sample and arrive at a photoelectric tube that determines how much light got through, which is called the *percent transmittance*. For example, if no light got through, the transmittance would be 0%, and if all light got through, the transmittance would be 100%. However, we are most interested in how much light was absorbed by the sample, and this can be determined mathematically by the equation:

$$\text{Absorbance} = \log_{10}(1/\text{Transmittance})$$

Determining the Maximal Absorbance

The first step is to determine which wavelength of light a particular colored solution will absorb maximally. We want to use this wavelength in our subsequent work to get the most accurate and precise results. This is accomplished by placing a colored solution in the spectrophotometer and then passing light through the sample in increments of wavelength of 25 nm. White light consists of light with wavelengths from about 400 nm (purple) to about 700 nm (red). There is an interesting, inverse relationship between the color of a solution and the wavelength of light it absorbs; for example, a blue solution maximally absorbs light with wavelengths at the red end of the visible spectrum (~ 700 nm) while a red solution maximally absorbs light with wavelengths at the blue end of the spectrum (~ 400 nm). This is because our eyes perceive the blue light reflected by blue solutions and the red light reflected by red solutions.

The Beer-Lambert Law

Before we can measure the concentration of glucose in a plasma sample, we have to know the linear relationship between the glucose concentration and the intensity of the color produced by the chemical reaction. This linear relationship is known as a *standard curve*. To make a standard curve, the first step is to take a solution of known glucose concentration and dilute it, producing a series of solutions of decreasing glucose concentration. Then the color-producing chemicals (chromogens) are added, the color is generated, and then the spectrophotometer is used to determine the absorbance of each tube with a solution of known glucose concentration. If we plot the concentration of glucose (the independent variable) on the x-axis and the absorbance of the colored solution (dependent variable) on the y-axis of a graph, we get the standard curve. The linear relationship between the concentration of a colored solution and its light absorbance is known as the Beer-Lambert law. Then we can use this curve to graphically determine the concentration of glucose in a sample from a patient:

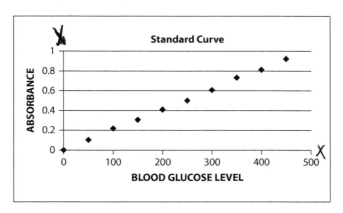

Determining the Unknown

If we plot the curve with the dependent variable (absorbance) on the x-axis and the independent variable (concentration) on the y-axis, and we determine the mathematical equation of the straight line of the standard curve, we can then mathematically determine the concentration of the patient sample from its absorbance. This would also enable us to calculate the confidence interval on our estimate of the patient's blood glucose level using advanced statistics (see Chapter 1, page 4).

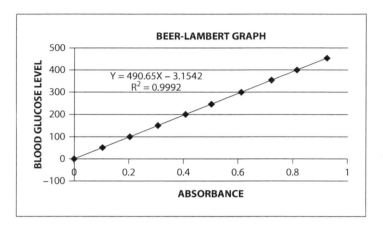

Procedure for Today's Experiment

Part One

In general, you will be estimating the number of beads in a large container by taking various samples of beads from the container and weighing them. You will then use a variety of statistical tests to estimate the total number of beads, and the number of beads of each color in the container. How close will you get?

1. There should be two beakers at your workstation, one empty and one full of colored beads. There should also be a plastic weighing boat.

2. Weigh the empty beaker as shown in Figure 4-2 and record its weight in Table 4-1. Then fill the empty beaker by adding 10 beads of each color to the beaker. Weigh the full container as shown in Figure 4-3

FIGURE 4-2 Weighing empty beaker.

FIGURE 4-3 Weighing beaker full of beads.

TABLE 4-1	Data table for weights of beads and containers
Weight of empty beaker (g)	—
Weight of beaker + 60 beads (g)	—
Weight of 60 beads (g)	32.10
Weight of empty weight boat	—
Weight of weight boat + 10 beads	—
Weight of 10 beads	5.24
Weight of empty weight boat	—
Weight of weight boat + 15 beads	—
Weight of 15 beads	8.04
Weight of empty weight boat	—
Weight of weigh boat + 20 beads	—
Weight of 20 beads	10.62

and record its weight in Table 4-1. Determine the total weight of the beads by subtracting the weight of the empty beaker from the weight of the full beaker.

3. Shake the beaker full of beads to mix the colored beads. Then take a "random" sample of 10 beads from the beaker and place your sample in the plastic weight boat. Be sure to weigh the plastic weight boat before putting the beads into it as shown in Figure 4-4 and record the weight in Table 4-1. Then weigh the plastic boat with the beads as shown in Figure 4-5 and record the weight in Table 4-1. Then determine the weight of the beads in your sample by subtracting the weight of the empty weight boat from the weight of the boat and beads in Table 4-1. Also record the number of beads of each color in your sample in Table 4-2. Then return the beads in the sample to the beaker and mix the beads again.

FIGURE 4-4 Weighing weigh boat.

Image courtesy of Edward O. Keith, 2011.

FIGURE 4-5 Weighing 10 beads.

Image courtesy of Edward O. Keith, 2011.

TABLE 4-2 *Data table for recording composition by color of samples of beads*

	Number of beads (n = 10)	Number of beads (n = 15)	Number of beads (N = 20)
Green	3	4	30
Purple	0	1	2
Yellow	1	2	4
Blue	2	3	4
Red	3	4	6
Pink	1	1	1
Total	10	15	20

4. Estimate the total number of beads in the full beaker using the data from your sample:

$$\text{Estimated \# of beads in full beaker} = \text{\# of beads in sample} \times \frac{\text{weight of 60 beads (population)}}{\text{weight of sample}}$$

Record this result as "Total Estimate" in the "Sample Size 10" column in Table 4-3.

5. Determine the accuracy of your estimate by calculating the percent error your estimate of the number of beads to the actual number of beads you placed in your beaker using the following equation:

$$\text{Percent error} = \frac{\text{Estimated \# of beads in full beaker (from above)} - \text{Actual \# of beads in full beaker}}{\text{Actual \# of beads in full beaker}} \times 100\%$$

Record this result as "Percent Error" in the "Sample Size 10" column in Table 4-3.

6. Estimate the number of beads of each color in the full beaker (population) using the following equation for red beads as an example:

$$\begin{array}{ccc}\text{Estimated \# of read beads} \\ \text{in the full container}\end{array} = \begin{array}{c}\text{Total \# of beads} \\ \text{in the full container}\end{array} \times \frac{\text{\# of red beads in sample}}{\text{Total \# of beads in sample}}$$

Record these results as "Number of red beads" in the "Sample Size 10" column in Table 4-3.

Repeat this part for beads of each color and record your results in Table 4-3 as above.

7. Repeat steps 3, 4, 5, and 6 by taking samples of 15 and 20 beads from the full beaker of beads (population), and record your results as "Total Estimates 15"; "Total Estimate 20"; "Percent Error 15"; "Percent Error 20"; "Number of beads of each color" and "Number of beads of each color 20" in Table 4-3.

8. Give your data in Table 4-3 to the instructor so that every group's data can be entered into the class data sheet and posted on the class web page.

9. In your lab report, compare the accuracy of each of your three estimates of the total number of beads and the number of beads of each color. How precise were your three estimates of the total number of beads and the number of beads of each color?

TABLE 4-3	Table for calculation of color composition of population of beads and estimating the total number of beads in the population					
	Number of beads (n = 10)		Number of beads (n = 15)		Number of beads (N = 20)	
Green	18	80%	16	60%	9	-55%
Purple	0	0%	4	-73.3%	6	-60%
Yellow	6	-40%	8	-46.6%	12	-40%
Blue	12	20%	12	-20%	12	-40%
Red	18	80%	16	60%	18	-10%
Pink	6	-40%	4	-73.3%	3	-85%
Sample size	10		15		20	
Total estimate	61.25		59.89		60.95	
Percent error	2.08%		-0.18%		0.75%	

Image courtesy of Edward O. Keith, 2011.

FIGURE 4-6 Weighing 15 beads.

Image courtesy of Edward O. Keith, 2011.

FIGURE 4-7 Weighing 20 beads.

Part Two

1. There are four vials at your work station: one with a known glucose concentration (200 mg/dL), a second one with a solution of known glucose concentration (500 mg/dL), a third with a solution of unknown glucose concentration (patient sample), and a fourth containing the chromogen solution. Following the directions in Table 4-4, use the micropipette to add 2.0 mL of the 500 mg/dL stock solution and 20 μL of distilled water to a cuvette. This will be the "blank" cuvette. To a second cuvette, add 20 μL of the 500 mg/dl solution and then add 2.0 mL of the chromogen solution. This will be the "test" cuvette.

TABLE 4-4	Mixing directions for the two cuvettes in part two		
Cuvette	500 mg/dL glucose stock solution	Chromogen stock solution	Distilled water
Blank	0 μL	2.0 mL	20 μL
Test	20 μL	2.0 mL	0.0 mL

2. Incubate both cuvettes in the 37° water bath for five minutes, remove, and dry the outside of the cuvettes.

3. Set the wavelength of the spectrophotometer to 400 nm. Insert the blank cuvette into the spectrophotometer. Set the absorbance reading to zero, and remove the blank cuvette.

4. Insert the test cuvette into the spectrophotometer, and read the absorbance. Record the absorbance value in Table 4-5. Remove the test cuvette.

5. Set the wavelength of the spectrophotometer to 425 nm. Insert the blank cuvette, set the absorbance reading to zero, and remove the blank cuvette.

6. Insert the test cuvette, and read the absorbance. Record the absorbance in Table 4-5, and remove the colored cuvette.

7. Repeat these steps (#5 and #6) in wavelength increments of 25 nm up to 700 nm. Be sure to set the absorbance of the blank cuvette each time after you change the wavelength.

8. Make a graph with the wavelength on the x-axis and the absorbance on the y-axis, and determine the wavelength of light that the colored cuvette absorbed maximally. The graph below shows an example of such a curve. Note that your curve will probably look different and yield a different wavelength where the colored cuvette absorbed maximally.

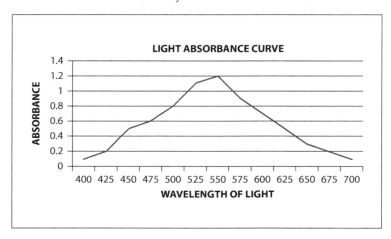

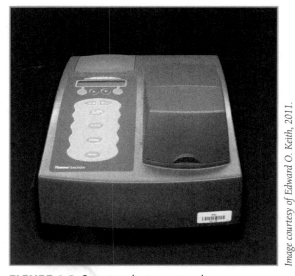

FIGURE 4-8 Spectrophotometer alone.

Data table for absorbance values
TABLE 4-5 at different wavelengths

Wavelength (nm)	Absorbance (A)
400	.162
optimal 425	.183
450	.18
475	.17
500	.15
525	.13
550	.09
575	.06
600	.04
625	.04
650	.03
675	.03
700	.02

Part Three

Following the directions in Table 4-6 and the instructions below, prepare a series of cuvettes of known glucose concentration. Note that the "test" cuvette you prepared in the previous section has a glucose concentration of 500 mg/dl. Also note that you will use the same "blank" cuvette in this section that you prepared in the previous section.

1. Put 10 μL of the 200 mg/dL glucose solution into a clean cuvette and then add 10 μL of water. This results in a solution with a glucose concentration of 100 mg/dL. Then, into a second cuvette, put 20 μL of the 200 mg/dL glucose solution.

2. Put 20 μL of the 500 mg/dL glucose solution into a third clean cuvette and then add 10 μL of water. This results in a solution with a glucose concentration of 250 mg/dL. The "test" cuvette you prepared in Part Two (previously) already has a glucose concentration of 500 mg/dL.

3. Finally, take 20 μL from the vial with the patient sample (unknown glucose concentration), and place it into a fourth cuvette.

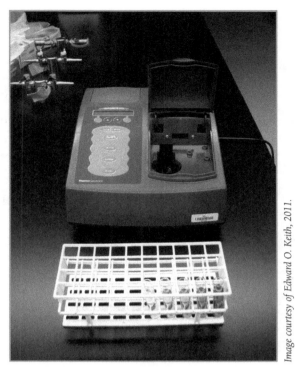

FIGURE 4-9 Spectrophotometer open.

4. Add 2.0 mL of the chromogen solution to the four tubes you just prepared and incubate them at 37° for 5 minutes. Remove the cuvettes and dry them.

5. Set the wavelength of the spectrophotometer to the wavelength that you determined was absorbed maximally by the chromogen (Part Two—step 8). Using the blank cuvette, set the absorbance to zero.

TABLE 4-6 *Mixing directions for the Cuvettes in Part Three—Pipette Larger Volumes First.*

Cuvette	Relative glucose concentration (mg/dL)	Chromogen stock solution	Distilled water (DH$_2$0)	200 mg/dL stock solution	500 mg/dL stock solution	Patient sample
1 = "Blank" from Part 2	0	2 mL	2.0 mL	—		—
2	100	2 mL	10 μL	10 μL	—	—
3	200	2 mL	—	20 μL	—	—
4	250	2 mL	10 μL	—	10 μL	—
5 = "Test" from Part 2	500	2 mL	—	—	20 μL	—
6	**Unknown**	20μL	—	—	—	20 μL

Image courtesy of Edward O. Keith, 2011.

6. Read the absorbance of all five cuvettes, and record them in Table 4-7.

TABLE 4-7	Data table for recording absorbances of known and unknown glucose solutions	
Concentration (mg/dL)		**Absorbance (A)**
D2	100	0.22
D3	200	0.18
D4	250	0.19
D5	500	0.17
D6 Patient Sample ("Unknown")		0.20

Handwritten notes to the right of the table:

0.378
0.369
0.800
1.890
0.539

SD 0.524464

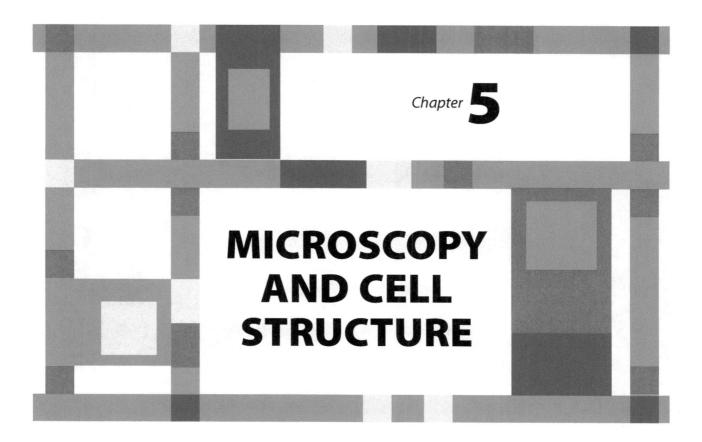

Chapter **5**

MICROSCOPY AND CELL STRUCTURE

Overview

In this lab, you will learn the parts of the microscope and its function and how to use compound and dissecting microscopes. Then, using these microscopes, you will observe a wide variety of biological specimens under the microscope and describe their similarities and differences. Finally, you will learn how to do a wet mount.

Background

The first microscopes were made about 1600 in the Netherlands (Holland). These were primitive magnifying glasses that took time, patience, and a lot of light to use. Galileo Galilei constructed one of the first compound microscopes that had two lenses to focus the light, and the name "microscope" was coined for Galileo's instrument. Marcelo Malpighi in Italy and Robert Hooke in England conducted extensive studies using primitive compound microscopes in the 1660s and 1670s. Antoni von Leeuwenhoek did some of the most ground-breaking work discovering red blood cells, spermatozoa, and microorganisms in the 1670s.

Since that time microscope technology has advanced significantly, and microscopes are now used in all kinds of scientific endeavors. Light microscopes use visible light to visualize small structures. High-powered compound microscopes allow for magnification up to about 1000x, while dissecting microscopes allow for magnification up to about 100x.

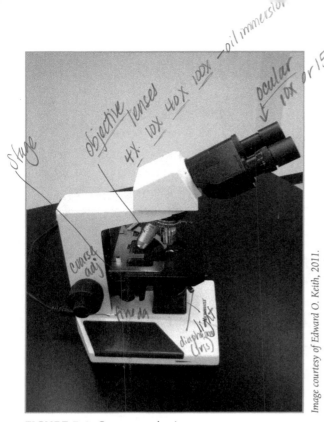

FIGURE 5-1 Compound microscope.

Image courtesy of Edward O. Keith, 2011.

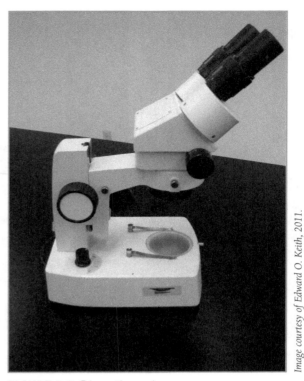

FIGURE 5-2 Dissecting microscope.

Image courtesy of Edward O. Keith, 2011.

↑magnification ↓ Field size   ↓ Depth of field (3 threads)*

There are two major properties of light microscopes. The first is magnification, which is the ratio of the size of the image seen in the microscope to the actual size of the object. This is usually written as a magnification factor, e.g., 100×, which in this case means that the image visible in the microscope is 100 times larger than the actual size of the object. In a compound microscope, the magnification is set by turning the objective lenses just above the stage of the microscope. The magnification of a light microscope is limited by the wavelength of visible light (400–700 nm) and is generally considered to be about 1200×.

The other property is the resolution, which is the ability of the microscope to resolve, or separate, two points. The resolution is determined by the quality of the lenses in the microscope, the diameter of the lenses, the wavelength of light and the visual acuity of the microscope user. Magnification is not a parameter in the equation used to predict resolution, but one would hope that as the magnification increases the resolution would also increase. This is not always the case, especially with microscopes with inexpensive, poor-quality lenses.

Another factor that will influence your ability to visualize objects with the light microscope is the focal plane. At higher magnifications, the microscope focuses light in increasingly thin sections. As you move the microscope stage up and down, attempting to visualize some structure in a thin section of material, you sometimes focus above or below the desired object and thus must adjust the stage to visualize the structure of interest.

In order to overcome the magnification limit imposed by visible light, electron microscopes have been developed that use electron beams to visualize very small structures and cellular features. Because the wavelength of electrons is much shorter than that of visual light, the magnification achieved by electron microscopes is also much greater (~1,000,000x). However, in order to visualize materials in an electron microscope, they must be coated with metal ions, and this process kills living specimens.

There are two types of electron microscopes: transmission and scanning. Transmission electron microscopes (TEM) are conceptually analogous to compound optical microscopes in that the beam of electrons passes through the sample and is then used to produce an image. Scanning electron microscopes (SEM) produces three-dimensional images of the surfaces of objects.

Orientation "e"

Procedure for Today's Experiment

In this exercise, you will be viewing many different types of cells and structures. While doing that, you should be asking yourself questions about how cell shape relates to its function. In particular, you should pay attention to similarities/differences between animal cells, plant cells, fungal cells, and protist cells and to visible differences between living cells and dead cells.

You will be looking at ~20 different biological specimens, most by using the compound microscope and some by using the dissecting scope. Every person should get a compound microscope and become familiar with its operation. There are a limited number of dissecting scopes, so you will have to share these.

Work as a team in your group. Each person in the group should get a specimen properly magnified and focused under the scope, and then everyone should go around and look in each other's microscope. Draw what you see using the report form. Be sure to label the structures you observe.

100x lens → needed Oil immersion

Par-focal. Once in focus @ 1 power
its almost in focus @ next power
Use fine focus

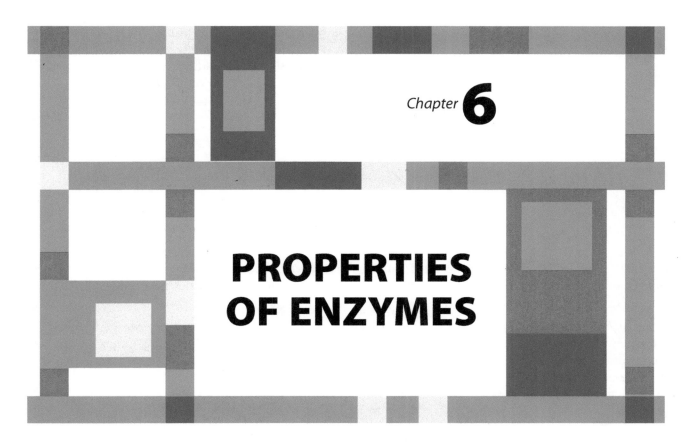

Chapter **6**

PROPERTIES OF ENZYMES

Overview

In this lab, you will examine the effects of temperature, pH, and enzyme concentration on the catalytic rate of various enzymes. Some of these enzymes are involved in human digestion, and some are involved in clinical tests for certain diseases.

(handwritten) ⊛ substrate (reactant) —Enzyme→ product

Background

(handwritten) ⊛ Enzymes ↓ energy for activation need for a reaction to occur.

This laboratory exercise is divided into four parts:

1. Determining the effects of pH on the digestive enzyme pepsin from the stomach
2. Determining the effects of pH on digestive enzymes from the pancreas *(handwritten)* ⊛ Factors pH Temp Concentration
3. Determining the effect of enzyme concentration on catalytic rate
4. Determining the effect of temperature on catalytic rate

Enzymes are extremely important for a variety of reasons. First of all, they are catalytic proteins that increase the rate of chemical reactions by decreasing the activation energy required for the reaction to occur. Every chemical reaction that occurs inside the cell is catalyzed by an enzyme. Thus, life itself would probably be impossible without the participation of enzymes in living processes. Second, enzymes help us digest the food we eat. Without these enzymes, we would die from lack of nutrients and energy. Third, enzyme assays are used to diagnose a wide variety of diseases and are therefore incredibly valuable in the practice of medicine.

Enzymes are different from inorganic catalysts because their activity is affected by many factors and controlled in many ways. The control of enzyme activity can be subdivided into three different categories: (1) the actual properties of the enzyme, (2) the kinetics of the enzyme, and (3) the type of enzyme. In this experiment, you will examine the effect of the environment on the properties and catalytic rate of a number of different enzymes.

(handwritten) Rate of rxn   pH

(handwritten) Rate of rxn will peak @ optimum pH.

(handwritten) Ho- Δ in pH has no effect rate of rxn

(handwritten) Hq- Δ in pH affects rate of rxn

The two environmental variables examined in this experiment are pH and temperature. Both of these have important effects in the enzymes involved in human digestion. An enzyme's activity is often limited to a relatively narrow pH. On either side of this range, enzymatic activity drops off rapidly, so a plot of rate versus pH frequently yields a bell-shaped curve:

[handwritten note, left margin] ▽ active site exposed at optimum in true shape

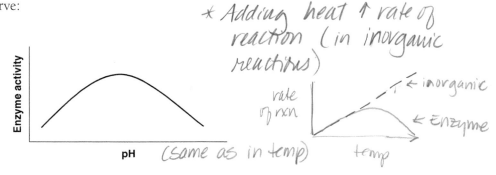

*[handwritten note, upper right] * Adding heat ↑ rate of reaction (in inorganic reactions)*

[handwritten graph] rate of rxn / ← inorganic / ← Enzyme / temp

[handwritten, under pH axis] (same as in temp)

[handwritten, right vertical margin] # - Concentration has ↑ effect in rate of rxn

[handwritten, left vertical margin] ↑ Temp will not affect rate of rxn   Ha ↑ in Temp will affect rate rxn

We call the pH at which an enzyme shows maximal activity the **optimum pH**. For most enzymes in the human body, the optimum pH is near neutrality (pH ≈ 7.0), but some enzymes have unusually high or unusually low pH optima, as you will see.

Similarly, enzymes have an **optimum temperature** at which they show maximal activity. Most enzymes have temperature optima between 20–40°C, although some enzymes have unusually high temperature optima and some have unusually low temperature optima. For most enzymes the rate of reaction doubles for every 10°C increase in temperature (Q_{10} effect). However, this effect is limited by the denaturing of the enzyme as temperature increases. Once denatured, the enzyme cannot catalyze its reaction.

Human digestion occurs by a series of hydrolysis reactions, which break down large polymeric food molecules into smaller monomers that our bodies can absorb. An enzyme catalyzes each of the hydrolytic reactions. Pepsin is found in the stomach and hydrolyzes proteins into smaller polypeptides. These polypeptides are then completely hydrolyzed into their constituent amino acids by other proteases in the small intestine. Pancreatin contains a mixture of digestive enzymes, all produced in the pancreas and secreted into the small intestine. There are enzymes to hydrolyze each of the three major food polymers in pancreatin. Pancreatic proteases digest protein in a manner similar to gastric pepsin.

Many diseases produce elevations in the concentration of specific enzymes in the blood plasma. This can lead to cell injury and/or death caused by the disease and the consequent release of cell contents into the circulatory system. In other cases, diseased cells overproduce certain enzymes and release them. Some released enzymes are specific for a given disease, and these "marker enzymes" can be used to diagnose the condition. For example, the enzyme alkaline phosphatase can be used to diagnose a variety of diseases such as bone cancer, jaundice, and cirrhosis of the liver.

Alkaline phosphatase (ALP) catalyzes the hydrolysis of a phosphate group attached to proteins or lipids *in vivo*. In this experiment, we will use an *in vitro* substrate, para nitrophenol-phosphate (pNPP), which is colorless. Hydrolysis of the phosphate yields para nitrophenol, which is yellow. The appearance of the yellow product will be monitored over time and used as an index of the rate of reaction.

[handwritten] (colorless) pNPP → ALP → pNP (removes phosphate) yellow

[handwritten] ⊛ By monitoring color we monitor rate of rxn ⊛

Procedure for Today's Experiment

Part One

Estimating the optimum pH for stomach pepsin activity:

1. Following the instructions in Table 6-1, prepare four test tubes as follows. Place 2.0 mL of homogenized egg white into each of four numbered test tubes. To tube #1, the control (no enzyme), add 2.0 mL of distilled water and 2.0 mL of 0.2 M HCl. To tube #2, neutral pH, add 2.0 mL of pepsin solution and 2.0 mL of distilled water. To tube #3, acidic, add 2.0 mL of pepsin solution and 2.0 mL of 0.2 M HCl. To tube #4, basic, add 2.0 mL of pepsin solution and 2.0 mL of 0.1 M Na_2CO_3 solution. Carfully mix each tube by covering with Parafilm and inverting the tube.

[handwritten graph, bottom] Rate of rxn / concentration

[handwritten, bottom right] All substrates are involved (in use) saturation curve

TABLE 6-1 Mixing instructions for Pepsin pH Experiment   *I*

Tube	Relative pH	Pepsin	Egg white solution	0.2 M HCl	0.1 M Na$_2$CO$_3$	Distilled water	Total volume	
1 (Control) *Clear*	Acidic	—	2 mL	2 mL	—	2 mL	6 mL	pH 2
2 *milky*	Neutral	2 mL	2 mL	—	—	2 mL	6 mL	pH 7
3	Acidic	2 mL	2 mL	2 mL	—	—	6 mL	pH 1
4	Basic	2 mL	2 mL	—	2 mL	—	6 mL	pH 10

2. Place a strip of broad-range pH paper on a clean, dry, watch glass, and immediately after mixing, remove a drop of each solution and place the drop on the pH paper to estimate the pH of the solution. Record these measurements and the tube from which they were taken in Table 6-5 on page 54.

3. Place the four test tubes in the 40°C water bath. Periodically agitate the tubes to mix them, and observe the mixtures. Record the time required for any changes in the appearance of the tubes. Keep the tubes in the bath for at least one hour, or until the contents of one of the tubes clears. What was the change you observed? Why did this change occur? After one hour, record the appearance of each tube next to the pH data recorded in Table 6-5 on page 54. Compare and contrast the appearance of each tube.

4. Pour the contents of the tubes down the drain with cold, running water. Wash the test tubes and rinse with distilled water. Discard the used pH paper in the appropriate receptacle. Wash and dry the watch glass.

Part Two

(Trypsin)

Estimating the optimum pH for pancreatic protease activity:

1. Following the instructions in Table 6-2, prepare four test tubes as follows. Place 2.0 mL of homogenized egg white into each of four numbered test tubes. To tube #1, the control (no enzyme), add 2.0 mL of distilled water and 2.0 mL of 0.1 M Na$_2$CO$_3$. To tube #2, neutral pH, add 2.0 mL of pancreatin solution and 2.0 mL of distilled water. To tube #3, acidic, add 2.0 mL of pancreatin solution and 2.0 mL of 0.2 M HCl. To tube #4, basic, add 2.0 mL of pancreatin solution and 2.0 mL of 0.1 M Na$_2$CO$_3$ solution. Carefully mix each tube by covering with Parafilm and inverting the tube.

2. Place a strip of broad-range pH paper on a clean, dry, watch glass, and immediately after mixing, remove a drop of each solution and place the drop on the pH paper to estimate the pH of the solution. Record these measurements and the tube from which they were taken in Table 6-6 on page 54.

TABLE 6-2 Mixing instructions for Pancreatin pH Experiment   *II*

Tube	Relative pH	Pancreatin	Egg white solution	0.2 M HCl	0.1 M Na$_2$CO$_3$	Distilled water	Total volume	
1 (Control) *Clear*	Basic	—	2 mL	—	2 mL	2 mL	6 mL	pH 10
2 *milky*	Neutral	2 mL	2 mL	—	—	2 mL	6 mL	pH 7
3 *yellow*	Acidic	2 mL	2 mL	2 mL	—	—	6 mL	pH 2
4	Basic	2 mL	2 mL	—	2 mL	—	6 mL	pH 10

3. Place the four test tubes in the 40°C water bath. Periodically agitate the tubes to mix them, and observe the mixtures. Record the time required for the first cloudy mixture to clear. Keep the tubes in the bath for at least one hour or until the contents of one of the tubes clears. Why does one of the tubes become clear? At that time, record the appearance of each tube next to the pH data recorded in Table 6-6 on page 54. Compare and contrast the appearance of each tube.

4. Pour the contents of the tubes down the drain with cold, running water. Wash the test tubes and rinse with distilled water. Discard the used pH paper in the appropriate receptacle. Wash and dry the watch glass.

Part Three

Determining the effect of enzyme concentration on catalytic rate:

1. Put 12.5 mL of stock Solution A (alkaline buffer solution) into a beaker. Add 12.5 mL of stock Solution B (para nitro phenolphosphate (pNPP) substrate 0.003 M) to the same beaker, and gently swirl the beaker to mix. **Caution: Alkaline phosphate buffer solution and pNPP substrate are irritants. Prevent eye, skin, and clothing contact.**

2. Place 3.0 mL of the mixed buffer and substrate solution into eight cuvettes, marked 1a, 1b, 2a, 2b, 3a, 3b, 4a, and 4b.

3. Place cuvette 1b in the refrigerator (approximately 4°C). Leave cuvette 2b at room temperature (approximately 23°C). Place cuvette 3b in a 32°C water bath. Place cuvette 4b in a 40°C water bath.

4. Set the spectrophotometer to zero absorbance at 405 nm using cuvette 1a (the blank) before you add enzyme. Do not adjust the zero absorbance again during this experiment. Check Table 6-3 to verify that all cuvettes have been prepared properly and that you are ready to take data using the spectrophotometer. Do not add solution C or D until you are ready to actually take the readings with the spectrophotometer. Add solution C or D to one tube at a time and do not add to the next tube until you have recorded all of the data from the first tube. Be sure that someone has a watch with a second hand or a digital readout. Also, have a small square of Parafilm ready.

5. Using the micropipette, add 100 µL of solution C (low ALP concentration) to cuvette 1a, **quickly** cover with Parafilm, invert to mix, remove Parafilm, and place into spectrophotometer. Do this as rapidly as possible, and then begin to record the absorbance readings. Read the absorbance every

| TABLE 6-3 | *Mixing instructions for the effect of enzyme concentration on catalytic rate* |

Notice the Dark Bold Line in the table! Do not add solution C or D until you are ready to actually take the readings with the spectrophotometer. Add C or D to one tube at a time and do not add to the next tube until you have recorded all of the data from the first tube.

Cuvette	Relative enzyme concentration	Solutions A&B (buffer/substrate stock solution)	Solution C low ALP (enzyme) concentration	Solution D high ALP (enzyme) concentration
1a Blank (No Enzyme)	0	3 mL	—	—
1a	Lowest	3 mL	100 µL	—
2a	Medium	3 mL	500 µL	—
3a	Higher medium	3 mL	—	100 µL
4a	Highest	3 mL	—	500 µL

minute for 10 minutes after you insert the mixed cuvette into the spectrophotometer, and record your data in Table 6-7 in the Laboratory Report Form.

6. Using the micropipette, add 500 μL of solution C (low ALP concentration) to cuvette 2a, **quickly** cover with Parafilm, invert to mix, remove Parafilm, and place into spectrophotometer. Do this as rapidly as possible, and then begin to record the absorbance readings. Read the absorbance every minute for 10 minutes after you insert the mixed cuvette into the spectrophotometer, and record your data in Table 6-7 in the Laboratory Report Form.

7. Using the micropipette, add 100 μL of solution D (high ALP concentration) to cuvette 3a, **quickly** cover with Parafilm, invert to mix, remove Parafilm, and place into spectrophotometer. Do this as rapidly as possible, and then begin to record the absorbance readings. Read the absorbance every minute for 10 minutes after you insert the mixed cuvette into the spectrophotometer, and record your data in Table 6-7 in the Laboratory Report Form.

8. Using the micropipette, add 500 μL of solution D (high ALP concentration) to cuvette 4a, **quickly** cover with Parafilm, invert to mix, remove Parafilm, and place into spectrophotometer. Do this as rapidly as possible, and then begin to record the absorbance readings. Read the absorbance every minute for 10 minutes after you insert the mixed cuvette into the spectrophotometer, and record your data in Table 6-7 in the Laboratory Report Form.

Part Four

Determining the effect of temperature on catalytic rate: Check Table 6-4 to verify that all cuvettes have been prepared properly and that you are ready to take data using the spectrophotometer. Do not add solution C until you are ready to actually take the readings with the spectrophotometer. Add solution C to one tube at a time and do not add to the next tube until you have recorded all of the data from the first tube.

1. Using the micropipette, add 100 μL of solution C (low ALP concentration) to cuvette 1b, **quickly** cover with Parafilm, invert to mix, remove Parafilm, and place into spectrophotometer. Do this as rapidly as possible, and then begin to record the absorbance readings. Read the absorbance every minute for 10 minutes after you insert the mixed cuvette into the spectrophotometer, and record your data in Table 6-7 in the Laboratory Report Form.

2. Using the micropipette, add 100 μL of solution C (low ALP concentration) to cuvette 2b, **quickly** cover with Parafilm, invert to mix, remove Parafilm, and place into spectrophotometer. Do this as rapidly as possible, and then begin to record the absorbance readings. Read the absorbance every minute for 10 minutes after you insert the mixed cuvette into the spectrophotometer, and record your data in Table 6-7 in the Laboratory Report Form.

TABLE 6-4 *Mixing instructions for the effect of temperature on catalytic rate*

Notice the Dark Bold Line in the table! Do not add solution C until you are ready to actually take the readings with the spectrophotometer. Add C to one tube at a time and do not add to the next tube until you have recorded all of the data from the first tube.

Tube	Temperature (°C)	Solutions A/B (Buffer/substrate stock solution)	Sol C Low ALP (Enzyme) concentration
1b	4	3 mL	100 μL
2b	23	3 mL	100 μL
3b	32	3 mL	100 μL
4b	40	3 mL	100 μL

3. Using the micropipette, add 100 μL of solution C (low ALP concentration) to cuvette 3b, **quickly** cover with Parafilm, invert to mix, remove Parafilm, and place into spectrophotometer. Do this as rapidly as possible, and then begin to record the absorbance readings. Read the absorbance every minute for 10 minutes after you insert the mixed cuvette into the spectrophotometer, and record your data in Table 6-5 in the Laboratory Report Form.

4. Using the micropipette, add 100 μL of solution C (low ALP concentration) to cuvette 4b, **quickly** cover with Parafilm, invert to mix, remove Parafilm, and place into spectrophotometer. Do this as rapidly as possible, and then begin to record the absorbance readings. Read the absorbance every minute for 10 minutes after you insert the mixed cuvette into the spectrophotometer, and record your data in Table 6-7 in the Laboratory Report Form.

TABLE 6-5   Experimental Observations—effects of pH on pepsin activity

Tube	Relative pH	pH paper reading (estimated number)	Observations of solution
1 (Control—no enzyme)	Acidic	pH 2	Clear
2	Neutral	pH 7	Slightly milky
3	Acidic	pH 1	slightly milky
4	Basic	pH 10	slightly milky

TABLE 6-6   Experimental Observations—effects of pH on pancreatic enzyme activity

Tube	Relative pH	pH paper reading (estimated number)	Observations of solution
1 (Control—no enzyme)	Basic	pH 10	Clear
2	Neutral	pH 7	milky - yellow
3	Acidic	pH 2	milky - yellow
4	Basic	pH 10	milky - yellow

LABORATORY REPORT FORM
Lab 4

Name_____ Date_____

Properties of Enzymes

All answers to the following questions are to be turned in at the **beginning of the next lab meeting**. You must also include four graphs that you will be creating (see below). Make sure to write your name and date on every page of the worksheet and the pages containing the tables and figure.

Students should work individually to answer the following questions and to create the figure.

1. Why did one of the test tubes in the pepsin activity test become clear?

2. Describe the appearance of the three test tubes containing pepsin at the end of one hour, and explain how these results compare to the pH readings.

3. Why did one of the test tubes in the pancreatic protease activity test become clear?

4. Describe the appearance of the three test tubes containing pancreatic protease at the end of one hour, and explain how these results compare to the pH readings.

5. What are the optimum pH levels for the two enzymes in this experiment?

Enzyme	Optimum pH	Location in GI Tract
Pepsin	1-2	Stomach
Pancreatic protease	7.5-8.5	Sm. Intestine

6. Table 6-7.

TABLE 6-7 *Absorbance readings for each cuvette*

	C Concentration D				Temperature 10:30			
Time	**1a**	**2a**	**3a**	**4a**	**1b** 4°	**2b** room temp	**3b** 32	**4b** 40
Initial	0.86	0.411	0.130	0.576	.042	0.078	.089	0.92
1 min	0.109	0.471	0.218	0.808	.052	0.103	.110	0.117
2 min	0.125	0.529	0.253	1.026	.059	0.119	.132	0.145
3 min	0.141	0.586	0.311	1.232	.069	0.137	.155	0.174
4 min	0.157	0.643	0.370	1.472	.080	0.155	.180	0.200
5 min	0.173	0.698	0.428	1.669	.084	0.176	.206	.221
6 min	0.189	0.757	0.487	1.870	.098	0.189	.216	.244
7 min	0.205	0.812	0.545	2.056	.118	0.209	.232	.263
8 min	0.220	0.869	0.607	2.246	.137	0.225	.251	.287
9 min	0.236	0.927	0.667	2.478	.143	0.240	.276	.310
10 min	0.252	0.985	0.727	2.603	.170	0.254	.289	.328

Inversion was not immediate

7. Using the data above, plot the absorbance versus time for cuvettes 1a–4a on one graph. From this graph, determine the slope for each line (1a–4a). Then plot the absorbance versus time for tubes 1b–4b on a second graph. From this graph, determine the slope for each line (1b–4b). Attach these graphs to this report.

8. Using the slopes of each line in the first graph as an index to reaction rate, make another graph with enzyme concentration on the *x*-axis and slope (reaction rate) on the *y*-axis. Make a similar graph for the temperature data, with temperature on the *x*-axis and slope (reaction rate) on the *y*-axis. From this graph, attempt to determine the optimum temperature for the enzyme. Attach these graphs to this report.

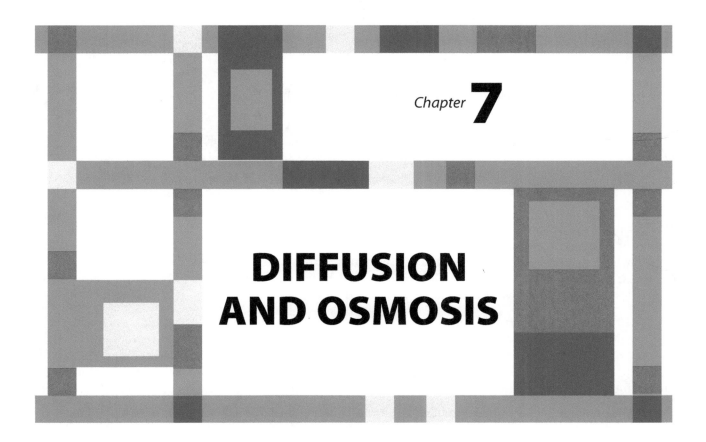

Chapter **7**

DIFFUSION AND OSMOSIS

Overview

In this lab, you will learn about the processes of diffusion and osmosis, both in an artificial system and in living cells.

Background

This laboratory exercise is divided into two parts:

1. Measuring the diffusion of a variety of solutes and the osmosis of water into and out of a dialysis bag (artificial system)

2. Measuring the osmosis of water into and out of living potato cells

Diffusion is the net movement of like molecules or ions from an area of high concentration to an area of low concentration (Figure 7-1). This process requires no energy input; in fact, a concentration gradient represents potential energy and as the molecules move they release kinetic energy. The difference in concentrations between the adjoining regions is called a concentration gradient, and molecules always have a tendency to flow DOWN a concentration gradient (from high to low).

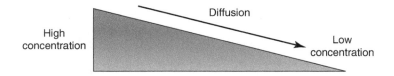

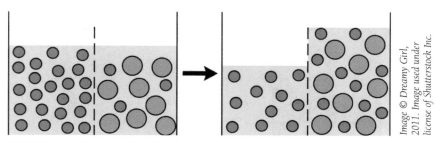

FIGURE 7-1 Small molecules (red) diffuse through a selectively permeable membrane until the concentrations on both sides are equal. Larger molecules (blue) cannot pass through the membrane.

Water follows the same diffusion rules of other substances: it will move from an area of high water concentration to an area of low water concentration. But, when is there a difference in water concentrations? This occurs when there is a difference in solute concentration across a membrane and the solutes are too big or otherwise unable to diffuse themselves. This can occur, for example, in the cell membrane that allows small molecules to pass but that won't allow large, or charged, molecules to pass.

In this situation, when there is a lot of nondiffusible solute, most of the water molecules will be in shells around the solute and unavailable for diffusion. This results in a relatively low water concentration. However, in areas where there is little or no nondiffusible solute, most of the water molecules are "free" and able to diffuse. Thus, water will diffuse from an area of low solute concentration (high free water concentration) to an area of high solute (low free water) concentration. This movement of water is called osmosis.

We can examine the effects of osmosis and define three terms useful to compare the effects of osmosis by examining how osmosis affects cells. We will use a red blood cell from the blood as our "experimental subject." The cytosol of the red blood cell contains many solutes, some of which can diffuse across the plasma membrane of the cell, and some which are too big, or charged, and subsequently cannot diffuse. If we drop a red blood cell into a solution of seawater, the seawater has more total solute than the cytosol of the red blood cell, and so water will move out of the red blood cell. This will cause the red blood cell to shrink (crenate). We can say that the seawater (environment) is hypertonic to the red blood cell (Figure 7-2 right).

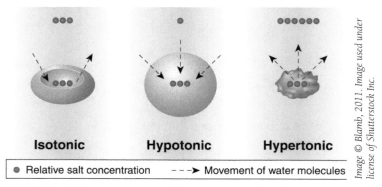

• Relative salt concentration   - - -> Movement of water molecules

Isotonic   **Hypotonic**   **Hypertonic**

FIGURE 7-2 The movement of water across the plasma membrane of a red blood cell in three different environments.

Conversely, if we drop a red blood cell into a distilled water solution, the cell cytosol has more solutes than the distilled water, and water will move into the red blood cell. The cell will expand and eventually burst as the hydrostatic pressure of the water inside the cell overwhelms the strength of the cell membrane. We can say that the distilled water (environment) is hypotonic to the red blood cell (Figure 7-2 center).

Finally, we can drop a red blood cell into a solution that has the same solute concentration as the cytosol of the cell, e.g., 5% glucose or 0.9% NaCl. In this case, although water is moving into and out of the cell, there is no net movement of water, and the cell remains the same size. We can say that the solution (environment) is isotonic to the cell (Figure 7-2 left). As an aside, if we need to give a patient an intravenous injection of a drug to treat some disease, we might dissolve the drug in one of the solutions, e.g., 5% glucose or 0.9% NaCl, so that when we inject the drug, the solution we inject is isotonic to the blood plasma and does not cause any problems with osmosis.

What factors determine how much/how fast water flows across a membrane? One is the differences in solute concentration across the membrane. The greater the difference (steeper the concentration gradient), the more water will cross the membrane (and it will move faster). The second is the hydrostatic pressure on the membrane. This is the water pressure created as water moves into or out of the cell. Because plant cells have cell walls, they will not burst when placed in distilled water, as the red blood cell did above. In the case of a plant cell placed in a hypotonic solution, water will move into the cell until the pressure of the water attempting to drive water out of the cell (the hydrostatic pressure) is equal to the osmotic pressure created by the solute causing water to enter the cell. At this point, even though water is moving into and out of the cell, the rates of water movement in both directions are equal, and the system is at equilibrium.

In today's laboratory exercise, you will study osmosis and diffusion in plant cells. You will also examine these processes in an artificial system using dialysis tubing. Dialysis tubing is an artificial plastic membrane that contains small holes (pores) of very specific sizes. These pores passively allow substances to pass across the plastic membrane. Dialysis membranes are commercially available with a wide variety of pore sizes that will allow molecules of various molecular weights to pass or will prevent them from passing. Because water molecules are very small relative to other biological macromolecules, dialysis tubing can allow for both osmosis and the diffusion of solutes. One important difference between real cell membranes and dialysis tubing is that real membranes are much more selective in terms of what they will allow to pass through themselves. The dialysis tubing experiment takes more time, so you will start with that experiment.

Procedure for Today's Experiment

H₂O 18 Daltons [handwritten]

Part One

1. Obtain a 20 cm section of dialysis tubing that has been soaking in a beaker of distilled water. Wear gloves when handling the dialysis tubing to keep oils and dirt from your fingers from clogging the pores in the tubing. Flush the inside of the tubing with some distilled water and squeeze it to expel all excess water. Tie off, or fold and clip, one end of the tube, to form a pouch, and then place 3 mL of the starch (molecular weight > 100,000 Daltons) and sodium sulfate (Na_2SO_4; MW = 142 Daltons) solution in the bag. Tie off, or fold and clip, the other end of the bag, wash the bag in distilled water, blot it dry, and then weigh it and record the weight as "initial water weight" in Table 7-1. Also, add 1.0 mL of the starch/sodium sulfate solution to each of four test tubes labeled "bag start."

2. Place the bag in a beaker containing a solution of albumin (MW ~ 64,000 Daltons) and glucose (MW = 180 Daltons). Be sure the albumin/glucose solution completely covers the bag. Add 1.0 mL of the albumin/glucose solution to each of four test tubes labeled "solution start."

3. Keep the bag in the albumin/glucose solution for 120 minutes. Every 15 minutes, gently swirl the beaker containing the bag and the albumin/glucose solution.

4. At the end of 120 minutes, take four 1.0 mL samples of the albumin/glucose solution from the beaker, and add them to four test tubes marked "solution end."

5. Remove the bag from the solution, and rinse it with distilled water. Carefully and gently blot it dry, and then weigh it and record the weight as "final water weight" in Table 7-1.

6. Carefully open the bag and dump the contents into a beaker. Take four 1.0 mL samples of the starch/sodium sulfate solution from the bag and add them to four test tubes marked "bag end."

7. To test for the presence of glucose, dip a glucose "dip-and-read" strip into the first test tube from each group of samples, i.e., "bag start," "solution start," "bag end," and "solution end." The pad of paper at the end of the strip will change color if glucose is present in the solution.

Molecules not → does it affect diffusion [handwritten, left margin]

8. To test for sodium sulfate in the solution and bag samples, add a few drops of 2% barium chloride ($BaCl_2$) to the second test tube from each group of samples, i.e., "bag start," "solution start," "bag end," and "solution end." If sodium sulfate is present in the solution, the sulfate ion will precipitate with the barium ion, forming white particles.

9. Dip a protein "dip-and-read" strip into the third test tube from each group of samples, i.e., "bag start," "solution start," "bag end," and "solution end." The pad of paper at the end of the strip will change color if protein is present in the solution.

10. Add a few drops of iodine solution to the fourth test tube from each group of samples, i.e., "bag start," "solution start," "bag end," and "solution end." If starch is present in the solution, it will turn blue-black when the iodine is added.

Part Two

1. Place 50 mL of each solution labeled 0.2 M sucrose, 0.4 M sucrose, 0.6 M sucrose, 0.8 M sucrose, 1M sucrose, distilled water, and unknown into different labeled plastic cups.

2. Slice a potato into discs that are approximately 3 cm thick.

3. Use a cork borer to cut 28 potato cylinders from the discs. Do not include any skin on the cylinders. You need four cylinders for each solution in step 1.

4. Separate the cylinders into seven groups of four. Keep the cylinders covered until you are ready to weigh them.

5. Determine the mass of each group of cylinders, and then place the groups into the beakers.

6. Record the initial masses in Table 7-2 on the laboratory report form.

7. Let stand for one hour at room temperature.

8. Remove the potato cores from each beaker, blot them gently on a paper towel, and determine their final mass.

9. Record the final masses in Table 7-2 on the laboratory report form, and calculate the percentage change using the following equation:

$$\text{Percent change} = \frac{\text{Ending mass} - \text{Starting mass}}{\text{Starting mass}} \times 100\%$$

Record your data in Table 7-2 on the laboratory report form. Record the data from other groups in Table 7-3.

TABLE 7-1

Complete the table below with + or – for each of the substances and record the weight to indicate water movement.

	Glucose	Sulfate ion	Protein	Starch	Water weight (g)
Inside bag					
Initial	(–)	+	(–)	+	5.92 g
Final	+	+	(–)	+	6.15 g
Outside bag					
Initial	+	(–)	+	(–)	
Final	+	+	+	(–)	

equilibrium

Due 10/22   Report-full (proper)

LABORATORY REPORT FORM
Lab 5

Name_____ Date_____

Diffusion and Osmosis

All answers to the following questions are to be turned in at the **beginning of the next lab meeting**. You must also include printouts of the figure and two tables that you will be creating (see below). Make sure to write your name and date on every page of the worksheet and the pages containing the tables and figure. This laboratory exercise also requires a formal lab report write-up. Detailed instructions will be provided by your instructor.

Students should work individually to answer the following questions and to create the figure.

Part One

1. Which substances (i.e., sodium sulfate, glucose, starch, albumin, and water) moved through the dialysis tubing? Which direction did they move relative to their concentration gradient?

2. Compare the movement of the substances to their molecular weight. Can you estimate the molecular weight cut-off (size of the pores) in the dialysis tubing from your data?

3. Did water move through the dialysis tubing into or out of the bag? What data do you have to support your answer?

TABLE 7-2

Contents in beaker	Initial mass	Final mass	Mass difference	% Change in mass	Class average % change in mass
a. Distilled Water	2.205 g	2.456	.251	11.38	
b. 0.2 M Sucrose	1.962 g	2.039	.077	3.92	
c. 0.4 M Sucrose	2.412 g	2.236	.176	7.29	
d. 0.6 M Sucrose	2.518 g	2.171	.387	15.36	
e. 0.8 M Sucrose	2.250 g	1.792	.458	20.35	
f. 1 M Sucrose	2.724 g	2.107	.617	22.65	
g. Unknown	2.144 g	1.880	.264	12.31	

TABLE 7-3

Treatment	Group 1	Group 2	Group 3	Group 4	Group 5	Group 6	Total	Average
a. Distilled Water								
b. 0.2 M Sucrose								
c. 0.4 M Sucrose								
d. 0.6 M Sucrose								
e. 0.8 M Sucrose								
f. 1 M Sucrose								

1. Make two bar histograms, one of your group's percent change in mass data from Table 7-2 and one of the class averages and standard deviations for the percentage change in mass from Table 7-2.

2. Determine the molar concentration of the potato and record this in your results. Do this by drawing a graph with sucrose concentration on the x-axis and the average percent change in mass on the y-axis. The data should form a straight line. Where the line crosses the x-axis represents the sucrose concentration where the mass change would be zero and corresponds to the molar concentration of the potato.

3. Determine the molar concentration of the unknown solution by drawing a line from the mass change in this solution on the y-axis horizontally to the line of data and then up or down vertically to the concentration of sucrose. You could also use a spreadsheet program to determine the equation for the line, and then solve for x to calculate the molar concentration of the unknown solution.

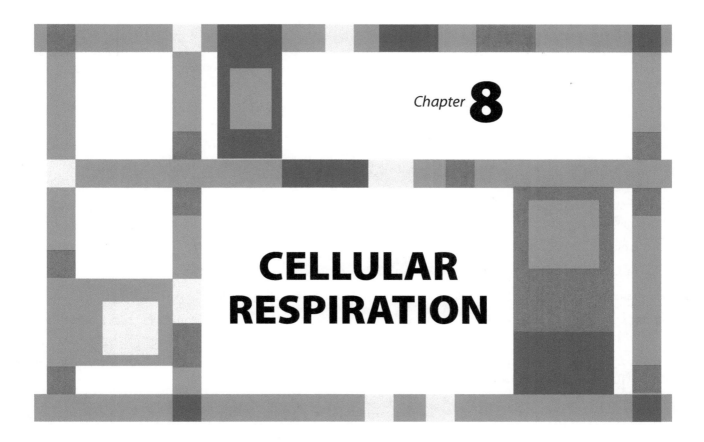

Chapter 8

CELLULAR RESPIRATION

Overview

In this experiment, you will work with seeds that are living but dormant. A seed contains a plant embryo and a food supply surrounded by a seed coat. When the necessary conditions are met, germination occurs, and the rate of cellular respiration greatly increases. In this laboratory you will measure oxygen consumption during germination. You will measure the change in gas volume in respirometers containing either germinating or nongerminating pea seeds. In addition, you will measure the rate of respiration at two different temperatures, cold and warm.

Objectives

Before doing this laboratory experiment, you should understand:

1. How a respirometer works

2. The general processes of metabolism in living organisms

After doing this laboratory experiment, you should be able to:

1. Calculate the rate of cell respiration from experimental data

2. Relate gas production to respiration rate

3. Test the effect of temperature on the rate of cell respiration in ungerminated versus germinated seeds in a controlled experiment

Background

Cellular respiration is the release of energy from organic compounds by metabolic chemical oxidation in the mitochondria within each cell. Cellular respiration involves a series of enzyme-mediated reactions.

The equation below shows the complete oxidation of glucose. Oxygen is required for this energy-releasing process to occur.

$$C_6H_{12}O_6 + 6\ O_2 \rightarrow 6\ CO_2 + 6\ H_2O + 686 \text{ kilocalories of energy/mole of glucose oxidized}$$

By studying the equation above, you will notice there are three ways cellular respiration could be measured. One could measure the:

1. Consumption of O_2 (How many moles of O_2 are consumed in cellular respiration?). 6
2. Production of CO_2 (How many moles of CO_2 are produced in cellular respiration?). 6
3. Release of energy during cellular respiration. 686 kcal / glucose mole

In this experiment, the relative volume of O_2 consumed by germinating and nongerminating (dry) peas at two different temperatures will be measured.

A number of physical laws relating to gases are important to the understanding of how the apparatus that you will use in this exercise works. The laws are summarized in the general gas law that states:

$$PV = nRT$$

where:

P is the pressure of the gas

V is the volume of the gas

n is the number of molecules of gas

R is the gas constant (its value is fixed), and

T is the temperature of the gas (in °K).

This law implies the following important concepts about gases:

1. If temperature and pressure are kept constant, then the volume of the gas is directly proportional to the number of molecules of the gas.
2. If the temperature and volume remain constant, then the pressure of the gas changes in direct proportion to the number of molecules of gas present.
3. If the number of gas molecules and the temperature remain constant, then the pressure is inversely proportional to the volume.
4. If the temperature changes and the number of gas molecules are kept constant, then either the pressure or volume (or both) will change in direct proportion to the temperature.

It is also important to remember that gases and fluids flow from regions of high pressure to regions of low pressure.

In this experiment, the CO_2 produced during cellular respiration will be removed by potassium hydroxide (KOH) and will form solid potassium carbonate (K_2CO_3) according to the following reaction:

$$CO_2 + 2\ KOH \rightarrow K_2CO_3 + H_2O$$

$$C_6H_{12}O_6 + 6O_2 \rightarrow 6CO_2 + 6H_2O + 686 \text{ Kcal ATP}$$

Since the CO_2 is being removed, the change in the volume of gas in the respirometer will be directly related to the amount of O_2 consumed.

In the experimental apparatus, if water temperature and volume remain constant, the water will move toward the region of lower pressure. During respiration, O_2 will be consumed. Its volume will be reduced because the CO_2 produced is being converted to a solid. The net result is a decrease in gas volume within the tube and a related decrease in pressure in the tube. The vial with glass beads alone will permit detection of any changes in volume due to atmospheric pressure changes or temperature changes.

The amount of O_2 consumed will be measured over a period of time. Six respirometers should be set up as follows:

Respirometer	Temperature	Contents
1	Room	Germinating seeds
2	Room	Dry seeds and beads
3	Room 23°	Beads
4	10°C 5°	Germinating Seeds
5	10°C	Dry seeds and beads
6	10°C	Beads

Procedure for Today's Experiment

1. Both a room-temperature bath (approximately 25°C) and a cold temperature (approximately 10°C) bath should be set up immediately to allow for time to adjust the temperature of each. Add ice to attain 10°C.

2. **Respirometer 1**: Obtain a 100 mL graduated cylinder, and fill it with 50 mL of H_2O. Drop in 10 germinating peas and determine the amount of water that was displaced (which is equivalent to the volume of the peas). Record the volume of 10 germinating peas. Remove those peas, and place them on a paper towel. They will be used in respirometer 1.

3. **Respirometer 2**: Refill the graduated cylinder with 50 mL of water. Drop 10 dried peas (not germinating) into the graduated cylinder, and then add enough glass beads to attain a volume equivalent to that of the germinating peas. Remove these peas and glass beads and place them on a paper towel. They will be used in respirometer 2.

4. **Respirometer 3**: Refill the graduated cylinder with 50 mL of water. Determine how many glass beads are required to attain a volume equivalent to that of the germinating peas. Remove these beads, and place them on a paper towel. They will be used in respirometer 3. ✱ control ✱

5. Repeat the procedures above to prepare a second set of germinating peas, dry peas plus glass beads, and beads alone for use in respirometers 4, 5, and 6, respectively.

6. To assemble the six respirometers, obtain six weighted vials and six stoppers with pipettes. Place a small wad of absorbent cotton in the bottom of each vial and, using a dropper, saturate the cotton with 15% KOH. Make sure that the respirometer vials are dry on the inside. Do not get KOH on the sides of the respirometer. Place a small wad of dry nonabsorbent cotton on top of the KOH-soaked cotton (Figure 8-1). **It is important that the amounts of cotton and KOH be the same for each respirometer**.

7.

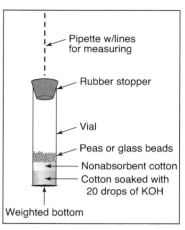

FIGURE 8-1 Components of a respirometer.

8. Place the first set of germinating peas, dry peas and beads, and beads alone in vials 1, 2, and 3, respectively. Place the second set of germinating peas, dry peas and beads, and beads alone in vials 4, 5, and 6, respectively. Insert the stopper fitted with a calibrated pipette. Wrap with Parafilm to seal.

9. Make a sling out of tape attached to each side of the water baths (Figure 8-2) to hold the pipettes out of the water during an equilibrium period of 7 minutes. Vials 1, 2, and 3 should rest in room temperature water and vials 4, 5, and 6 in 10°C water. While waiting for your respirometers to equilibrate in their temperature baths, you should practice reading water levels in the pipettes of practice respirometers set up by your instructor.

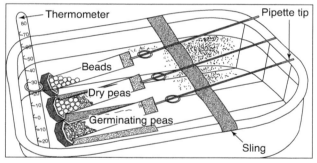

FIGURE 8-2 Reespirometers equilibrating in a water bath.

10. After the equilibration period of 7 minutes, immerse all six respirometers entirely in their water baths. **Make sure the tips of the pipettes are below the surface of the water so water can enter the pipette.** Water will enter the pipettes for a short distance then stop. If the water continues to move into a pipette, check for leaks in the respirometer. Work swiftly and arrange the respirometers so that they can be read through the water at the beginning of the experiment. They should not be shifted during the experiment. Hands should be kept out of the water bath after the experiment begins. Make sure that a constant temperature is maintained.

11. Allow the respirometers to equilibrate for 3 more minutes, then record, to the nearest 0.01 mL, the initial position of water in each pipette (time 0). Check the temperature in both baths, and record in Table 8-1. Every 5 minutes for 20 minutes, take readings of the water's position in each pipette, and record the data in Table 8-1.

12. After entering your data into Table 8-1 (next page), complete the table by calculating the difference between the initial reading (time 0) and the reading at the time X for the beads alone. For example, if your initial reading was 0.02 mL, and your reading after 10 minutes was 0.05 mL, the difference

Dependant variable output

TABLE 8-1

8°c Temp. °C	Time (min)	Beads Alone: Reading at time X	Beads Alone: Difference A	Germinating Peas: Reading at time X	Germinating Peas: Difference B	Germinating Peas: Corrected difference B–A	Dry Peas and Beads: Reading at time X	Dry Peas and Beads: Difference C	Dry Peas and Beads: Corrected difference C–A
Cold	Initial - 0	2.0		2.2			.6		
	5	2.4	0.4	4.3	2.1	1.7	1.1	0.5	0.1
	10	2.4	0.4	5.3	3.1	2.7	1.4	0.8	0.4
	15	2.4	0.4	6.2	4.0	3.6	1.7	1.1	0.7
	20	2.4	0.4	6.3	4.1	3.7	1.8	1.2	0.8
Warm	Initial - 0	0.1		1.3			1.0		
25°c	5	0.2	0.1	1.5	0.2	0.1	1.1	0.1	0
	10	0.2	0.1	2.5	1.2	1.1	1.2	0.2	0.1
	15	0.2	0.1	4.2	2.9	2.8	1.2	0.2	0.1
	20	0.2	0.1	5.2	3.9	3.8	1.3	0.3	0.2

independent variable

$C_6H_{12}O_6 + 6O_2 \rightarrow 6CO_2 + 6H_2O$

(initial reading – time X reading) is –0.03 mL. Enter these values in the difference column under beads alone (labelled Difference A). Notice that there is no difference for time 0.

13. Likewise calculate the difference between the initial reading (time 0) and the reading at time X for the germinating peas, and enter these values in the difference column under germinating peas (labelled Difference B). Do the same for the difference column under dry peas and beads (labelled Difference C).

14. Then correct your difference calculations for the germinating peas and dried peas and beads for the changes that occurred with the beads alone. For each row except the time 0 row in Table 8-1, subtract the difference value in the beads alone column from the difference value for the germinating peas (column Difference B – column Difference A), and enter this number in the corrected difference column under germinating peas. Likewise, subtract the difference value in the beads alone column from the difference value under dried peas and beads (column Difference C – column Difference A) and enter this value in the corrected difference column under germinating peas. For example, if your difference value after 10 minutes under germinating peas was –0.12 mL, then subtract that from the difference value at 10 minutes under the beads alone (–0.03 above) for a corrected difference value of 0.09.

LABORATORY REPORT FORM
Lab 6

Name_____ Date_____

Cellular Respiration

All answers to the following questions are to be turned in at the **beginning of the next lab meeting**. Make sure to write your name and date on every page of the worksheet and the page containing the figure.

Students should work individually to answer the following questions and to create the figure.

1. In this activity, you are investigating both the effect of germination versus nongermination and warm temperature versus cold temperature on respiration rate.

   Identify the hypotheses being tested in this activity.

   Temperature plays a role in cellular respiration rate of germinating peas. Cold temp will inhibit cellular respiration.

2. This activity uses a number of controls. Identify at least three of the controls, and describe the purpose of each control.

   KOH

   glass beads - Pressure and production of CO_2 will remain constant

   Temperature - Maintains all specimens under exact same conditions to allow/inhibit cellular respiration

   Volume - Allows for calculations of ↑ ↓ of vol

3. Graph the results from the corrected difference column for the germinating peas and dry peas at both room temperature and at 10°C and label it Figure 1. For this graph you will need to determine the following:

   a. The *independent variable* _____*O_2 consumed (ml)*_____ Use this to label the horizontal (*x*) axis.

   b. The *dependent variable* _____*Time*_____ Use this to label the vertical (*y*) axis.

   c. Be sure to **title** the graph.

   Cellular Respiration @ 8° 25°

4. Describe and explain the relationship between the amount of O_2 consumed and time.

   At time ↑ consumption of O_2 ↑

5. From the slope of the four lines in Figure 1, determine the rate of O_2 consumption of germinating and dry peas during the experiments at room temperature and at 10°C. Recall that rate = $\Delta Y/\Delta X$.

Condition	Show Calculations Here	Rate in mL O_2/Minute
Germinating Peas @ 10°C	*3.7 - 1.7/20 = 2.0/20*	*0.1 mL O_2/min*
Germinating Peas @ Room Temperature	*3.9 - 0.2/20 = 3.7/20*	*0.2* *0.185 mL O_2/min*
Dry Peas @ 10°C	*0.8 - 0.1/20 = 0.7/20*	*.04* *.035 mL O_2/min*
Dry Peas @ Room Temperature	*0.3 - 0.1/20 = 0.2/20*	*0.01 mL O_2/min*

6. Why is it necessary to correct the readings from the peas with the readings from the beads?

   Beads are the baseline that measurement for peas are compared ē. Beads did not consume O_2

7. Explain the effect of germination (versus nongermination) on pea respiration.

   Germinating peas are actively carrying on cellular respiration, thus having a ↑ rate of of O_2 consumption than Dry peas.

8. What is the purpose of the KOH in this experiment?

   Removal of CO_2 making O_2 consumption measurable

9. Why did the vial have to be completely sealed around the stopper?

For pressure to remain constant
ē gas consumption/production
ē environmental influence (such as water or air)

10. If you used the same experimental design to compare the rates of respiration of a 25 g reptile and a 25 g mammal at 10°C, what would you expect? Explain your reasoning.

Rate of respiration would be higher in a 25g mammal because its body would need to keep optimal temp to ensure survival. Reptiles have slower metabolism as they acquire heat from the environment vs. cellular resp.

11. If respiration in a small mammal were studied at both room temperature (21°C) and 10°C, what results would you predict? Explain your reasoning.

↑ CR in 10°

12. Explain why water moved into the respirometers' pipettes.

N/A

13. Design an experiment to examine the rates of cellular respiration in peas that have been germinating for 0, 24, 48, and 72 hours. What results would you expect and why?

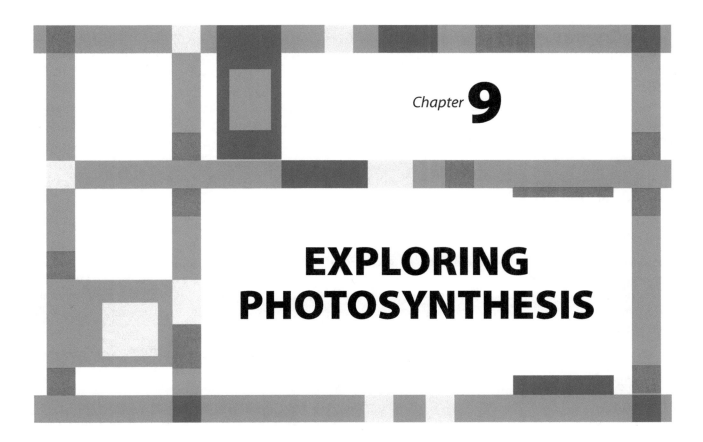

Chapter **9**

EXPLORING PHOTOSYNTHESIS

Overview

In this laboratory experiment, you will measure the rate of photosynthesis in isolated chloroplasts. The measurement technique involves the reduction of the dye, 2,6 dichlorophenol indophenol (DPIP). The transfer of electrons during the light-dependent reactions of photosynthesis reduces DPIP, changing it from blue to colorless.

Objectives

Before doing this laboratory experiment, you should understand:

1. The process of photosynthesis

2. The functions of plant pigments

3. The relationship between light wavelength and photosynthetic rate

4. The relationship between light intensity and photosynthetic rate

After doing this laboratory experiment, you should be able to:

1. Describe a technique to determine photosynthetic rates

2. Compare photosynthetic rates at different temperatures, different light intensities, or different light wavelengths using controlled experiments

3. Explain why the rate of photosynthesis varies under different environmental conditions

Bozemans Science → (handwritten annotation)

Background

The Light Reactions

Light is a part of a continuum of radiation, or energy waves. Shorter wavelengths of energy have greater amounts of energy. For example, high-energy ultraviolet rays can harm living tissues. Wavelengths of light within the visible part of the light spectrum power photosynthesis.

When light is absorbed by leaf pigments, electrons within each photosystem are boosted to a higher energy level, and this energy is used to produce ATP and to reduce $NADP^+$ to NADPH. ATP and NADPH are then used to incorporate CO_2 into organic molecules, a process called carbon fixation.

The Experiment

Photosynthesis may be studied in a number of ways. For this experiment, a dye-reduction technique will be used. The dye-reduction experiment tests the hypothesis that light and chloroplasts are required for the light reactions to occur. In place of the electron acceptor, $NADP^+$, the compound DPIP (2,6-dichlorophenol-indophenol) will be substituted. When light strikes chloroplasts, electrons boosted to high energy levels will reduce DPIP and it will change from blue to colorless.

In this experiment, chloroplasts are extracted from spinach leaves and incubated with DPIP in the presence of light. As the DPIP is reduced and becomes colorless, the resultant increase in light transmittance is measured over a period of time using a spectrophotometer. The experimental design matrix is presented in Table 9-1.

Electrons from H_2O (H^+) will reduce DPIP (handwritten annotation)

TABLE 9-1 *Experimental design matrix*

	Cuvettes				
	1 Blank	**2** Unboiled chloroplasts Dark (foil)	**3** Unboiled chloroplasts Light	**4** Boiled chloroplasts Light	**5** No chloroplasts
Phosphate buffer	1 mL	1 mL	1 mL	1 mL	1 mL
Distilled H_2O	4 mL	3 mL	3 mL	3 mL	3 mL + 3 drops
DPIP	— *green*	1 mL *b/g*	1 mL *b/g*	1 mL *b/g*	1 mL *blue*
Unboiled chloroplasts	3 drops	3 drops	3 drops	—	—
Boiled chloroplasts	—	—	—	3 drops	—
		b/g	*green*	*b/g*	*blue — expectations*

(handwritten annotations below row)

Procedure for Today's Experiment

1. Turn on the spectrophotometer to warm up the instrument and set the wavelength to 605 nm by adjusting the control.

2. Set up an incubation area that includes a light, water flask, and test tube rack. The water in the flask acts as a heat sink by absorbing most of the light's infrared radiation while having little effect on the light's visible radiation (Figure 9-1).

FIGURE 9-1 Chloroplast incubation set up.

Image courtesy of Edward O. Keith, 2011.

3. You will be provided with two beakers, one containing a solution of boiled chloroplasts and the other containing unboiled chloroplasts. Be sure to keep these on ice at all times.

4. At the top rim, label cuvettes 1 through 5, respectively. Using lens tissue, wipe the outside walls of each cuvette (Remember: handle cuvettes only near the top). Cover the walls and bottom of cuvette 2 with foil, and make a foil cap cover for the top. Light should not be permitted inside cuvette 2 because it is a control for this experiment.

5. Refer to Table 9-1 to prepare each cuvette. **Do not add unboiled or boiled chloroplasts yet**. To each cuvette, add 1 mL of phosphate buffer. To cuvette 1, add 4 mL of distilled H_2O. To cuvettes 2, 3, and 4, add 3 mL of distilled H_2O. To cuvettes 2, 3, and 4, add 1 mL of DPIP. To cuvette 5, add 1 mL phosphate buffer, 3 mL plus 3 drops of distilled H_2O, and 1 mL DPIP.

6. Set the spectrophotometer to 100% Transmittance. Cover the top of cuvette #1 with Parafilm and invert to mix. Insert cuvette #1 into the sample holder in the spectrophotometer. **Only reset the spectrophtometer to 100% Transmittance with cuvette #1 ("blank") when you change the wavelength on the spectrophotometer.** In other words, you will measure the light transmittance through the other samples as a percentage of the light transmitted through cuvette #1 at each wavelength. For each reading, make sure that the cuvettes are inserted into the sample holder so that they face the same way as for the previous reading. This keeps the distance that the light travels through the sample constant.

7. Obtain the unboiled chloroplast suspension, stir to mix, and transfer 3 drops to cuvette 2. Immediately cover and mix cuvette 2. Then, remove it from the foil tube and insert it into the sample holder, read the % transmittance, and record it as the Time 0 reading in Table 9-2. Replace cuvette 2 into the foil sleeve, and place it in the incubation test tube rack. Turn on the floodlight. Take and record additional readings at 5, 10, and 15 minutes. Mix the cuvettes' contents just prior to each reading. Remember to use cuvette 1 occasionally to check and adjust the spectrophotometer to 100% transmittance.

8. Obtain the unboiled chloroplast suspension, mix, and transfer 3 drops to cuvette 3. Immediately cover and mix cuvette. Insert into the sample holder, read the % transmittance, and record in Table 9-2 as Time 0. Place cuvette 3 in the incubation test tube rack next to cuvette 2. Take and record additional readings at 5, 10, and 15 minutes. Mix the cuvettes contents just prior to each reading. Remember to use cuvette 1 occasionally to check and adjust the spectrophotometer to 100% transmittance.

9. Obtain the boiled chloroplast suspension, mix, and transfer 3 drops to cuvette 4. Immediately cover and mix cuvette 4. Insert into the sample holder, read the % transmittance, and record in Table 9-2 (as Time 0). Place cuvette 4 in the test tube rack next to tubes 2 and 3. Take and record additional readings at 5, 10, and 15 minutes. Mix the cuvettes contents just prior to each reading. Remember to use cuvette 1 occasionally to check and adjust the spectrophotometer to 100% transmittance.

10. Cover and mix cuvette 5. Insert it into the sample holder, read the % transmittance, and record in Table 9-2 (as Time 0). Place cuvette 5 in the test tube rack next to tubes 2, 3, and 4. Take additional readings at 5, 10, and 15 minutes. Mix the cuvettes contents just prior to each reading. Remember to use cuvette 1 occasionally to check and adjust the spectrophotometer to 100% transmittance.

3+ tubes as tube #2

TABLE 9-2 Individual group transmittance data for each cuvette (individual lab group data only)

Cuvette	0 mins	5 mins	10 mins	15 mins
2 Unboiled/Dark	A. 23.13 SD.0.14 26.3 SD. 8.20 A. 28.48 g. 37.0 b. 32.8 27.43	A. 27.45 SD.6.02 28.7 SD.6.34 A. 27.85 g. 37.0 b. 34.5 A. 26.93	25.68 SD. 2.42 29.2 SD 6.00 A. 28.43 g. 37.0 b. 34.5 A. 28.3	26.10 SD.2.37 29.5 SD.5.58 A. 29.2 A.83 g. 37.0 b. 37.0 A.25.88
3 Unboiled/Light	A 22.87 SD.1.92 SD. 2.10 25.9	97.93 SD.5.73 SD 8.83 109.5	98.20 SD.41.6 SD.9.62 110.8	97.98 SD.11.21 SD.9.94 110.9
4 Boiled/Light	32.03 SD.4.44 39.1	36.70 SD.4.57 45.3	4030 SD.5.09 47.0	41.28 SD.5.18 47.2
5 No Chloroplasts	A. 33.96 SD.480 40.1	33.43 SD.4.65 40.2	33.99 SD.447 40.2	34.18 SD.474 40.3

Name _____ Date _*11.05.13*_____

Exploring Photosynthesis

All answers to the following questions are to be turned in at the **beginning of the next lab meeting**. You must also include printouts of a figure and a table that you will be creating (see below). Make sure to write your name and date on every page of the worksheet and the pages containing the table and figure.

Students should work individually to answer the following questions and to create the graphs.

1. Data presentation
   a. **Table 9-3** (Transmittance readings)—Individual group data will be entered during class. Average the class data and calculate the standard deviation at each time point. Give the table a descriptive title and turn in.
   b. **Figure 9-1**—Using the data from Table 9-3, **graph the average percent transmittance for the 4 conditions (unboiled/light, boiled/light, unboiled/dark, no chloroplasts)**. The *x*-axis should be time (min) and the *y*-axis should be light transmittance (%). It should be a line graph that contains four lines. The standard deviations should be included in the graph.

2. What was the purpose of DPIP in this experiment?

   Act as NADPH would under normal photosynthesis

3. What molecule found in the chloroplasts does DPIP replace in this experiment?

   NADPH

4. What is the source of the electrons that reduced the DPIP?

   H_2O – H^+ reduces

5. What was measured with the spectrophotometer in this experiment?

Amt of light absorbed by chlorophylls

6. What purpose did the flask of water serve? What would have happened if you accidentally left it out?

Absorb heat while transmitting light

7. What results would you have expected if the light source only emitted green light?

no photosynthesis

8. Data analysis

   a. What is the effect of darkness on the reduction of DPIP? Explain. (For example, what happens to electron movement in the dark?)

   b. What is the effect of boiling the chloroplasts on the subsequent reduction of DPIP? Explain. (For example, why might boiling be harmful?)

9. What reasons can you give for the difference in the percent transmittance between the live chloroplasts that were incubated in the light and those that were kept in the dark?

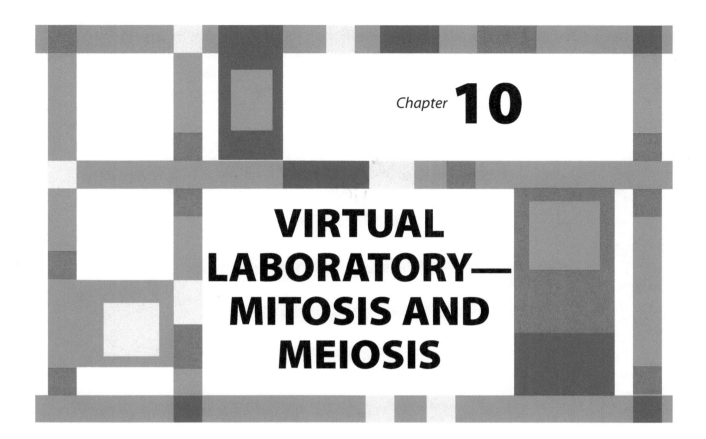

Chapter 10

VIRTUAL LABORATORY— MITOSIS AND MEIOSIS

Introduction

You may work together with your lab partner, but your written responses to the questions and your drawings must be your own. Otherwise, you will receive no credit for this lab. Make sure you understand all aspects of this lab. There will be questions from this lab on your quizzes and tests.

Overview

In this virtual laboratory, you will use some resources available on the Internet to investigate the process of mitosis and meiosis. The first part is a study of mitosis. You will examine slides of whitefish and onion cells undergoing mitosis. You will be able to make comparisons of mitosis in plant and animal cells. The second part is a study of meiosis. You will examine slides of meiosis taking place in *Lillium spp.* anthers. These plants are related to the familiar traditional Easter lilies. Finally, you will make graphic comparisons between cells undergoing mitosis and those undergoing meiosis. You will be taking some online self-quizzes to test your knowledge of both meiosis and mitosis.

Procedures and Analysis Questions

A. Mitosis in Onion Root-Tip Cells and in Whitefish Cells.
  Go to the website: http://biog-1101-1104.bio.cornell.edu/biog101_104/tutorials/cell_division.html. To find the site easily without having to type in the long web-page address, do an Internet search for "Cornell

Biology Mitosis," and select "Cell Division Tutorials" and then "Review—Onion Root Tip." If this link is no longer active, the instructor will provide one for you. You may also use the mitosis images in your textbook.

1. Sketch the slides that you see at this website for onion root-tip cells undergoing mitosis on the laboratory report form. (See: Review—Onion Root Tip.) Label all the parts of your sketch.

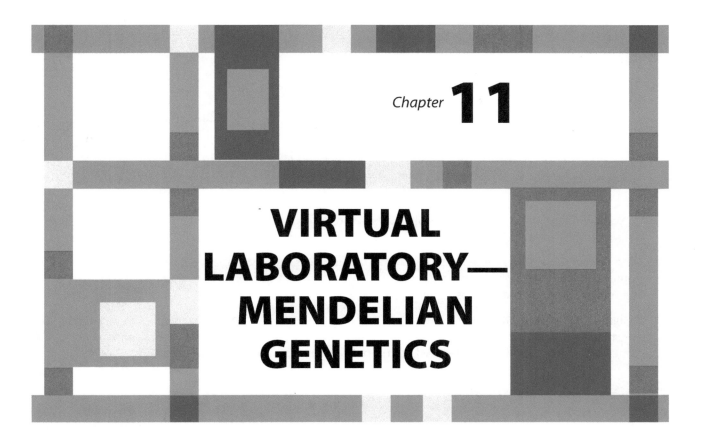

Chapter **11**

VIRTUAL LABORATORY— MENDELIAN GENETICS

Overview

In this lab exercise, you will use the virtual Fly Lab website at www.biologylabsonline.com[1] to help you predict the outcome of monohybrid (one gene), dihybrid (two gene), and trihybrid (three gene) genetic crosses between individual fruit flies, *Drosophilia melanogaster*. You will also make use of the chi-square χ^2 test statistic to help assess whether or not there is a difference in the number of individuals that were observed and expected in each phenotypic category. This lab will also serve to help make sure you understand the law of multiplication and are able to use it to your full advantage. By the end of this lab, you should not be slave to the Punnet square, but instead a master of it. You will also use Fly Lab to explore the effects of lethal mutations, epistasis, and X-linked genes on the outcomes of genetic crosses in both monohybrid and dihybrid examples.

Background

Tracking inheritance of genes from parents to offspring has been an interesting and important field within the study of biology. Groundbreaking work was begun in this field by Gregor Mendel in the 1800s who grew countless numbers of generations of pea plants and tracked their phenotypic traits. This type of study was continued by Thomas Hunt Morgan, who extensively studied fruit flies. Morgan was awarded the Nobel Prize in Physiology or Medicine in 1933 for his discovery of the X-linked white-eyed mutation in fruit flies. Work in this field continues to advance as additional details of genetics in various organisms become better known.

This lab consists of a series of exercises to help you better understand the following components of genetics crosses through one and two generations (F_1 and F_2).

---

[1] The virtual Fly Lab website is provided by Pearson Publishing, Inc., as a collaboration between the California State University System and Benjamin Cummings, Inc., an imprint of Pearson Publishing, Inc.

I. **Exercise 1 (Simple Mendelian Genetics)**: Exploration of Mendelian genetics by comparing the expected phenotypic outcomes with the outcomes observed as a result of the Fly Lab simulation for the offspring of matings involving:

1. One gene (monohybrid)

2. Two genes (dihybrid)

3. Three genes (trihybrid)

II. **Exercise 2 (Lethal Mutations)**: Exploration of lethal mutations by comparing the expected phenotypic outcomes and the observed phenotypic outcomes in the offspring of matings involving lethal mutations in one and two genes (monohybrid and dihybrid examples).

III. **Exercise 3 (Epistasis)**: Exploration of epistasis by comparing the expected phenotypic outcomes and the observed phenotypic outcomes in the offspring of flies containing epistatic genes (a dihybrid example).

IV. **Exercise 4 (X-Linked Genes)**: Exploration of X-linked genes by comparing the expected phenotypic outcomes and the observed phenotypic outcomes in the offspring of flies containing X-linked genes (monohybrid and dihybrid examples).

Your assignment is to approach each exercise and take clear notes, showing all your work and completing the worksheets provided. You need to use the virtual Fly Lab as a genetics calculator to check your work. Check with your professor to confirm precisely what you need to turn in from this lab.

Things to keep in mind as you complete these exercises:

1. Each individual (fly) has two alleles (forms) of each gene (trait or character). *For example, if the gene is for body color, an individual has two alleles for body color. One could be ebony and one could be the wild-type (dominant allele).*

2. Each individual fly's gametes have half the number of alleles as its adult body cells. In other words, gametes are haploid, and adult body cells are diploid.

3. The offspring flies' cells will have two of each allele for each gene (one from the mother and one from the father).

Using the "Virtual Fly Lab" Genetics Cross Calculator

1. Go to the website www.biologylabsonline.com.

2. Select Fly Lab.

3. You will be given a username and password from your instructor. Write this down.
   Username: _NSUBIDL1500 01_
   Password: _BIDL1500 01_

4. You may use this to access the fly lab after the laboratory session is finished to complete this laboratory assignment.

5. Press the Start Lab button. Wait/watch the computer screen, and follow the directions.

6. Get familiar with the website by exploring the buttons/options as described below. As soon as you log in, an applet will load. This will allow you to be able to visualize flies with different traits on the computer.

7. Select the number of offspring to result from the matings. The choices are 100, 1,000 or 10,000. It is best to pick 10,000 (the maximum value). Always make sure that Fly Lab is set to this maximum number of offspring. Why do you think it is best to use the maximal number of offspring? Remember, having offspring that are all female is much more likely to happen if you only have four offspring. But,

individuals are much more likely to have a gender distribution closer to 50:50 if there have been more offspring produced.

8. On the computer, you should see two flies, one labeled female (on the left) and the other labeled male (on the right). There is a Design button under each fly. Click on the Design button under the female fly. Now you will see a series of genes pop up on the left such as bristle, body color, antennae, etc. When you select Bristle, you will then see a list of options such as wild-type, forked, shaven, etc., going from left to right across the screen. These are the various alleles (forms) that correspond to the particular gene. Notice that the Fly Lab calculator designates the wild-type with the symbol "+". Unless you are told otherwise, the wild-type allele corresponds to the dominant allele. Then Fly Lab gives various symbols (probably not the ones you would have selected on your own) to note each of the other alleles. You should assume that the other alleles are all recessive options, unless you learn otherwise.

9. In this way you are able to select the genes and alleles corresponding to these genes for both the male and female fly. Unless you have specifically selected a gene and its alleles, the fly is given the default, wild (dominant) and true breeding (homozygous) genotype. Unless told otherwise, assume that flies are true-breeding (homozygous) for any given gene.

10. Once you select the traits for the male and female fly (by pressing the Select button under each fly), the Mate button appears between them. Once you select the Mate button, you will see simulations of the phenotypic categories of flies produced as a result of this mating. You are able to analyze results by pressing the Analyze Results button. Once the analyze results button is pressed, you are taken to a separate screen where you can choose to either Ignore Sex or not. Unless you suspect the gene you selected is sex-linked or you notice that the offspring ratios are greatly skewed from 50/50, press the Ignore Sex button.

11. There is also a Chi-Square Analysis button, which tells the computer to perform this type of statistical analysis (more information later).

12. There is also an Add Data to Notebook button; when you press this, the computer will keep a log of the data you accumulate throughout all the exercises.

13. Check with your instructor to see if they want you to turn in a computer-generated notebook printout. It is always a good idea to save often if you use this feature as it can "lock-up." Be sure to write down the results of the chi-square tests to make sure you understand the process (space given in the worksheet).

14. Once you are finished with the analysis screen, click the Return to Lab button and now you can make the current offspring the new parents by pressing the Select button under the male and female. Then you will be able to press the Mate button to see the phenotypic classes of the offspring that result from this new mating of the offspring. Once again, you will be able to press the Analyze Results button if desired/requested.

15. Now, let's get started on some genetics problems and learn to use this Fly Lab genetics calculator.

16. Press the New Mate button and let's move on!

Complete the Fly Lab exercises using the following worksheet pages.

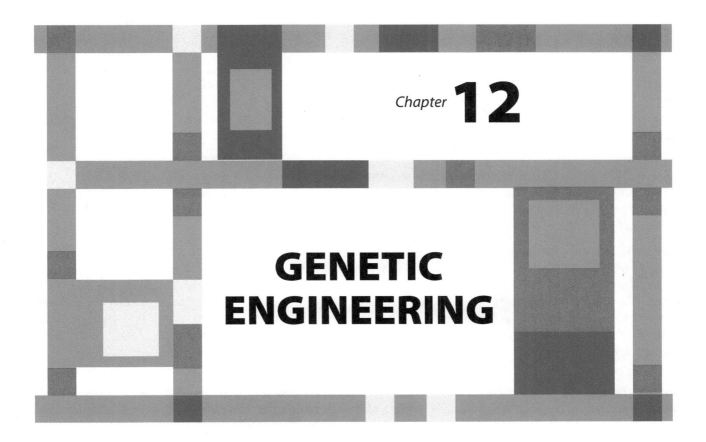

Chapter **12**

GENETIC ENGINEERING

Overview

In this lab, you will perform a procedure known as genetic transformation. Genetic transformation occurs when a cell takes up and expresses a new piece of genetic material, i.e. DNA. This new genetic information can provide the organism with a new trait that is identifiable after transformation. Genetic transformation literally causes genetic changes in cells and involves the insertion of one or more new gene(s) into a cell in order to change its traits.

This process is used in many areas of biotechnology. In agriculture, genes coding for traits such as frost, pest, or drought resistance can be genetically transformed into plants. In bioremediation, bacteria can be genetically transformed with genes enabling them to digest oil spills. In medicine, diseases caused by defective genes are beginning to be treated by gene therapy, that is, by genetically transforming a sick person's cells with healthy copies of the defective gene that causes their disease.

Genes can be taken from human, animal, or plant DNA and placed inside bacteria. For example, a healthy human gene for the hormone insulin can be put into bacteria. Under the right conditions, these bacteria can make authentic human insulin. This insulin can be isolated and purified, and then used to treat patients with diabetes that is caused by a lack of insulin (as you already know from a previous laboratory exercise).

Biotechnology – application of tech on a living system

Objectives

1. To do the genetic transformation
2. To determine the degree of success in your efforts to genetically alter an organism

Bacterial cell
1 single circular chromosome
several plasmids (1-several gene)

GMO's
genetically
modified
organisms

Background

Using a commercially available transformation kit, you will use a simple procedure to transform bacteria with a gene that codes for green fluorescent protein (GFP). The real-life source of this gene is the bioluminescent jellyfish *Aequorea victoria*, and GFP causes the jellyfish to fluoresce and glow in the dark. Following the transformation procedure, the bacteria express their newly acquired jellyfish gene and produce the fluorescent protein, which causes them to glow a brilliant green color under ultraviolet light.

In addition to their single large chromosome, bacteria often naturally contain one or more small circular pieces of DNA called *plasmids*. Plasmid DNA usually contains genes for one or more traits that may be beneficial to bacterial survival. In nature, bacteria can transfer plasmids back and forth, allowing them to share these beneficial genes. This natural mechanism allows bacteria to adapt to new environments. The occurrence of bacterial resistance to antibiotics is often due to the transmission of plasmids.

You will use a unique plasmid that contains the gene for GFP and a gene for resistance to the antibiotic ampicillin. The plasmid also incorporates a special gene regulation system that can be used to control expression of the fluorescent protein in the transformed cells. The gene for GFP can be switched on in transformed cells simply by adding the sugar arabinose to the cell's nutrient agar. Selection for cells that have been transformed with the plasmid DNA is accomplished by growing the bacteria on antibiotic-containing nutrient agar. Transformed cells will appear white (wild-type phenotype) on plates that do not contain arabinose and fluorescent green when arabinose is included in the nutrient agar.

You will increase the bacterial uptake of the plasmid DNA using a process called *heat shock*, where you briefly expose the bacterial cells to a higher temperature. It is important that you follow the directions regarding time. Also important is the rapid temperature change and the duration of the heat shock. For optimal results, the tubes containing the cell suspensions must be taken directly from ice, placed into the water bath at 42°C for 50 seconds, and returned immediately to the ice. For example, the absence of the heat shock will result in a tenfold decrease in plasmid DNA uptake, while a 90-second heat shock will reduce plasmid DNA uptake by about one-half as many as would occur with a 50-second heat shock.

Procedure for Today's Experiment

Special Precautions

Whenever one works with and cultures bacteria, it is important not to introduce contaminating bacteria into the experiment. Because contaminating bacteria are ubiquitous and are found on fingertips, bench tops, etc., it is important to avoid these contaminating surfaces. When you are working with the inoculation loops, pipettes, and agar plates, the round circle at the end of the loop, the tip of the pipette, and the surface of the agar plate should not be touched or placed on contaminating surfaces. While some contamination will not likely ruin the experiment, the use of sterile technique is an important skill to learn. Using sterile technique is also an important aspect of human cleanliness and safety.

The host bacterium for the plasmid is a strain (K-12) of *Escherichia coli* (or *E. coli*) that is not pathogenic such as the *E. coli* O157:H7 strain that has been implicated recently in human disease. However, handling of the *E. coli* K-12 requires the use of standard microbiological practices. These practices include decontaminating work surfaces on a daily basis and after any spill of viable material. All contaminated liquid or solid wastes are to be decontaminated in the autoclave before disposal. You should wash your hands after you handle materials that may have contacted bacteria containing recombinant DNA molecules and before leaving the laboratory. All procedures are to be performed carefully to minimize the creation of aerosols.

Mechanical pipetting devices are to be used; as you know, mouth pipetting is prohibited in the laboratory. Eating, drinking, smoking, and applying cosmetics are not permitted in the work area. Wearing protective eyewear and gloves is strongly recommended.

Procedure

1. Label one closed micro–test tube "+Plasmid" (+pGLO) and another "–Plasmid" (–pGLO). Label both tubes with your group's name. Place them in the foam tube rack.

2. Open the tubes, and using a sterile transfer pipette, transfer 250 µL of transformation solution (CaCl₂) as shown in Figure 12-1.

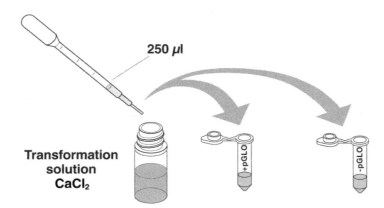

FIGURE 12-1   *Image © Bio-Rad Laboratories, Inc.*

3. Place the tubes on ice.

4. Use a sterile loop to pick up a single colony of bacteria from your starter plate. Pick up the +Plasmid (+pGLO) tube and immerse the loop into the transformation solution at the bottom of the tube. Spin the loop between your index finger and thumb until the entire colony is dispersed in the transformation solution as shown in Figure 12-2 (with no floating chunks). Place the tube back in the tube rack in the ice. Using a new sterile loop, repeat for the –Plasmid (–pGLO) tube.

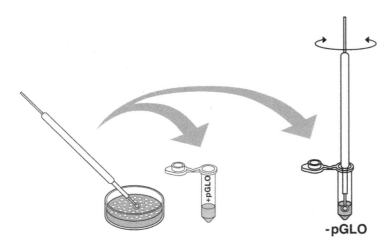

FIGURE 12-2   *Image © Bio-Rad Laboratories, Inc.*

5. Examine the tube containing the plasmid DNA solution with the UV lamp. Note your observations. Immerse a new sterile loop into the plasmid DNA stock tube. Withdraw a loopful. There should be a film of plasmid solution across the ring. This is similar to seeing a soapy film across a ring for blowing soap bubbles. Mix the loopful into the cell suspension of the +Plasmid (+pGLO) tube as shown in Figure 12-3. Close the tube and return it to the rack on ice. Also, close the –Plasmid (–pGLO) tube. Do not add plasmid DNA to the –Plasmid (–pGLO) tube. Why not?

From *Biotechnology Explorer™, pGLO Bacterial Transformation Kit*, Catalog Number 166-0003EDU. Reprinted with permission from Bio-Rad Laboratories, Inc.

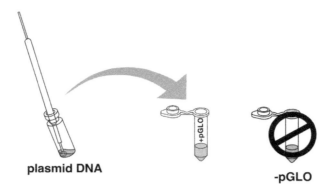

plasmid DNA

-pGLO

FIGURE 12-3   *Image © Bio-Rad Laboratories, Inc.*

6. Incubate the tubes on ice for 10 minutes. Make sure to push the tubes all the way down into the rack so the bottoms of the tubes stick out and make contact with the ice.

7. While the tubes are sitting on ice, label your four agar plates on the bottom (not the lid) as follows: Label one LB/amp plate: "+Plasmid"; label the LB/amp/ara plate: "+Plasmid"; label the other LB/amp plate: "–Plasmid"; and label the LB plate: "–Plasmid."

8. Heat shock. Using the foam rack as a holder, transfer both the +Plasmid ((+) pGLO) and –Plasmid ((–) pGLO) tubes into the water bath set at 42°C, for exactly 50 seconds. Make sure to push the tubes all the way down into the rack so the bottom of the tubes stick out and make contact with the warm water. When the 50 seconds have passed, place both tubes back on ice. For the best transformation results, the change from the ice (0°C) to 42°C and then back to the ice must be rapid. Incubate tubes on ice for 2 minutes.

9. Remove the rack containing the tubes from the ice, and place on the bench top. Open a tube and, using a new sterile pipette, add 250 μL of LB nutrient broth to the tube and then reclose it. Repeat with a new sterile pipette for the other tube as shown in Figure 12-4 (top). Incubate the tubes for 10 minutes at room temperature.

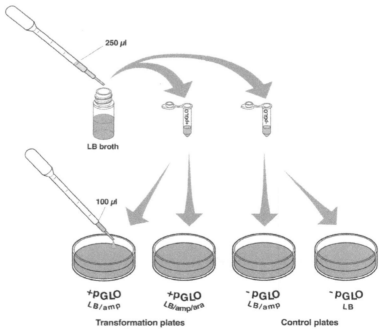

FIGURE 12-4   *Image © Bio-Rad Laboratories, Inc.*

10. Tap the closed tubes with your finger to mix. Using a new sterile pipette for each tube, pipette 100 μL of the transformation and control suspensions onto the appropriate plates as shown in Figure 12-4 (bottom).

11. Use a new sterile loop for each plate and spread the suspensions evenly around the surface of the agar by quickly skating the flat surface of a new sterile loop back and forth across the plate surface as shown in Figure 12-5.

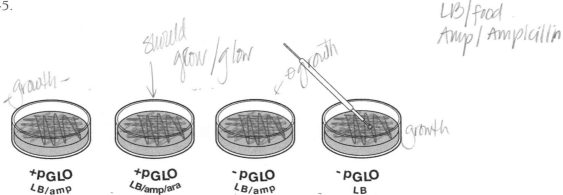

+growth−

should grow / glow

−growth

LB/food
Amp / Amplcillin

growth

FIGURE 12-5

Image © Bio-Rad Laboratories, Inc.

+PGLO
LB/amp

+PGLO
LB/amp/ara

−PGLO
LB/amp

−PGLO
LB

12. Stack up your plates and tape them together. Put your group name and class period on the bottom of the stack, and place the stack upside down in a cool, dry place as directed by the lab assistant until the next laboratory period.

Dec. 3rd

From *Biotechnology Explorer™*, *pGLO Bacterial Transformation Kit*, Catalog Number 166-0003EDU. Reprinted with permission from Bio-Rad Laboraties, Inc.

activates
arabinose
arabinose
receptor

GFP

DNA

Ampicillin
resistant
gene

(*) Plasmid tranferred to Bacteria E.coli
by Heat shock.

(*) Transformed Bacteria c̄ a new DNA
new / glows / Ampicillin resistant.
green c̄ light

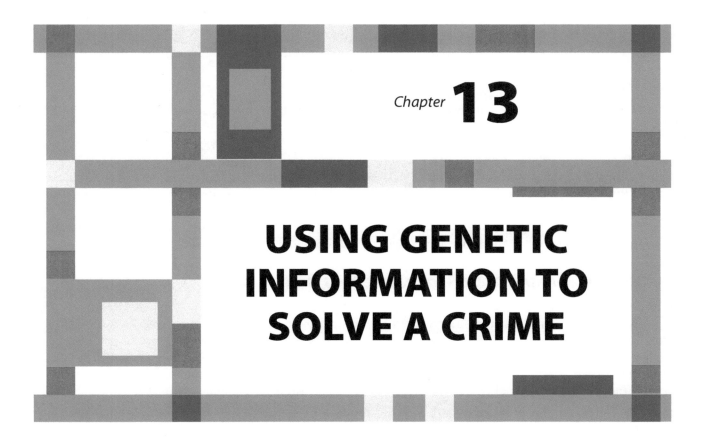

Chapter **13**

USING GENETIC INFORMATION TO SOLVE A CRIME

Overview

You are about to conduct real-world forensic DNA (deoxyribonucleic acid) profiling. As a crime scene investigator, you will use the polymerase chain reaction (PCR) and agarose gel electrophoresis to analyze the DNA samples obtained from a hypothetical crime scene and four suspects. Your job is to identify the perpetrator. In this analysis, a genotype is the particular set of genetic markers, or alleles, in a DNA sample. Every person's genotype is their own uniquely personal genetic barcode. In this experiment, you'll be revealing the genetic barcodes of several individuals and looking for a match.

Objectives

1. To amplify the genetic marker using the polymerase chain reaction.

2. To visualize the products of the amplification using electrophoresis.

Background

How Can DNA Evidence Solve Crimes?

DNA profiling refers to the use of molecular genetic methods used to determine the genotype of a DNA sample. This powerful tool is routinely used around the world for investigations of crime scenes, missing persons, mass disasters, human rights violations, and paternity. Crime scenes often contain biological evidence (such as blood, semen, hairs, saliva, bones, pieces of skin) from which DNA can be extracted. If the DNA profile obtained from evidence discovered at the scene of a crime matches the DNA profile of a suspect, this person is included as a potentially guilty person; if the two DNA profiles do not match, the individual is probably innocent.

A Brief History of Forensic Analysis

Forensic science occurs at the boundary between science and the law. Forensic science can just as easily convict someone of a crime as free someone wrongly convicted. The earliest uses of forensic science for criminal investigations involved photographs to document crime scenes. Fingerprint evidence has been in use for the past 100 years or so. The first genetic evidence to be collected for investigative work involved the use of blood group typing. The 1980s saw the first use of a DNA-based forensic test, restriction fragment length polymorphism (RFLP) analysis. Although RFLP analysis has its limitations, it has been the workhorse of forensic analysis for nearly 20 years. Only with the advent of polymerase chain reaction (PCR) has this aspect of the criminal justice system become truly modernized. Modern forensic DNA profiling makes it possible to distinguish between any two people on the planet (with the exception of identical twins), living or dead.

PCR Is DNA Replication Gone Crazy in a Test Tube

PCR produces large amounts of a specific piece of DNA from trace amounts of starting material (template). The template can be any form of double-stranded DNA. A researcher can take trace amounts of DNA from a drop of blood, a single hair follicle, or a cheek cell and use PCR to generate millions of copies of a desired DNA fragment. In theory, only a single template strand is needed to generate millions of new DNA molecules. Prior to PCR, it would have been impossible to do forensic or genetic studies with this small amount of DNA. The ability to amplify the precise sequence of DNA that a researcher wishes to study or manipulate is the true power of PCR.

One of the main reasons PCR is such a powerful tool is its simplicity and specificity. The specificity of PCR is its ability to target and amplify one specific segment of DNA a few hundred base pairs in length out of a complete genome of over 3 billion base pairs. In addition, all that is required for PCR is at least one DNA template strand, DNA polymerase, two DNA primers, the four nucleotide building block subunits of DNA [adenine (A), guanine (G), thymine (T), cytosine (C)], and reaction buffer. PCR allows forensic scientists to reveal personal details about an individual's genetic makeup and to determine the most subtle differences in the DNA of individuals—from the tiniest amount of biological material. The fact that millions of exact copies of a particular DNA sequence can be produced easily and quickly using PCR is the basis for modern forensic DNA testing.

What Kinds of Human DNA Sequences Are Used in Crime Scene Investigations?

There are about 3 billion base pairs in the human genome, and more than 99.5% do not vary between different human beings. However, a small percentage of the human DNA sequence (<0.5%) does differ, and these differences are known as polymorphisms. Polymorphic sequences are used in forensic applications. By universal agreement, DNA sequences used for forensic profiling are "anonymous"; that is, they come from loci that are not expressed and have no known functions. A single locus may have different forms or types and these different forms are called alleles. A locus may be bi-allelic, having only two different forms, or it may be polymorphic, as described above. The DNA sequences used in forensic labs are noncoding regions that contain segments of Short Tandem Repeats (STRs). STRs are very short DNA sequences that are repeated in direct head-to-tail fashion. The example below shows a locus (known as TH01) found on chromosome 11; its specific DNA sequence contains four repeats of [TCAT].

..C C C T C A T T C A T T C A T T C A T T C A..

Image © Bio-Rad Laboratories, Inc.

From *Biotechnology Explorer™, Crime Scene Investigator PCR Basics™ Kit*, Catalog Number 166-2600EDU. Reprinted with permission from Bio-Rad Laboratories, Inc.

DNA —denature ī heat ī Thermocycler

For the TH01 STR locus, there are many alternate polymorphic alleles that differ from each other by the number of [TCAT] repeats present in the sequence. Although more than 20 different alleles of TH01 have been discovered in people worldwide, each of us still has only two of these, one inherited from our mother and one inherited from our father. For example as shown in Figure 13-1, suspect A has one allele with 6 repeats, and one allele with 3 repeats, giving a DNA profile for the TH01 locus of 6–3.

Suspected A's DNA type for the TH01 locus is (5–3)		Suspect B's DNA type for TH01 locus is (6–10)	
CCC ☐☐☐☐☐☐AAA	5*	CCC ☐☐☐☐☐☐AAA	6*
CCC ☐☐☐AAA	3*	CCC ☐☐☐☐☐☐☐☐☐☐AAA	10*

* Number of [TCAT] repeats

FIGURE 13-1   *Image © Bio-Rad Laboratories, Inc.*

How Are STR Alleles Detected?

The key to DNA profiling is amplification of the number of copies of the allele present in the small amounts of evidentiary DNA using the polymerase chain reaction (PCR). Using primers specific to the DNA sequences on either side of the [TCAT] STR, billions of copies of each of the two original TH01 alleles in any one person's DNA type are synthesized in the reaction. These copies contain the same number of STRs present in the original DNA copies and can be visualized using agarose gel electrophoresis. By comparison with a DNA size standard, or allele ladder (the control), that corresponds to the known sizes of TH01 alleles, the exact sizes of the PCR products from the sample DNAs can be determined and compared.

A diagram of the results for TH01 typing of suspect A and suspect B is shown in Figure 13-2. In this cartoon example, PCR has been performed on DNA from two suspects using primers specific for the TH01 locus. Following gel electrophoresis, which separates the PCR products according to their size, the pattern of bands is compared to the allele ladder to identify the alleles present in the original samples.

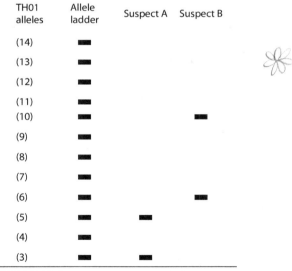

FIGURE 13-2   *Image © Bio-Rad Laboratories, Inc.*

PCR Amplification *(Replication)*

PCR amplification is DNA replication in a test tube. The portion of the DNA that you want to copy is called the target sequence. The sample of DNA obtained at a crime scene and the suspect's DNA samples contain the target sequence.

From *Biotechnology Explorer™, Crime Scene Investigator PCR Basics™ Kit*, Catalog Number 166-2600EDU. Reprinted with permission from Bio-Rad Laboraties, Inc.

PCR relies on three principles of molecular biology:

1. Denaturation—melting double-stranded DNA template into single stands *č heat*
2. Annealing—complementary DNA strand hybridization via DNA primers
3. Extension—DNA strand synthesis via DNA polymerase *will allow elongation*

Denaturation: Before new DNA synthesis can begin the double stranded DNA template must be unwound and separated into single strands. In cells this is carried out by a family of enzymes. In PCR, heat is used to melt apart—or denature—the double stranded DNA template.

Annealing: Before a target region of DNA can be amplified, one must determine short sequences of DNA upstream (at the 5' end) and downstream (at the 3' end) of the target loci region of interest. These areas are then used to make short pieces of DNA, called primers or oligonucleotides, which are complementary to regions upstream and downstream of the target loci region (Figure 13-3). Primers serve as start and stop points for amplifying the target region of the DNA to be copied.

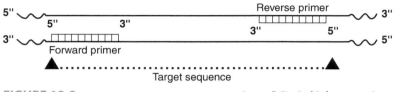

FIGURE 13-3   *Image © Bio-Rad Laboratories, Inc.*

In PCR, complementary strand hybridization takes place when oligonucleotide primers anneal, or bind, to their respective complementary base pair sequences on the template. Hybridization is the process that describes the binding of the oligonucleotide primer to the template DNA. The two strands anneal to each other, forming a "hybrid." Like bookends, the two primers are designed and synthesized in the laboratory with a specific sequence of nucleotides so they will anneal at the opposite ends and on the opposite strands bracketing the target stretch of double-stranded DNA (template strand) to be amplified. Therefore, the target sequence is determined by the location where the primers anneal.

Extension: Primers are needed because the **DNA polymerase** requires an already existing nucleotide chain to bind and add nucleotides one at a time. Once the polymerase locates and binds to template DNA and the primer, it initiates the addition of nucleotides and synthesizes new copies of the double-stranded template DNA by adding nucleotides onto the primer and extending it. Therefore, primers provide a starting point for the DNA polymerase. These three steps—denaturation, annealing, and extension—together make up one PCR cycle. A complete PCR reaction involves many repetitions of a single PCR cycle. In this experiment, your PCR reactions will cycle 35 times.

The enzyme used in PCR, i.e., DNA polymerase, must be thermally stable because PCR cycles between temperatures of 52°C and 94°C. The thermostable DNA polymerase that performs the polymerization was isolated from a thermophilic bacterium, *Thermus aquaticus* (Taq), which lives in high-temperature steam vents such as those found in Yellowstone National Park.

Two template strands are created from the original template after each complete cycle of the strand synthesis reaction—denaturation, annealing, and extension. It is called the polymerase chain reaction because exponential growth of the number of template molecules occurs after each cycle is complete, i.e., the number of DNA copies doubles at each cycle. Therefore, after 35 cycles there will be 2^{35} times more copies than at the beginning. After 35 cycles, the DNA of interest has been amplified sufficiently to be visualized using gel electrophoresis and DNA stains. This allows researchers to determine the presence or absence of the desired PCR products.

From *Biotechnology Explorer™, Crime Scene Investigator PCR Basics™ Kit*, Catalog Number 166-2600EDU. Reprinted with permission from Bio-Rad Laboraties, Inc.

In order for PCR to happen efficiently, several components are needed. In addition to the template, the oligonucleotide primers, and the enzyme (Taq DNA polymerase), a special reaction buffer is also required, called a master mix. The master mix contains all of the components for PCR to occur, including the individual building blocks of DNA (nucleotides, or dNTPs), a special buffer to maintain optimum pH, salts, and $MgCl_2$. Salts and magnesium ions (also known as cofactors) are needed for the Taq DNA polymerase to perform optimally.

In this experiment, your instructor will provide you with a master mix that comes prepared with all of the ingredients listed above, but also includes colored primers and Taq polymerase mixed in. For this reason, it's important to keep the master mix cold before use, so that the enzyme doesn't start to work before you add your DNA templates.

In this part of the experiment, you will obtain DNA samples that have been collected from a crime scene and four individuals suspected of being involved in the crime. Your task is to amplify the region of interest (the BXP007 locus, a polymorphic allele) from the DNA samples. Once complete, you will analyze your PCR products using gel electrophoresis to determine the genotypes of the samples at the BXP007 locus and match the crime scene DNA to one of the suspects.

[handwritten: To replicate DNA]   *[handwritten: Nucleotides in Master Mix / Enzyme (polymerase) & primers]*   *[handwritten: FWD / Reverse]*

Procedure for Today's Experiment

1. You will have six tubes in a white foam rack at your workstation. You should have one yellow tube labeled "Master Mix" containing a blue liquid, and five tubes labeled "Crime Scene Evidence (CS)," "a DNA sample from suspect A (A)," "a DNA sample from suspect B (B)," "a DNA sample from suspect C (C)," and "a DNA sample from suspect D (D)."

2. You should also have five 0.2 mL PCR tubes nested into microcentrifuge tubes. Label the PCR tubes "CS," "A," "B," "C," and "D" and include your group name or initials as well.

The labels correspond to the following tube contents:

3. Using aerosol barrier pipette tips and an adjustable micropipette set to 20 μL, take 20 μL of DNA from each prelabeled tube and add it to each of the PCR tubes you just labeled. For example, for the crime scene evidence, transfer 20 μL of the sample into your CS-labeled PCR tube. **Important: Use a fresh pipette tip for each DNA sample**.

4. Using aerosol barrier pipette tips and an adjustable micropipette set to 20 μL, add 20 μL of the Master Mix to each tube as indicated in the table above. Mix the contents of your PCR tubes by gently pipetting up and down. **Important: Use a fresh pipette tip each time**. Once you've added Master Mix to a tube, close the cap. The solution in your PCR tubes should be blue. If it's not blue, talk to your instructor.

5. Give your tubes to the instructor or the lab assistant. They will conduct the PCR reaction using the thermocycler for you and provide the samples for electrophoresis in the next lab session.

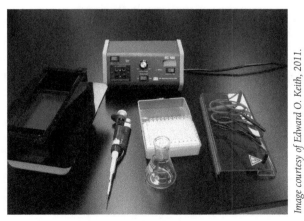

Image courtesy of Edward O. Keith, 2011.

FIGURE 13-4 Equipment used for this experi-

Procedure for Second Week of Experiment

1. Set up your gel electrophoresis apparatus as instructed. Directions below are specifically for using the "Dark Reader" gel electrophoresis system.

2. Obtain your five PCR reactions from the previous laboratory session.

3. Using aerosol barrier pipette tips and an adjustable micropipette set to 5 μL, add 5 μL of Orange G loading dye (from the tube labeled "LD") to each PCR reaction tube and mix well. **Important: Use a fresh tip each time**.

4. Make the agarose solution. The recommended gel concentration for this exercise is 1.5% agarose. Add 1.5 g of agarose to 100 mL of 1x TAE electrophoresis buffer in a 125 mL Erlenmeyer flask and swirl to suspend the agarose powder in the buffer.

5. Place the agarose solution into the microwave. Use a medium power setting and set to 3 minutes. Stop the microwave oven every 30 seconds, and swirl the flask to suspend any undissolved agarose. This technique is the fastest and safest way to dissolve agarose. Boil and swirl the solution until all of the small transparent agarose particles are dissolved. Set aside to cool to 60°C before pouring (it is cool enough when you can hold it in your hand). Then the instructor will add 6 μL of SYBR Safe (a DNA binding dye) to the warm, but not hot, agarose, right before pouring the gel into the electrophoresis chamber. Do not touch the SYBR Safe liquid or the gel containing SYBR Safe with your bare hands. Wear gloves when handling the gel and use caution because the SYBR safe will bind to your DNA too!

6. Pour no more than 50 mL of the liquid gel into the center of the electrophoresis tank. Place the comb in the tank so that the white teeth of the comb face the center of the gel with space between the teeth of the comb and the top of the gel tank. Allow the gel to solidify. It will be ready for the next step when it is white and translucent.

7. Fill the electrophoresis chamber with enough 1x TAE buffer to cover the gel. This will require ~220 mL of 1x TAE buffer as shown in Figure 13-5.

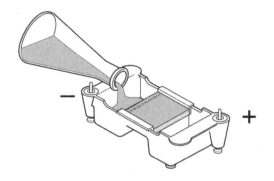

FIGURE 13-5   *Image © Bio-Rad Laboratories, Inc.*

From *Biotechnology Explorer™, Crime Scene Investigator PCR Basics™ Kit*, Catalog Number 166-2600EDU. Reprinted with permission from Bio-Rad Laboraties, Inc.

8. Using the table below as a guide, load 15 μL of the allele ladder and 15 μL of each sample into your gel in the order indicated below as shown in Figure 13-6.

Lane	Sample	Load volume
1	Allele Ladder	05 μL
2	Crime Scene	05 μL
3	Suspect A	05 μL
4	Suspect B	05 μL
5	Suspect C	05 μL
6	Suspect D	05 μL

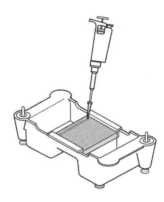

FIGURE 13-6   *Image © Bio-Rad Laboratories, Inc.*

9. Secure the lid on the gel chamber. The lid will attach to the base in only one orientation: red to red and black to black. Connect the electrical leads to the power supply.

10. Turn on the power supply and electrophorese your samples at 100 V for 30 minutes.

11. During the electrophoresis, turn on the UV light in the bottom of the gel chamber and observe the progress. You should be able to see the samples immediately and watch them move through the gel. The final separation should be visible after approximately 30 minutes. If the allele ladder has not spread sufficiently, electrophorese for another 15 minutes.

12. After you analyze your results and draw your gel, remove the gel and deposit it in the biohazard trash. Pour the buffer into the sink and rinse the gel chamber.

DNA ↑ phosphate (-) charge
DNA will run through the gel

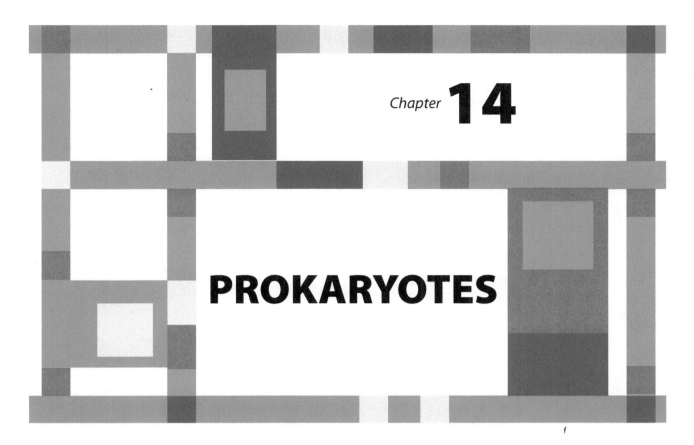

Chapter **14**

PROKARYOTES

Introduction

Prokaryotes include the simplest life forms and were the first living things to appear on earth. Their name, which reflects their simplicity, derives from the Greek roots *pro* (before) and *karuon* (kernel, or nut); these cells are so simple, they have no nucleus. Although almost all prokaryotes are microscopic (actually, extremely small), they are so numerous that they account for a biomass greater than all remaining living organisms put together. It has been estimated that there are 3×10^8 prokaryote cells on the skin of an average adult human, and another 7×10^{13} in the colon. Because they have adapted to a wider range of conditions than any other organisms, prokaryotes are found wherever life exists and often where other life forms cannot exist: from high in the atmosphere, to dry valleys deep in Antarctica, to hot sulfurous vents in the deep sea. They have even been found in exploratory oil wells as deep as 2.7 km below ground. Although several thousand have been named as formal species, it is clear that this represents only a small percentage of real prokaryote diversity. Traditional species concepts (such as the Biological Species Concept and Phylogenetic Species Concept) are difficult to apply to prokaryotes, because they have relatively few traditional distinguishing features, such as cell shape, colony form, metabolic and nutritional requirements, pathogenicity, and oxygen and antibiotic tolerance. As a result, more and more species are distinguished on the basis of differences in their DNA sequences. Also, microbiologists have only been able to culture a very small percentage of prokaryotes in the laboratory. Having only a single cell limits what you can say about it.

Most prokaryotes are what we would consider bacteria, but the situation is not quite that simple. For many years, bacteria were treated as members of the plant kingdom. In 1866, the German scientist Ernst Haeckel placed almost all microscopic life (including bacteria) in the Protista, a third kingdom separate from the animal and plant kingdoms. A century later, Robert Whittaker formally recognized the distinction between prokaryotic and eukaryotic cells by placing all prokaryotes in a separate kingdom, Monera. In addition to not having a membrane-bound nucleus with DNA segregated inside, prokaryotic cells are characterized by the following features:

- Small cell size: chiefly 1–5 μm (though at least one species reaches 0.75 mm across).

- No complex organelles such as mitochondria or Golgi apparatus.

- No complex, membrane-bound packing of DNA together with histone proteins in chromosomes. The prokaryote chromosome is a single long loop of DNA, accompanied by smaller shorter loops of DNA called **plasmids**.

- Reproduction by **binary fission**; no mitosis, meiosis, or fertilization.

- A smaller distinctive ribosome.

- A cell wall composed of peptidoglycan instead of polysaccharides such as cellulose or chitin.

- Only limited multicellularity and cell specialization.

More recently, Carl Woese and others recognized that one group of prokaryotes, previously treated as just another group of bacteria called Archaebacteria, was actually more closely related to eukaryotes than to other bacteria. They divided living things into three Domains: Bacteria (sometimes called Eubacteria, or "true" bacteria), Archaea (formerly Archaebacteria), and Eucarya (all eukaryote organisms).

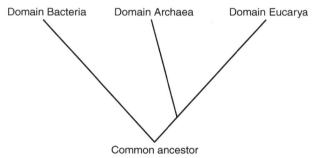

Diagram of evolutionary relationships among
the three named domains of living organisms.

Archaeans have a series of genes and metabolic pathways closer in common with those of eukaryotes (e.g., pathways involved in transcription and translation). As a result, they branch more closely to eukaryotes than to bacteria in the diagram above. Although we will not specifically examine archaeans in this laboratory exercise (because they basically look like regular bacteria), it is worth noting that they occur in a wide range of habitats, including harsh ones such as hot springs, as well as in soil, oceans, and our own intestines.

While we usually think of prokaryotes, and bacteria in particular, in negative terms as disease-causing agents, they are far more beneficial (or at least benign) as a whole. Although many species are responsible for such devastating conditions as tuberculosis, cholera, Black Plague, leprosy, botulism, anthrax, diphtheria, and rabies (to name just a few), they are also critical components in all the world's food webs, responsible for decomposition and nutrient recycling, as well as photosynthesis. Without them, we and all other living things would not be here. They even generate important components of earth's atmosphere. Prokaryotes produce protective chemicals such as streptomycin, neomycin, and tetracycline, which inhibit the growth of other microorganisms. We, of course, use these chemicals to our own advantage. We also use prokaryotes in many commercial, medical, and biotechnological processes, e.g., in the decomposition of sewage and petroleum spills; in the production of pesticides and other synthetic compounds; in the industrial mass culture of vitamins, antibiotics, and other compounds such as acetone; and in the manufacture of foods such as cheese and yogurt. The bacterium *Escherischia coli* (abbreviated *E. coli*) is probably the best understood organism and is used as a model in medical, genetic, and environmental research.

Prokaryotes have the widest range of metabolic processes of any living things:

- **Photoautotrophy (= photosynthesis)**—Use of light energy and small inorganic molecules (CO_2, H_2O) for energy acquisition and nutrient synthesis

- **Chemoautotrophy (= chemolithotrophy)**—Oxidation of small inorganic molecules (H_2S, CH_4, NH_4^+, Fe^{+2}) rather than use of light as an energy source, with CO_2 for nutrient synthesis

- **Photoheterotrophy**—Use of light energy and already-manufactured organic molecules for energy acquisition and nutrient synthesis

- **Chemoheterotrophy (= heterotrophy)**—Acquisition of energy and nutrients from already-manufactured organic molecules

- **Mixotrophy**—Energy and nutrient acquisition via alternation among or combination of any of the preceding metabolisms, e.g., switching between auto- and heterotrophy

Prokaryotes also exhibit a wide range of oxygen requirements. Some, like us, are **obligate aerobes** that require oxygen for survival. Others are **facultative aerobes** that can use oxygen when present yet survive when it is not, while still others are **obligate anaerobes** that are poisoned by oxygen. Because they often live in harsh or highly variable environments, prokaryotes may be extremely resistant. Many can dry up and regenerate when returned to a suitable moist environment. Some bacteria produce **endospores**, resting stages surrounded by a tough coating that can resist extreme conditions. Such protective coatings make the species that cause anthrax, tetanus, and botulism particularly difficult to destroy.

Exercises

1. Basic Prokaryote Forms

Because almost all prokaryote cells are extremely small, they are difficult to examine. In fact, the examples provided in this laboratory exercise will be the most difficult to find and study of any specimens you encounter in this course. However, once you have successfully learned how to examine prokaryotes, other specimen preparations will be much easier.

Because it is often difficult to locate prokaryotic cells on prepared microscope slides, the following procedure will help.

1. Place the microscope slide on the stage so that the edge of the cover slip (or, if this is not obvious, the edge of the opaque slide label) is in the middle of the viewing field, and focus on this at low (4×) magnification using the coarse focus adjustment knob. Also, make sure your eyepiece lenses are focused and the correct distance apart for your eyes.

2. Move the stage using the mechanical stage knobs so that the center of the cover slip lies in the middle of the viewing field. Now that you have focused correctly, you should be able to locate an irregular or ring-shaped colored area. This is where the stained cells will be, although they may be quite pale. Use the small handle on the condenser just underneath the stage to adjust the brightness and contrast of your image.

3. Increase the magnification by rotating the objective lens turret, first to 10× and then to 40×, focusing at each higher magnification by just slightly rotating the fine focus adjustment knob. You will also have to adjust the amount of light using the substage condenser. Higher magnifications require more light.

4. Drawing prokaryote cells under lower magnifications will show only unidentifiable masses. Make sure you can distinguish individual cells.

Figure 14-1 shows a prepared microscope slide of *Staphylococcus* under increasing magnification.

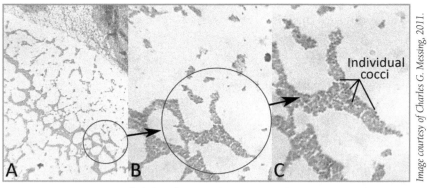

FIGURE 14-1 Prepared slide of *Staphylococcus* under increasing magnification. Individual cells cannot be resolved at low magnifications.

As mentioned above, prokaryotes do not exhibit a wide range of physical forms (Figure 14-2). The three most common and widespread cell shapes are:

Cocci (singular: coccus)—spheres.

Bacilli (singular: bacillus)—rods.

Spirilla (singular: spirillum)—spirals.

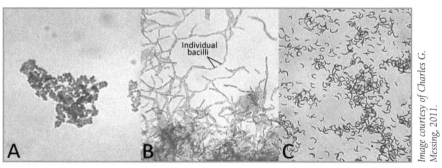

FIGURE 14-2 Common bacterial shapes. A. Coccus. B. Bacillus. C. Spirillum. A and B are Gram positive. C is Gram negative.

Of course, variations of these three exist. **Coccobacilli** are short wide rods intermediate between cocci and bacilli. Bacilli can be cylindrical or taper at both ends. Some spirilla, called **vibrios**, are so short that they look like commas. Examples of some of these variations are *Vibrio cholerae* and the coccobacillis *Haemophilus influenza*; their scientific names reflect the diseases that they may cause. Different species of prokaryotes may also aggregate in different arrangements. As examples, **diplococci** cluster in pairs, **streptococci** and **streptobacilli** (Figure 14-2B) link up in chains, and **staphylococci** cluster in irregular masses.

- Examine prepared slides of *Bacillus*, *Rhodospirillum rubrum* and *Staphylococcus aureus*. Illustrate representatives of each for your lab notebook. Note name, shape, color, and the magnification at which you make the drawing.

- Examine prepared slides of diplococci, and streptococci or streptobacilli. Illustrate representatives of each for your lab notebook, and note in particular how the cells are arranged in each case.

2. Prokaryote Colonies

In addition to cell shape and arrangement, different prokaryotes may produce very different appearances when huge numbers grow in culture to form colonies visible to the naked eye. In this exercise, you will examine the visible form of prokaryote colonies. During the week before this laboratory, different environmental samples were collected by brushing sterile swabs moistened with distilled water against surfaces (e.g., lawn soil, decaying leaf, bark, sidewalk, doorknob, chair seat, carpet). Each swab was then brushed against a culture medium in a petri dish in a zigzag pattern. Each dish was immediately covered, labeled with information about the sample habitat (e.g., surface, location, date), and then placed in an incubator.

■ Examine the variety of colonies visible on the agar culture dishes provided. Your instructor will provide you with information about the culture media and incubation time.

  • Illustrate representatives of several different colony forms for your laboratory notebook. Note size, color, texture, and any other feature you may observe.

  • Compare and contrast colonies from different habitats. Do you find any similar colonies in similar or different habitats? Suggest reasons for any consistencies among habitats.

■ To examine a greater diversity of possible bacterial habitats, your instructor will divide your laboratory section into groups. Each group will be provided with an agar culture dish and a sterile swab. You will leave the laboratory as a group to go outside and select an environmental sample for analysis of colony form.

A. Moisten the swab with distilled water.

B. Select a habitat (e.g., lawn soil, garden soil, leaf, bark, sidewalk, doorknob, carpet, chair seat). Use a marker to write the habitat name and your group name on the underside of the culture dish.

C. Brush the swab across or touch it to your chosen environmental surface; uncover the culture dish, and gently brush the swab against the culture medium surface in a zigzag pattern. Quickly cover the dish.

D. Return the dish to the laboratory and place it in the incubator (your instructor may do this).

E. Examine your culture dish during laboratory the following week.

  • Illustrate and describe the colonies that you observe. Note differences in size, texture, shape and color.

  • Compare and contrast colonies from different habitats. Do you find any similar colonies in similar or different habitats? Suggest reasons for any consistencies among habitats.

3. Prokaryote Cell Shape, Cell Wall and Gram Staining

To make individual prokaryote cells visible, as in the prepared slides in Exercise 1, they must be stained. Stains consist of a colored molecule dissolved in a solvent such as ethanol or water. Part of the colored molecule is a pigment that provides the color. Another part of the molecule carries a charge that allows it to attach to the cell surface, so the molecule dyes the cell with a specific color. A **simple** stain uses one staining compound.

The prokaryote cell wall, unlike that of eukaryotes, consists chiefly of the molecule **peptidoglycan**, which forms long chains of amino sugars (sugars that have an amine group, e.g., N, NH or NH_2, in place of an hydroxyl (-OH) group cross-linked together by polypeptide chains to form a mesh or lattice. Many prokaryotes, including bacteria of medical interest, exhibit one of two different cell wall structures, with either a thick peptidoglycan cell wall external to the typical phospholipid bilayer cell membrane, or a thinner peptidoglycan layer between an inner and outer cell membrane.

The Dane Hans Christian Gram (1853–1938) developed the staining procedure named after him to distinguish between two different bacteria that produced the same symptoms in humans. **Gram staining** differs from the simple stain in the previous exercise; it is a **differential stain** that uses two dyes, which allow the observer to distinguish among organisms or among different cells in one organism. In addition, Gram staining requires a critical de-colorizing step in which excess amounts of the first stain are rinsed away before a second stain is applied. Cells that retain the first stain are called **Gram positive**; those that lose the first stain but accept the second are called **Gram negative**. Gram positive bacteria have the well-developed outer peptidoglycan cell wall.

They are typically susceptible to antibiotics, which inhibit formation of the cross-links and thus prevent cell wall development. Gram negative forms have the second membrane outside the thin cell wall. Lipopolysaccharides in the outer membrane are often toxic; the outer membrane prevents the first stain from reaching the cell wall and, in the case of pathogenic or parasitic species, also offers additional defenses against the host organism.

Gram staining is usually the first step in a clinical or research attempt to identify a bacterial cell, although the procedure does not distinguish every prokaryotic species, i.e., there are Gram indeterminate and Gram variable cells as well.

■ Prepare a slide smear and identify whether the cells are Gram positive or negative. Record cell shape, arrangement, and color according to the following procedure.

A. Place a small drop of water in the middle of a clean, glass microscope slide.

B. Heat an inoculating loop in a Bunsen burner flame to sterilize it; allow it to air cool for several seconds.

C. Touch the loop to the surface of the culture material so that a small amount attaches.

D. Transfer the culture material to the water on the slide, gently spreading the drop out. Do not splash or splatter as you mix.

E. Re-sterilize the loop in the flame.

F. Allow the mixture, called a **smear**, to air dry; it should be visibly cloudy when dry.

G. Pick up the slide with a slide holder, and pass the slide quickly through the upper part of the burner flame three times. Avoid overheating the slide. This **heat-fixing** both kills the prokaryotes and adheres them to the slide.

H. Allow the slide to cool in air.

I. Place the slide over a tray or jar to catch excess fluid; cover the smear with **crystal violet** stain (the **primary stain**) for 1 min.

J. Using a slide holder, tilt the slide over the tray, jar, or sink, and rinse the slide with distilled water.

K. Place the slide again over the tray or jar to catch excess fluid; cover the smear with iodine stain for 1 min. Iodine enhances the color of the first stain by forming a crystal violet–iodine complex.

L. Using a slide holder, tilt the slide over the tray, jar, or sink, and rinse the slide with distilled water.

M. Still holding the tilted slide with a slide holder over the tray or jar (but not the sink), decolorize with one of the following as provided (95% ethanol, ethanol/acetone, or isopropyl alcohol/acetone). **This is the most important step. Too much decolorizing may leave pale pink rather than dark purple Gram positive cells. Too little decolorizing may leave purple Gram negative cells.**

N. Place the slide again over the tray or jar to catch excess fluid; cover the smear with **safranin stain** (the **counterstain**) for 1 min.

O. Using a slide holder, tilt the slide over the tray, jar, or sink, and rinse the slide with distilled water.

P. Blot the slide dry gently between paper towels or sheets of bibulous paper.

Q. Examine under the maximum microscope magnification (first focusing through the sequence of increasing magnifications, 4×, 10×, 40×) using immersion oil as follows:

    i. Once you focus under 40× power, rotate the objective turret between the 40× lens and the 100× lens.

    ii. Place a drop of immersion oil on the center of the slide.

    iii. Rotate the turret to the 100x lens; focus and observe.

iv. **IMPORTANT: ONCE YOU USE THE HIGH POWER 100X LENS, DO NOT RETURN THE SLIDE TO A LOWER MAGNIFICATION. THIS WILL GET IMMERSION OIL ALL OVER THE LOWER MAGNIFICATION LENS.**

R. Illustrate for your lab notebook. Note cell shape and arrangement, color, and magnification.

S. Dispose of the slide according to instructions given in lab.

T. **IMPORTANT: Gently and thoroughly wipe the high magnification lens with lens paper, so that no oil is visible on the lens paper. DO NOT RETURN THE SLIDE WITH OIL ON IT TO A LOWER MAGNIFICATION LENS.**

4. Cyanobacteria

Formerly called blue-green algae, cyanobacteria are photoautotrophic bacteria with plantlike photosynthesis, splitting H_2O as an electron donor and yielding O_2 as an electron acceptor. The basic equations are the same in cyanobacteria and plants:

$$CO_2 + 2H_2O \rightarrow (CH_2O)_n + H_2O + O_2$$

Also as in plants, they contain photosystems II and I. Their photosynthetic pigments are chlorophyll *a* as well as accessory blue phycobilin and red phycoerythrin pigments. As a result, they may appear green, blue green, or reddish brown. They live in freshwater, terrestrial, and marine habitats, and also occur as symbionts inside some lichens and sponges. Marine species are important primary producers and major contributors to the nitrogen cycle. *Prochlorococcus*, an extremely small single-celled form discovered in 1986, is responsible for over half of the photosynthesis in the open ocean. Cyanobacteria are often much more resistant to environmental extremes than eukaryotic algae. Some produce toxins that can cause harmful algal blooms. Different species may occur as single cells (unicellular), as a variety of multicellular (many-celled) **colonies** (Figure 14-3A), or with cells lined up as **filaments** (Figure 14-3B). Cells in colonial species secrete external gelatinous capsules or mucous sheaths that allow them to stick together and also may make them distasteful to potential grazers. No species have flagella, and motile filaments move by gliding.

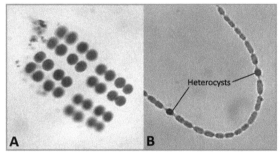

FIGURE 14-3 Cyanobacteria. A. Preserved *Merismopedia*. B. Preserved *Anabaena*.

Image courtesy of Charles G. Messing, 2011.

■ Examine the live cultures of cyanobacteria.

A. Make a wet mount of the two forms provided as living cultures: filamentous *Oscillatoria* and colonial *Merismopedia*.

B. Withdraw a small portion of culture containing cells using a dropper designated for that culture. If the culture is provided in a test tube, invert the CLOSED tube several times to suspend the cells uniformly. If the culture is provided in a jar, stir it gently with the dropper to suspend cells.

C. **ALWAYS USE THE DROPPER DESIGNATED FOR A SPECIFIC CULTURE TO AVOID CONTAMINATION.**

D. Place a small droplet of culture in the middle of a clean microscope slide.

E. Place the side of a clean coverslip on the microscope slide adjacent to the culture droplet and lower it onto the slide so as not to trap any air bubbles (which will appear under the microscope as little black tires or bagels).

F. Examine as you would a prepared slide. Cyanobacterial cells and filaments are often larger than those of nonphotosynthetic bacteria, so you will not have to use the highest magnification.

G. Illustrate each preparation for your lab notebook. Note cell shape and arrangement, color, and magnification.

■ Examine the prepared microscope slides of cyanobacteria: *Oscillatoria*, *Merismopedia*, and *Nostoc* or *Anabaena*.

A. Compare and contrast the appearances of these preserved *Oscillatoria* and *Merismopedia* with the live cultures in the previous exercise.

B. Look for enlarged cells in the cell chains of *Nostoc* or *Anabaena*. These are specialized nonphotosynthetic cells called **heterocysts** that contain the enzyme **nitrogenase**, which permits these cells to fix atmospheric gaseous nitrogen (N_2) into a more usable form such as ammonium (NH_4^+).

C. Illustrate each preparation for your lab notebook. Note cell shape and arrangement, color, and magnification.

Questions

1. How do prokaryotes differ from eukaryotes?

2. Briefly describe the diversity of form among (all) prokaryotes.

3. Why and how does the Gram stain work?

4. Describe at least two differences visible between living and preserved versions of the two cyanobacteria compared in laboratory. Offer an explanation for the differences.

References

Eiler, A. 2006. Evidence for the ubiquity of mixotrophic bacteria in the Upper Ocean: implications and consequences. *Applied Environmental Microbiology* 72 (12): 7431–7.

Herrero A., and Flores E., eds. 2008. *The Cyanobacteria: molecular biology, genomics, and evolution*. Norfolk, UK: Caister Academic Press.

Jernigan, J. A., Stephens, D. S., Ashford, D. A., Omenaca, C., Topiel, M. S., Galbraith, M., Tapper, M., Fisk, T. L., et al. 2001. Bioterrorism-related inhalational anthrax: the first 10 cases reported in the United States. *Emerging Infectious Diseases* (Internet serial), 7 (6) (December).

Sogin, M. L., Morrison, H. G., Huber, J. A., Welch, D. M., Huse, S. M., Neal, P. R., Arrieta, J. M., and Herndl, G. J. 2006. Microbial diversity in the deep sea and the underexplored "rare biosphere." *Proceedings of the National Academy of Sciences* 103 (32): 12115–20.

Ward, B. B. 2002. How many species of prokaryotes are there? *Proceedings of the National Academy of Sciences* 99 (16): 10234-6.

Whitman, W. B., Coleman, D. C., and Wiebe, W. J. 1998. Prokaryotes: the unseen majority. *Proceedings of the National Academy of Sciences* 95 (12): 6578–83.

Woese, C., Kandler, O., and Wheelis, M. 1990. Towards a natural system of organisms: proposal for the domains Archaea, Bacteria, and Eucarya. *Proceedings of the National Academy of Science USA* 87 (12): 4576–9.

Materials and Supplies

Prepared Microscope Slides

Bacteria, three types, separate smears

Staphylococcus aureus

Bacillus

Rhodospirillum rubrum

Streptococcus or *Streptobacillus*

Diplococcus

Oscillatoria

Merismopedia

Nostoc or *Anabaena*

Living Cultures

Gram positive bacterium

Gram negative bacterium

Oscillatoria

Merismopedia

Equipment

Bibulous paper

Bunsen burners and gas tubes

Burner lighters

Compound microscopes

Disposable droppers

Glass coverslips

Glass microscope slides

Inoculation loops

Laboratory tape

Lens paper

Nalgene squirt bottles

Permanent markers

Petri dishes for culture media

Slide holders

Small glass jars or beakers, or trays for stain overflow and waste

Sterile swabs

Test-tube holders for live culture tubes (if needed)

Supplies

Acetone

Agar culture media

Crystal violet stain

Distilled water

Immersion oil

Iodine stain

Methylene blue stain

Saffranin stain

95% ethanol

Prelaboratory Preparation

Bacterial cultures in petri dishes should be established using a variety of possible sources one week before the laboratory exercise, e.g., air, floor dust, skin scraping, soil, or underside of shoe.

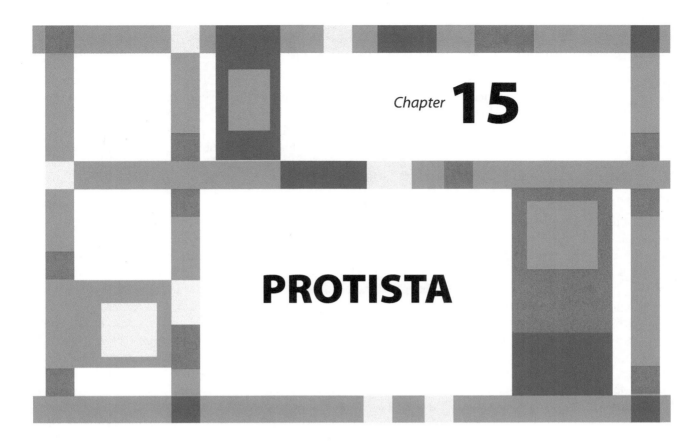

Chapter **15**

PROTISTA

Introduction

The preceding laboratory exercise mentioned that the taxon Protista was introduced by Ernst Haeckel to differentiate microscopic organisms, including bacteria, from the animal and plant kingdoms. More recently, the concept was refined to exclude prokaryotes and just include all single-celled eukaryotes and their immediate relatives (such as seaweeds). However, this definition is based on absent characters. It simply includes all eukaryotes without those specific features that define an organism as an animal, plant, or fungus. No characteristics uniquely define protists as a group. Also, it is clear that some protists are more closely related to either plants, animals, or fungi than they are to other protists. The group is thus **paraphyletic**—it is a group that includes a common ancestor (the first eukaryote) but not all of the descendants—it omits the animals, plants, and fungi. The name is therefore a grouping with no evolutionary significance. We have assembled representatives of these chiefly microscopic but often-unrelated organisms together in one exercise simply for convenience.

Protists, like animals, plants, and fungi, are all eukaryotes. They arose from prokaryotic ancestors at least in part through repeated **endosymbiosis**, in which, for example, once free-living aerobic bacteria and single-celled cyanobacteria became internal symbionts within another cell, eventually diminishing as mitochondria and chloroplasts, respectively. Eukaryotic cells exhibit the following features:

- Larger cell size: chiefly 10–100 μm

- DNA segregated into a membrane-bound nucleus

- Complex internal membrane system and organelles such as mitochondria and Golgi apparatus

- DNA extensively complexed with histone proteins and packaged together as chromosomes

- Cell division via mitosis

- Meiosis, fertilization, sexual recombination, and crossing over

■ Extensive multicellularity and cell differentiation

■ Larger eukaryotic ribosome

Because most protists consist of a single cell, they must be able to carry out all life processes, including feeding themselves and reproducing in their environment. As a result, they exhibit **cellular differentiation**; that is, they have evolved specialized organelles and membrane structures, such as axopods, extrusomes, membranelles (sheets of fused cilia), axostyle, kinetoplasts, or a stalk, not found in typical animal or plant cells. By contrast, the cells of multicellular species do not carry out every life process. Such cells demonstrate **histological differentiation**; they are typically specialized for different functions, often forming different tissues (e.g., a muscle, skin, or nerve cell cannot survive on its own).

As a result of cellular differentiation, protists inhabit a tremendous range of environments. All require water, even if only a thin film surrounding sediment or soil particles, although many can survive lengthy dry or otherwise unfriendly environmental conditions as **cysts** or spores with tough outer coatings. Cell size also ranges widely; the smallest species, at ~5 μm, are no larger than many prokaryotes, while the largest multicellular seaweeds may exceed 100 m in length. With their diversity, protists exhibit a substantial range of metabolisms, including all of those listed for prokaryotes, except chemoautotrophy. However, the vast majority are aerobic. **Photoautotrophic** species include both single- and many-celled algae and seaweeds. All have chlorophyll as do plants, but also a wide range of accessory pigments and different storage compounds. Some diatoms are **photoheterotrophs**, carrying out photosynthesis while taking up some organic molecules such as amino acids. **Heterotrophs**, which require already manufactured organic molecules, may obtain their nutrients via **phagotrophy**—ingesting particulate food—or **osmotrophy**—absorbing dissolved food. Phagotrophic protists are chiefly single-celled species formerly placed in the animal kingdom as "Protozoa" ("first animals," such as *Amoeba* and *Paramecium*). Protozoa is a polyphyletic group with no evolutionary meaning or taxonomic status. Osmotrophic protists are parasites and decomposers, also chiefly single-celled. These include species such as the malarial parasites that were also formerly classified as protozoans, and fungus-like decomposers. In addition, **mixotrophs** (technically photoheterotrophs) include single-celled algae that carry out photosynthesis but also have heterotrophic nutritional requirements. As a final layer of variation, protists exhibit a tremendous diversity of life cycles. Protists may be asexual or sexual; the haploid or diploid phase may dominate; a flagellated **swarmer stage** may be present, and even mitosis varies. For example, in dinoflagellates the nuclear envelope remains intact during mitosis.

NOTE: The classifications in this and subsequent chapters do not include categories such as kingdom, phylum, and class. The taxonomy of many groups is not well defined, and the traditional categories established by Linnaeus are not easily applicable in many cases. To distinguish more inclusive groups from smaller groups within them, we apply a series of different, successively indented fonts, beginning with the most inclusive. The following chapters that discuss different groups of organisms will each begin with a list that outlines the hierarchical classification used in the chapter.

The classification of protists has changed repeatedly over the last few decades as new technologies such as electron microscopy and DNA sequencing have revealed new characteristics and relationships. As a result, the classification outlined here (Table 15-1) will likely change in the future. Also, this classification includes only a few representative groups and specific examples. The diversity is far greater than we could cover, even in an entire course devoted just to protists.

TABLE 15-1 *Classification summary of protists discussed in this chapter.*

EXCAVATA
  Parabasalia
    TRICHOMONADIDA
    TRICHONYMPHIDA
  Euglenozoa
    EUGLENOIDEA (OR EUGLENIDA)
    KINETOPLASTIDA
ALVEOLATA
  Ciliophora (ciliates)
  Dinoflagellata
STRAMENOPILA
  Bacillariophyceae (diatoms)
  Phaeophyceae (brown algae)
RHIZARIA
  Foraminifera
  Radiolaria
AMOEBOZOA
  Lobosea
  Mycetozoa (slime molds)

EXCAVATA

Excavates may or may not represent a monophyletic group. They are chiefly single cells with two, four, or more flagella (up to several hundred), and many have no mitochondria. The name derives from a conspicuous feeding groove supported by microtubules.

Parabasalia

Parabasalids are anaerobic, either endosymbiotic or parasitic, single cells with no mitochondria, and with flagella clustered at the anterior end of the cell. They are named after the **parabasal body**, a complex of fibers arising from the basal bodies of flagella, Golgi apparatus, and microtubules.

TRICHOMONADIDA

Trichomonads are endosymbiotic and parasitic flagellates with 4–6 flagella at one end. One of these runs along the cell body as an undulating membrane. A sheet of microtubules called the **axostyle** projects beyond the end of the cell like a needle (Figure 15-1). *Trichomonas vaginalis* is a parasite of the human urogenital system. It is the most common protist parasite in the United States, although men are usually asymptomatic.

■ Examine a prepared microscope slide of *Trichomonas vaginalis*. Illustrate in your lab notebook. Look for flagella, nucleus, and needle-like axostyle.

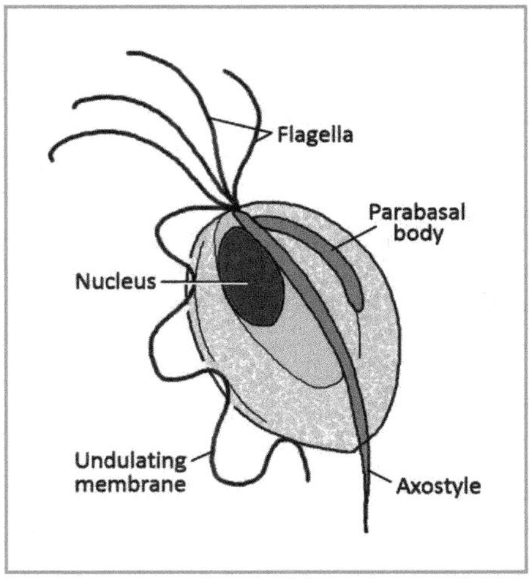

TRICHONYMPHIDA

Trychonympha is a pear- or teardrop-shaped parabasalid, one of several found in the intestine of most termite species, where it contributes to digestion of wood that the termite consumes. Actually, symbiotic bacteria within *Trichonympha* produce the enzyme cellulase that digests the wood's cellulose. This protist bears hundreds of flagella (hence, an older name for its group: Hypermastigida, from the Greek roots for "excessive" and "whip").

FIGURE 15-1 Excavata, Parabasalia, Trichomonadida: *Trichomonas vaginalis* diagram.

Image courtesy of Charles G. Messing, 2011.

■ Examine living parabasalid symbionts in the hindgut of a termite. These may also include *Trichomonas* and other genera in addition to *Trichonympha*.

• Obtain a clean glass microscope slide and coverslip.

• Using a dropper, place a drop of sterile saline solution in the center of the slide.

• Obtain a live termite in a small dish. Make sure you do not allow it to escape.

• Using a forceps, gently grasp the termite by its midsection.

• Holding the termite over the drop of saline solution, use a second forceps to gently squeeze the midsection of the termite, which should cause it to release a pale fluid from its hind end.

• Dip the termite's hind end in the drop of saline.

• Cover the drop with a coverslip in the same way you have previously made a wet mount.

• Examine under 40✕ magnification.

• Work quickly; the symbionts will eventually die outside their host.

• Note the manner in which the symbionts move. Draw the different forms that you observe. Can you see any wood fragments within the symbionts?

Euglenozoa

These single cells usually have two flagella that arise from a pouch or **reservoir** at or near one end of the cell. The pouch is supported by microtubules and may also serve as a **cytostome**, or cell mouth. Euglenozoan flagella are uniquely supported by a complex lattice of microtubules in addition to the usual 9 + 2 microtubule construction. Species include absorbers (including parasites), phagotrophs that feed on bacteria and smaller eukaryotes, and photosynthetic forms. Typically, asexual, longitudinal division produces mirror-image daughter cells.

EUGLENOIDEA (OR EUGLENIDA)

Because some euglenids are photosynthetic and others heterotrophic, while others may alternate between the two metabolisms, they were claimed by both botanists and zoologists, which helped prompt the development of the Protista as a separate group. These flagellates are named for their reddish **stigma**, or eyespot, of carotenoid pigment grains next to the pouch (from the Greek *eu*: "true"; *glene*: "eyeball" or "socket") that probably acts as a shield for a much smaller photoreceptor. Spiral strips of protein under the cell membrane create a flexible or rigid **pellicle**. Most live in fresh water. Figure 15-2 shows several preserved and stained Euglena, which do not show internal structure well.

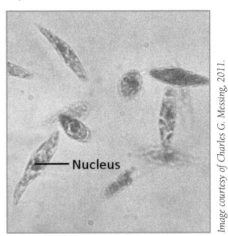

FIGURE 15-2 Excavata, Euglenozoa, Euglenoidea: *Euglena*, preserved and stained microscope slide. Note differences in cell shapes associated with euglenoid movement. Flagella are not visible.

Image courtesy of Charles G. Messing, 2011.

- Examine live cultures of photosynthetic *Euglena* and heterotrophic *Peranema*.

   A. Make separate wet mounts on separate slides of the two forms provided as living cultures.

   B. Withdraw a small portion of culture containing cells using a dropper designated for that culture. **ALWAYS USE THE DROPPER DESIGNATED FOR A SPECIFIC CULTURE TO AVOID CONTAMINATION.**

   C. Place a small droplet of culture in the middle of a clean microscope slide.

   D. Place a smaller drop of "Detain" or "Protoslo" on the culture droplet. This will slow the activity of the organisms (and eventually kill them, so don't dawdle).

   E. Place the side of a clean coverslip on the microscope slide adjacent to the droplet, and lower it onto the slide so as not to trap any air bubbles.

   F. Examine as you would a prepared slide.

      - Compare sizes and shapes of the two species. Which is larger under the same magnification?

      - Describe the changes in cell shape called **euglenoid movement** (permitted by the flexible pellicle) (Figure 15-2). Do both species exhibit such changes?

      - How does the activity of the flagellum differ in the two?

      - What differences in color between the two suggest that one species is photosynthetic and one is not?

      - Under high magnification, can you observe the reddish stigma in *Euglena* associated with phototaxis? Where is it located in the cell?

      - Illustrate both species for your lab notebook.

- To observe **phototaxis** in photosynthetic *Euglena*, your instructor will surround a culture jar with opaque heavy paper except for a slit on one side open to a light source (gooseneck microscope illuminator). During lab, briefly remove the opaque paper to reveal the distribution of cells in the culture (visible to the naked eye because of the green chlorophyll pigments).

  - Does the distribution of *Euglena* in the jar reflect positive (toward the light) or negative (away from the light) phototaxis? Note your observations in your lab notebook.

KINETOPLASTIDA

These are free-living and parasitic, heterotrophic flagellates characterized by a large mitochondrion with a DNA-containing **kinetoplast**. Parasitic *Trypanosoma* has one long flagellum that attaches along the cell body as an **undulating membrane** (Figure 15-3). Some members of this genus cause **sleeping sickness**, which is transmitted by **tsetse flies (*Glossina*)**.

- Examine a prepared microscope slide of *Trypanosoma*. To see any detail, you must increase magnification to the 40✕ lens. Illustrate for your lab notebook.

  - Look for the large dark-stained central nucleus, small dark-stained kinetoplast at one end of the cell, and undulating membrane. The large, pale, surrounding spheres are red blood cells. Illustrate for your lab notebook.

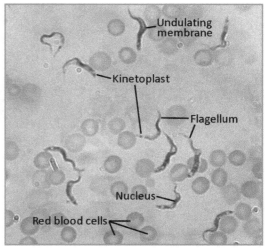

Image courtesy of Charles G. Messing, 2011.

FIGURE 15-3 Euglenozoa, Kinetoplastida: *Trypanosoma brucei*, the causative agent of sleeping sickness, also called trypanosomiasis. Preserved and stained microscope slide.

ALVEOLATA

The three groups of microorganisms included here appear very different from each other and were never considered at all closely related until recent advances in molecular biology and ultrastructure revealed important homologous similarities among them. The group name comes from the system of flattened sacs, or vesicles, called **alveoli**, under the cell membrane. These organisms also possess **extrusomes**—organelles that can extrude or release threads, usually for defense or anchoring. This exercise examines two of the groups. Members of the third group, the **Apicomplexa**, which include the organisms that cause malaria, are too small to observe usefully with our microscopes.

Ciliophora

Ciliates are single-celled heterotrophs that bear a complete or partial covering of hairlike **cilia**, a firm or somewhat flexible cell shape with a **cytostome** (permanent mouth opening), and both **micronuclei** (diploid; for reproduction) and a **macronucleus** (polyploid; for cell regulation). Cilia are used in locomotion, feeding, and sensory functions. They share with flagella the same basic internal organization of microtubules, but cilia are typically shorter, more numerous, exhibit a different pattern of undulation with a power and recovery stroke, and are accompanied by a system of fibrils and microtubules below the cell membrane. Groups of cilia are often fused and function together as sheets (**membranelles**) or bristles (**cirri**). Reproduction occurs either asexually via transverse **binary fission**, or sexually via **conjugation**, in which two cells join and exchange nuclear material before reproducing. Ciliates are important in all aquatic habitats, in moist soils, and as endosymbionts and parasites.

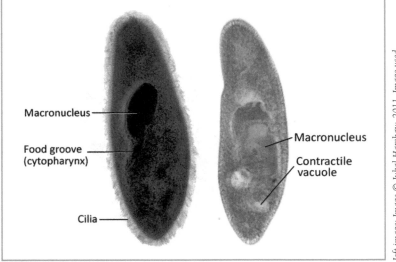

Macronucleus

Food groove
(cytopharynx)

Cilia

Macronucleus

Contractile
vacuole

left image: Image © Jubal Harshaw, 2011. Image used under license of Shutterstock, Inc. Right image: Courtesy of Charles G. Messing, 2011.

FIGURE 15-4 Alveolata, Ciliophora: *Paramecium*. Two stained preparations showing different anatomical features.

■ Examine prepared microscope slides of the ciliates *Paramecium* (Figure 15-4) and *Stentor*.

  • Compare and illustrate differences in cell shape and size. Note apparent differences in the structure and distribution of cilia and macronuclei.

■ Prepare and examine wet mounts from living cultures of *Paramecium* and *Stentor* following the instructions for *Euglena* and *Peranema* above.

  • Compare and contrast differences in cell shape between living and preserved samples.

  • Compare and contrast swimming behavior in the two species.

  • Under high magnification, examine specimens of both species that have been slowed down using "Detain" or "Protoslo." How are membranelles and separate hairlike cilia distributed differently in the two species? Observe the activity of the **contractile vacuoles**, which control water balance and appear as large, pale circles; they should disappear abruptly at intervals as they void excess water to the exterior, and then reappear as they swell with water from within the cell.

■ Prepare and examine a wet mount from pond water.

  • Look for various kinds of ciliates, such as bell-shaped, stalked *Vorticella*, J-shaped *Loxodes*, or flat, oval, *Euplotes* with bristles at both ends.

  • Have your instructor help you distinguish between ciliates and similarly sized **rotifers**, which are actually many-celled members of the animal kingdom (see Rotifera on page 222).

Dinoflagellata

Dinoflagellates are best known as photosynthetic single cells that are critical components at the base of marine food webs. They typically bear one ribbonlike flagellum in an encircling groove (cingulum) and one whip flagellum in a posterior groove (sulcus) (Figure 15-5) that together produce a whirling swimming motion. (While the "dino" in dinosaur and "dinoflagellate" both derive from Greek words, one comes from *deinos*, or "terrible," while the other comes from *dinos*, or "whirling.") As in plants, the storage product is starch, and the cell wall is composed of cellulose (often sculptured or armorlike); however, the dominant photosynthetic pigments are golden-brown (although preserved cells may be stained pink). Some species are

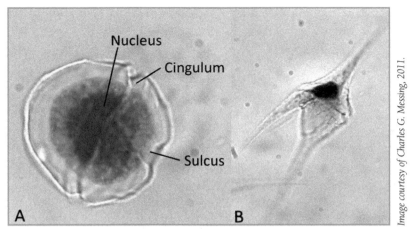

FIGURE 15-5 Alveolata, Dinoflagellata. A. *Peridinium*. B. *Ceratium* with long spines and dark nucleus. Preserved and stained microscope slides.

important endosymbionts called **zooxanthellae** ("little yellow animals") found in reef-building corals and giant clams, while others produce toxins and are responsible for the harmful algal blooms called **red tides**.

- ▪ Examine a prepared microscope slide of a dinoflagellate.

  - • Illustrate for your lab notebook. Look for the encircling and posterior grooves and nucleus.

STRAMENOPILA

This is an amazingly diverse group that in some ways parallels the evolution of the three "higher" kingdoms (Fungi, Plantae, Animalia). It includes funguslike, nonphotosynthetic water molds; animal-like, carnivorous, single-celled flagellates, and plantlike species ranging from single-celled photosynthetic algae to large brown seaweeds with complex internal structures. However, all are united by having a unique "tinsel" flagellum with fine, tubular side branches as well as one normal flagellum in at least some life history stage (usually a sexually reproducing stage). The name stramenopile means "straw hair." Most species are photosynthetic and contain chlorophyll c (plants have chlorophyll *a*) and accessory carotenoid pigments that produce a characteristic golden or golden-brown color. They store energy as oils or polysaccharides (other than starch), and many produce calcium carbonate or silica skeletons. This laboratory exercise examines representatives of two stramenopile groups.

Bacillariophyceae
("ba-sih-la-ree-oh-FYE-see")

Diatoms are golden-pigmented, photosynthetic single cells (or simple colonies) that produce a protective shell of silica and organic material in two nested pieces like a petri dish. These shells are elaborately ornamented and may be cylindrical, triangular, boat-shaped, or needle-shaped (Figure 15-6). Diatoms are nonmotile or capable of gliding on a thin layer of extruded slime. They occur in fresh and salt water, moist soil, and hypersaline lakes. Along with dinoflagellates, they are among the most important phytoplankton at the base of marine food webs, although many **benthic** (bottom-dwelling) forms also exist. Fossil diatom deposits known as **diatomaceous earth** are used as abrasives, filters, chalk, and talc and are important

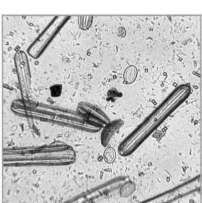

FIGURE 15-6 Stramenopila, Bacillar-iophyceae: diatom shells illustrating boat-shaped and elongated forms.

in reconstructing ancient environmental conditions. The precise ornamentation of their silica shells is used to test the optical clarity of microscope lenses.

- Examine a prepared microscope slide of diatoms.

  • Illustrate for your lab notebook. Note the detailed ornamentation. Compare your illustrations with those of other students; different microscope slides may have differently shaped species.

Phaeophyceae (or Phaeophyta) *("fay-oh-FYE-see")*

The **brown algae**, along with the green and red algae, comprise one of the three major traditional groups of seaweeds. However, they are not all closely related to each other and do not form a single **monophyletic** group with a common ancestor separate from all other algae and plants. Brown algae are all marine and range in size from microscopic to gigantic kelps up to 100 m long (none are single celled). The **thallus** (body) of large species is often divided into a basal **holdfast**, a **stipe** (stalk), and broad **blades**. Gas-filled **flotation sacs** that buoy the photosynthetic blades toward the sun are often present. Brown algae exhibit a complex life history that includes single-celled zoospores with the characteristic stramenopile flagellum and alternation of haploid and diploid generations. Many species, such as the kelps and rockweeds, are important components of temperate coastal ecosystems, where they serve as food for sea urchins, snails, and crustaceans. The brown alga *Sargassum* forms great floating masses in tropical seas; hence, the name Sargasso Sea.

- Examine the specimens of brown algae dried onto sheets of herbarium paper. Specimens may include temperate *Fucus* (rockweed), and tropical *Sargassum* (Gulf weed) and *Padina* (fan-shaped peacock algae).

  • Illustrate for your lab notebook. Note any differentiation of the thallus into holdfast, stipe, and blades, and any flotation sacs.

RHIZARIA

Members of this group are chiefly ameboid and nonphotosynthetic, with a variety of slender, root-, web-, or needlelike pseudopods (not the broad lobes typical of *Amoeba*). However, no characteristics unique to the group have been discovered. The only support for the Rhizaria comes from molecular data (rRNA and actin), although it is robust and consistent. Many species produce mineral shells or skeletons, which may be quite complex.

Foraminifera

Foraminifers (forams, for short) are single-celled, marine ameboid organisms. They produce a network of fine, meshlike pseudopods that arise from openings in a multi-chambered shell (**test**) of calcium carbonate ($CaCO_3$), or one of fine mud (Figure 15-7A). Their complex life cycle includes sexual reproduction and alternation of haploid and diploid generations. Large species may reach 2 cm across, with numerous nuclei in a common cytoplasm. Although most are benthic, some are important members of the **zooplankton**. For millions of years, their sand-grain–sized tests have accumulated to form thick layers of deep-sea mud that provide an important record of global climate changes. The great pyramids of Egypt were built from sandstone composed chiefly of giant fossil foraminiferans.

- Using the dissecting stereomicroscope, examine dry tests of planktonic and benthic foraminifers.

  • Illustrate a variety of tests for your lab notebook.

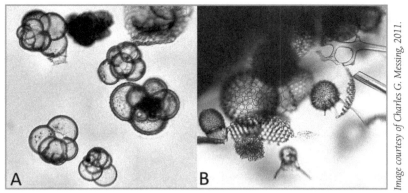

Image courtesy of Charles G. Messing, 2011.

FIGURE 15-7 Rhizaria. A. Multi-chambered tests of foraminiferans. B. Spherical (and broken) tests of radiolarians. Microscope slides.

Radiolaria

Radiolarians are also important members of the ocean's zooplankton, but they produce needlelike pseudopods that radiate from delicate spherical or basketlike tests of **silica** rather than calcium carbonate (Figure 15-7B). As with planktonic foraminiferans, the sinking tests of radiolarians contribute to vast expanses of deep-sea muds.

■ Examine a prepared microscope slide of radiolarian tests.

• Illustrate a variety of tests for your lab notebook.

AMOEBOZOA

This group includes the typical amoebas that produce broad, lobelike temporary extensions called **pseudopods**. The cytoplasm is divided into an interior **endoplasm** that contains the organelles and a clear exterior **ectoplasm** (Figure 15-8A). These cells move via **cytoplasmic flow**, in which the interior endoplasm flows forward in the direction of movement and turns into ectoplasm, which streams backward along the cell surface. Amoebozoans appear to be more closely related to fungi and animals than to plants.

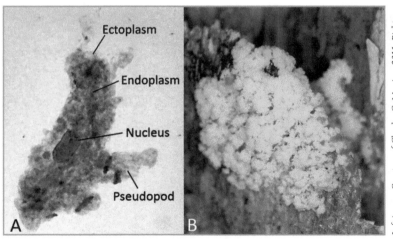

Left image: Courtesy of Charles G. Messing, 2011. Right image: Image © Torsten Lorenz, 2011. Image used under license of Shutterstock, Inc.

FIGURE 15-8 Amoebozoa. A. Lobosea: *Amoeba proteus*. Preserved and stained microscope slide. B. Mycetozoa: living yellow plasmodial slime mold on a dead tree stump.

Lobosea

Lobose amoebas are single cells that produce the typical lobelike pseudopods, although some move like little slugs with a single leading pseudopod. Others produce organic or mineral tests. They live in fresh water, moist soil, marine habitats, or as commensals or parasites (e.g., *Entamoeba histolytica* causes amebic dysentery). Not all amoebas belong to this group; the rare brain-eating amoeba, *Naegleria fowleri*, is included in the Excavata.

■ Examine a prepared microscope slide of fresh-water *Amoeba proteus*.

• Note the diversity of cell shapes resulting from the various shapes and numbers of pseudopods. Illustrate a variety of cell shapes for your lab notebook.

Mycetozoa

Commonly known as **slime molds** or **social amoebas**, members of this group all exhibit a life history stage in which a spore-producing structure (a **sorus**, as in ferns, or **fruiting body**, as in fungi) develops on a sterile stalk. They, along with some other unrelated forms also called slime molds, were formerly classified as fungi; the name means "fungus-animal." These slime molds spend much of their life history as individual amoebas, feeding on bacteria, spores, and organic material, most commonly in soil, lawns, rotting logs, and forest floors, but also in tropical trees and flowers. Under certain conditions, however, the individual amoebas gather together; in one group, the **plasmodial slime molds**, the amoebas fuse together as a **plasmodium**, a single membranous cytoplasm that may be brightly colored, reach meters across, and contain vast numbers of nuclei. Sliming their way across suburban lawns, these creatures have been misidentified as alien life forms. In another group, the **cellular slime molds**, when nutrients become depleted, the individual amoebas aggregate into a sluglike mass that moves as a single organism (though the individual cells remain distinct). These slime molds demonstrate among the simplest examples of cell communication and differentiation and so are used as important models for understanding early embryological development in humans as well as the evolution of multicellular organisms.

■ Using the dissecting stereomicroscope, examine a germinating culture of the plasmodial slime mold, *Physarum polycephalum*.

• Observe and take notes on the nature of cytoplasmic streaming.

Questions

1. In Biology I, you covered the basic structure of cellular organelles. As examples of cellular differentiation, briefly describe how the structure and functions of many of these organelles have been modified in protists discussed in this laboratory exercise. Include in your answer at least the following: flagellum, cilia, microtubules, Golgi apparatus, mitochondrion. Feel free to investigate beyond this exercise (cite any sources to which you refer).

2. Why do you suppose that microscopic fresh-water organisms such as *Paramecium* and *Amoeba* are often distributed around the world?

References

Cavalier-Smith, T. 2002. The phagotrophic origin of eukaryotes and phylogenetic classification of Protozoa. *International Journal of Systematic and Evolutionary Microbiology* 52 (2): 297–354.

Moreira, D., von der Heyden, S., Bass, D., López-García, P., Chao, E., and Cavalier-Smith, T. 2007. Global eukaryote phylogeny: combined small- and large-subunit ribosomal DNA trees support monophyly of Rhizaria, Retaria and Excavata. *Molecular Phylogenetics and Evolution* 44 (1): 255–66.

Nikolaev, S. I., Berney, C., Fahrni, J. F., Bolivar, I., Polet, S., Mylnikov, A. P., Aleshin, V. V., Petrov, N. B., and Pawlowski, J. 2004. The twilight of Heliozoa and rise of Rhizaria, an emerging supergroup of amoeboid eukaryotes. *Proceedings of the NationalAcademy of Science, USA* 101(21): 8066–71.

Rivkin, R. B., and Putt, M. 2007. Heterotrophy and photoheterotrophy by Antarctic microalgae: light-dependent incorporation of amino acids and glucose. *Journal of Phycology* 23 (3): 442–52.

Soper, D. 2004. Trichomoniasis: under control or undercontrolled? *American Journal of Obstetrics and Gynecology* 190 (1): 281–90.

Materials and Supplies

Living Specimens

Termite (for extraction of gut symbionts, e.g., *Trichonympha*)

Living Cultures

Euglena

Paramecium

Peranema

Physarum polycephalum (see under Prelaboratory Preparations, below)

Stentor

Pond water cultures

Prepared Microscope Slides

Amoeba proteus

Dinoflagellates (e.g., *Ceratium*)

Diatoms

Foraminifera

Paramecium caudatum or *multimicronucleatum*

Stentor coeruleus

Radiolaria

Trichomonas vaginalis

Trypanosoma brucei (may be labeled *gambiense* or other subspecies)

Dried Specimens on Herbarium Paper

Phaeophyta (brown algae), e.g., *Fucus, Sargassum, Padina, Laminaria*

Equipment

Compound microscopes

Dissecting stereomicroscopes

Disposable droppers

Fine forceps

Glass cover slips

Glass microscope slides

Gooseneck microscope illuminator

Heavy (card stock at least) opaque paper

Laboratory tape

Lens paper

Permanent markers

Scissors

Transparent tape

At least two 500-mL beakers

Supplies

"Protoslo" or "Detain"

Sterile saline solution

Prelaboratory Preparations

(Preceding week): Collect two or more 500-mL beakers of pond water, including fragments of aquatic plants, filamentous algae, and mud or detritus. Let stand on laboratory counter for at least one week; one beaker under bench lights, one beaker in the dark.

(Preceding week): Follow kit instructions for *Physarum polycephalum* (slime mold) germinating culture (from Carolina Biological or Ward's). Follow kit instructions.

Place incubated prokaryote culture dishes from previous week on lab counter for examination by students.

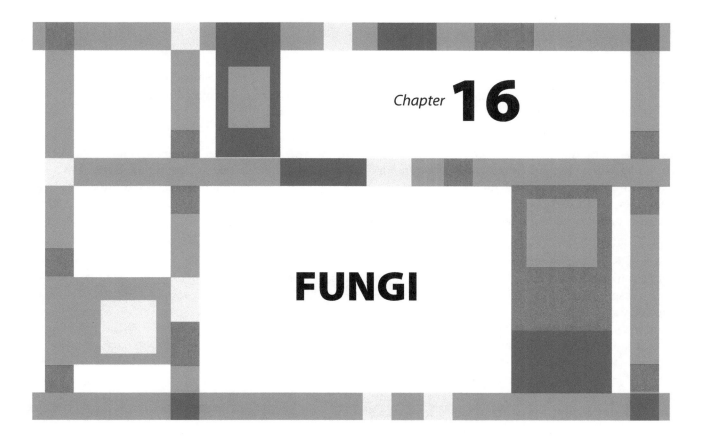

Chapter **16**

FUNGI

Introduction

Fungi (or **Mycota**, from the Greek *mykus* meaning mushroom) represent a major group of heterotrophic eukaryotes usually ranked as a kingdom. Although a few species are familiar as mushrooms, molds and mildews, we tend to overlook most fungi because the great majority remain hidden in soil, decaying vegetation, or as symbionts within other organisms. Yet, there are easily over 100,000 species. They occur from tropical rain forests to the tundra and on the sea floor. Fungi obtain nutrients via **osmotrophy**—the absorption of organic material broken down by secreted **exoenzymes**. As a result they are important **saprobes**, or decomposers, as well as parasites. None are photosynthetic. The decomposers are critical recyclers, releasing minerals and carbon dioxide from dead organic material and making them available again to food webs. Unfortunately, such decomposers also destroy vast amounts of stored food and agricultural products every year. Thousands of parasitic species attack members of pretty much every other group of living things, including amoebas, insects, plants, worms, and mammals. Over 5,000 species attack agricultural crops, and species in about a dozen genera cause a wide range of pathogenic conditions in humans, from vaginal thrush (*Candida*) to lymphocutaneous sporotrichosis (*Sporothrix*). Every organ system may be affected. On the other hand, no fungi = no bread, wine, cake, or beer. Certain species produce antibiotics, while others produce powerful hallucinogenic compounds such as psilocybin, or some of the most powerful toxic and carcinogenic substances known (e.g., aflatoxin).

Although some fungi exist as single cells, called **yeasts**, the great majority are multicellular. Unlike plants and animals, the body of a fungus

Image courtesy of Charles G. Messing, 2011.

FIGURE 16-1 Basidiomycota: group of mushrooms.

does not exist as a single solid mass. Instead, it consists of a **mycelium**—a network of fine tubular filaments called **hyphae** (singular: hypha). It is only in the reproductive stage that part of the mycelium of some fungi develops into an obvious compact mass such as a mushroom or toadstool. Yet, despite not having a massive body, fungi may include some of the largest organisms on earth. In northeastern Oregon, the mycelium of *Armillaria ostoyae*, a species pathogenic on the roots of northern conifer trees, spread over an area of 161 km^2 (= 62 mi^2) and may have begun growing as many as 8,650 years ago.

Fungal hyphae may be divided by cross walls into individual cells (**septate**), or they may have a continuous cytoplasm with many nuclei (**coenocytic**; pronounced *see-no-SIH-tic*). In parasitic species, branching hyphae, called **haustoria** (singular: haustorium), are modified for penetrating the cells of host organisms. All hyphae grow from their tips, unlike filamentous algae, which lengthen as cells divide and increase in number all along the filament. Unlike plants, the cell walls of fungi lack cellulose; instead, they consist of a combination of polysaccharides called **glucans** and **chitin**.

Although most fungi reproduce both asexually and sexually, some reproduce only asexually. Much of the fungus life cycle is **haploid**—each nucleus contains only a single set of chromosomes. The basic pattern is similar in many species. In the asexual cycle, some hyphae develop stalked structures called **conidiophores** that produce **spores**. Asexual spores are often called **conidia**. A spore is a single-celled, dispersal stage surrounded by a tough, resistant cell wall. When released, spores disperse in the air or water; when they land on a suitable substrate, they germinate, begin absorbing nutrients, and develop into hyphae again. The sexual cycle begins when hyphae from two or more genetically different mycelia fuse together, a process called **plasmogamy**. Fungi do not have what we normally think of as sexes. Instead, mycelia with different alleles are referred to as mating types (often designated "+" or "−", although some have more than two). The fused cytoplasms of the hyphae develop into a secondary mycelium in which the nuclei from the two "parents" pair up but do not yet fuse. This new mycelium is referred to as a **heterokaryon** (from the Greek *heteros* meaning different, and *karuon*). Because more than two mating types may fuse together, the term **dikaryon** refers specifically to cases in which just two different mycelia fuse. Mycelia can remain and grow in the dikaryotic stage for years, with the paired but separate nuclei dividing via mitosis. The genetic composition of each remains intact, and no sexual recombination takes place. Eventually, and usually when nutrients become depleted, the paired haploid nuclei fuse together, a process called **karyogamy**. Often, this occurs in a portion of the dikaryotic mycelium called the **fruiting body**, modified for reproduction (although it has nothing to do with the fruits of flowering plants). The fused nuclei form a **zygote**, the only diploid stage in the fungal life cycle. However, this is a transient phase; the zygote quickly divides via **meiosis** to produce four nuclei that re-establish the haploid condition. Additional mitotic divisions eventually produce haploid spores that disperse to develop into the next generation of mycelia. Life cycle variations range from single-celled yeasts that only reproduce asexually via binary fission, to parasites called **rusts** that may require two different plant hosts and produce five different kinds of spores. **Mold** is a nontaxonomic term that refers to those fungi that do not produce discrete large fruiting bodies such as mushrooms. **Mildew** is a similar generic term for molds that typically grow on flat surfaces in moist environments (e.g., shower stalls), though it also refers specifically to some plant parasites (e.g., powdery mildew).

Because they are basically immobile and grow up from the soil, fungi were long classified as members of the plant kingdom. In 1969, Robert Whittaker elevated the Fungi to kingdom level as part of his five-kingdom system of classifying organisms. Some groups now recognized as fungi have also been placed among the protists in some classifications. Although there are eleven major fungal groups, including four of uncertain status, this exercise focuses on five major groups.

TABLE 16-1 *Classification summary of Fungi discussed in this chapter.*

CHYTRIDIOMYCOTA (chytrids)
ZYGOMYCOTA (conjugating fungi)
GLOMEROMYCOTA (endomycorrhizae)
ASCOMYCOTA (sac fungi and lichens)
BASIDIOMYCOTA (club fungi and ectomycorrhizae)

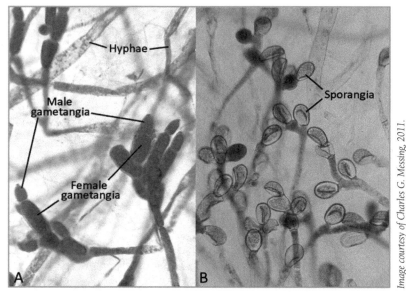

FIGURE 16-2 Chytridiomycota: *Allomyces*. A. Gametophyte showing male and female gametangia. B. Sporophyte showing egg-shaped sporangia. Preserved and stained microscope slides.

CHYTRIDIOMYCOTA *("kih-TRIH-dee-o-my-KOH-ta")*

Chytrids (*"KIT-rids"*) are the oldest known and most primitive living fungi (Figure 16-2). Unlike most fungi, they have a flagellated stage, and at least some have multicellular haploid and diploid life history stages. In the water mold, *Allomyces*, a decomposer widespread in moist soil and fresh water, the asexual stage is a diploid coenocytic branching filament that produces capsules (**sporangia**) containing diploid **zoospores**. Zoospores are so named because they have a flagellum and are motile (like the flagellates formerly included in the animal kingdom; hence, the prefix "zoo-") and represent a dispersal stage. Cells in some capsules undergo meiosis to produce haploid zoospores that develop into haploid mycelia bearing male and female **gametangia** (gamete-producing capsules). Although most chytrids are decomposers, others are important parasites. *Synchytrium endobioticum* causes an important disease of potatoes, and recently discovered *Batrachochytrium dendrobatidis* kills frogs in large numbers.

- Examine a prepared slide of the gametophyte of *Allomyces* (Figure 16-2A).

  • Gametangia occur as pairs of capsules, with the male gametangium at the tip and the female just below it.

  • Illustrate both sporophyte and gametophyte for your lab notebook.

- Examine a prepared slide of the sporophyte of *Allomyces* (Figure 16-2B).

  • Look for the egg-shaped reproductive structures along or at the tips of the hyphal branches. Diploid sporangia are single egg-shaped capsules that produce asexual diploid zoospores or, following meiosis, haploid zoospores.

ZYGOMYCOTA

These are the pin molds, sugar molds, and conjugating fungi. The latter refers to the life history stage when two mycelia fuse. Zygomycota literally means "yoke fungus," again referring to the stage when two mycelia unite, or yoke together. However, recent research suggests that the group is polyphyletic. Some members have been removed to the Glomeromycota (see below). Others, including "typical" zygomycotes such as the black bread mold (*Rhizopus*) examined in this exercise, are now treated as a group called Mucormycotina; it is not clear to which other fungi they are most closely related.

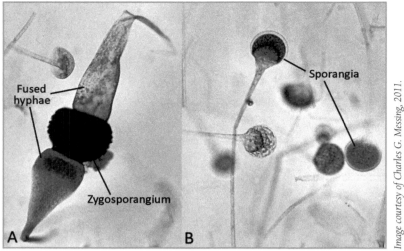

FIGURE 16-3 Zygomycota: black bread mold, *Rhizopus stolonifer*. A. Zygosporangium. B. Asexual sporangia. Preserved and stained microscope slides.

As in the chytrids, zygomycote hyphae are **coenocytic**; the cytoplasm is not divided into separate cells. However, these fungi do not produce flagellated zoospores. The asexual cycle follows the general pattern described for fungi above. To complete the sexual cycle, when hyphae of two different mating types meet, they develop swellings that grow toward each other. The swellings form **gametangia** containing several haploid nuclei as a partition separates each from its parent hypha. The two gametangia fuse (**plasmogamy**, remember?) to form a **zygospore** that contains numerous nuclei from both parent hyphae (so, it is not a spore in the true sense because it contains multiple nuclei). The zygospore develops a hard, rugged, resistant outer coating and is now called a **zygosporangium** (Figure 16-3A). This stage can withstand harsh environmental conditions and, indeed, must undergo a dormant period before it can complete the cycle. As favorable conditions return, the diploid nuclei undergo meiosis (including sexual recombination) to produce haploid nuclei that will be packaged as spores. As the zygosporangium germinates, it develops a stalked **sporangium** (Figure 16-3B) from which the spores will be released to disperse and develop into new mycelia.

Zygomycotes include both decomposers and symbionts. Many cause commercially important destructive rots of fruits in storage, particularly those with high sugar contents, such as strawberries. Others are important parasites on a wide range of organisms, including amoebas, roundworms, other fungi, and insects. Some of the latter may prove to be helpful biological controls of some insect pests, such as periodic cicadas. A few form ectomycorrhizal relationships with pine tree roots (See **Ectomycorrhizae** below).

The species examined here is the black bread mold, *Rhizopus stolonifer*. Other species of *Rhizopus* cause ocular and vascular infections in humans, especially in diabetics, and may induce abortions in cows and pneumonia in chicks.

■ Examine prepared microscope slides of both asexual and sexual spore-producing stages of *Rhizopus*. (Both may be on the same slide.)

• Look for asexual sporangia that appear as pink balloons and sexual zygosporangia that appear as dark knobby balls between two paler hyphal swellings. Colors may vary from pink to blue, depending upon the stain. Illustrate for your lab notebook.

GLOMEROMYCOTA

This important group of fungi was formerly included among the zygomycotes. They differ from other fungi in producing large spores with multi-layered walls and containing up to thousands of nuclei. Like zygomy-

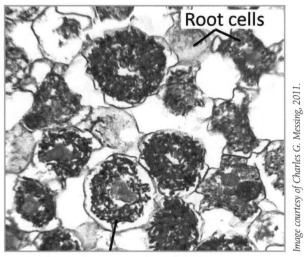

Root cells

Image courtesy of Charles G. Messing, 2011.

FIGURE 16-4 Glomeromycota: masses of red-stained threads are arbuscules of endomycorrhizal haustoria inside root cells. Preserved and stained microscope slides.

cotes and unlike the sac and club fungi, their hyphae are coenocytic (with no cell walls separating nuclei). They do not produce large visible reproductive structures. Most importantly, glomeromycotes form **mycorrhizae** ("*MY-co-RYE-zee*"; singular: "*MY-co-RYE-zuh*") with about 80% of land plant species. A mycorrhiza (from the Greek for "fungus-root") is a symbiotic relationship between a fungus and a plant root. These fungi form **endomycorrhizae**, in which specialized **haustoria** (penetrating hyphae) invade the root and typically form treelike structures called **arbuscules** that may fill individual root cells (Figure 16-4). Actually, the hyphae do not truly penetrate the root cell. Instead, they invaginate so that every branch of the hypha is completely surrounded by thin plant cell plasma membrane. The large surface area of the fungal mycelium increases mineral and water uptake into the plant, whereas the plant transfers carbohydrate products of photosynthesis to the fungus. Plants have had mycorrhizal relationships with fungi for at least 400 million years. Mycorrhizal relationships are often critical for agricultural crops by increasing both water and mineral uptake. They are so abundant that their mycelial network has been called the "Wood Wide Web."

◼ Examine a prepared microscope slide of endomycorrhizae.

- Look for the tight clusters of red- or purple-stained hyphae inside some of the plant cells. Illustrate for your lab notebook.

ASCOMYCOTA

The **sac fungi** are the largest group of fungi, with over 64,000 described species. The name derives from **ascus** (from the Greek *askos,* meaning "a wineskin" or "sac"), the spore-containing capsules produced during sexual reproduction. The group includes particularly important decomposers that produce enzymes capable of breaking down some of the most resistant components of living organisms: cellulose, lignin (wood), and collagen (tendons, ligaments, and connective tissue), as well as important molds that attack a wide variety of foods, causing them to rot before they can be harvested, shipped, or brought to the table. Numerous parasitic sac fungi include species that cause important plant (e.g., Dutch elm disease, chestnut blight) and human diseases (e.g., aspergillosis). Some produce seriously toxic compounds (e.g., ergotamine, aflatoxin). On the other hand, morels and truffles are highly prized as food. Edward Beadle and George Tatum won the Nobel Prize for their work with the red bread mold, *Neurospora crassa*, which led to the hypothesis that specific genes code for specific proteins. Members of the genus *Penicillium* are critical to the production of cheeses such as Brie and Camembert, as well as for producing antibiotics. Ascomycote yeasts include pathogenic *Candida*

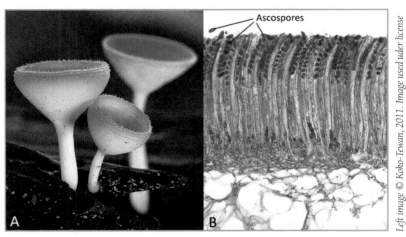

Left image © Koko-Tewan, 2011. Image used uder license of Shutterstock, Inc. Right image: Courtesy of Charles G. Messing, 2011.

FIGURE 16-5 Ascomycota. A. Open ascocarps (apothecia) of wine-cup fungus, *Cookeina*. B. Tightly packed column-like asci lining the apothecium of *Peziza;* each ascus contains a row of eight ascospores. Preserved and stained microscope slide.

species as well as *Saccharomyces cerevisiae*, the most thoroughly studied eukaryote apart from humans, and the critical contributor to brewing, baking, and wine-making.

In the asexual phase of the life cycle, haploid spores germinate and grow into mycelia, which develop **conidiophores**—stalked reproductive structures. Cells at the stalk tips undergo mitosis to produce asexual spores called **conidia**, which disperse in the air or water to settle and complete the cycle. Many sac fungi, such as *Penicillium* and *Aspergillus*, are exclusively asexual. Before molecular evidence identified them as ascomycotes, they were dumped together with all other exclusively asexual species as the Deuteromycota or Fungi Imperfecti, which is no longer a valid group. Other sac fungi, such as *Peziza*, never produce asexual spores.

The sexual cycle follows the general pattern for fungi. As the haploid hyphae of two genetically different mating types grow toward each other, they swell to form **gametangia**. One of these produces a fine hyphal thread that bridges the gap between the two, joining their cytoplasms (**plasmogamy**, again). Nuclei from the other gametangium migrate through the thread to join the nuclei in the first, establishing the dikaryotic condition. Although there are no sperm or eggs, the gametangium that gives up its nuclei is treated as the male **antheridium**, while the one that receives the nuclei is the female **ascogonium**. Dikaryotic hyphae (containing pairs of nuclei) grow out of the ascogonium and, together with haploid hyphae from each parent mycelium, interweave tightly and grow up into a fruiting body called an **ascocarp**. Nuclei in the tips of the dikaryotic hyphae fuse together (**karyogamy**) to form **zygotes**, the only diploid phase of the entire life cycle. The zygotes then divide via meiosis to produce four cells (haploid again); each divides again via mitosis to produce eight cells (**ascospores**) packaged inside an elongated sac (**ascus**; plural: asci) (Figure 16-5B), ready to disperse to complete the cycle. In some sac fungi, such as cuplike *Peziza* and the edible morels, the asci line the surface of the open fruiting body (**apothecium**) (Figure 16-5A). In others, such as truffles and powdery mildew, which parasitizes lilacs, the fruiting body is a closed spherical **cleistothecium** that must rupture or be broken open for the ascospores to disperse.

■ Examine a prepared microscope slide of a cross section of the ascocarp (also called an apothecium) of the ascomycote *Peziza*.

  • Look for the rows of asci containing ascospores lining the concave surface of the cross section.

  • How many ascospores can you count in an ascus that appears completely full?

  • Illustrate for your lab notebook. Make sure you can recognize the entire ascocarp as well as the rows of asci with their ascospores.

■ Examine a whole dried specimen of the edible morel, *Morchella*.

  • Note the mushroomlike shape. Can you find thin sheetlike gills on the underside of the tall cap?

  • The cap actually consists of numerous fused ascocarps. Where would you expect to find the spore-bearing asci? Illustrate for your lab notebook.

■ Examine prepared microscope slides of the mycelia of *Penicillium* and *Aspergillus*.

  • Look for the stalked conidiophores that bear asexually-produced spores (conidia).

  • Compare the shape of the conidiophores and arrangement of spores. How do they differ between the two genera? Illustrate for your lab notebook.

■ Prepare a wet mount of yeast (*Saccharomyces cerevisiae*) from the culture prepared before class. The culture was prepared by mixing sugar, water, and dried yeast. Using a disposable dropper, place a drop or two on a glass microscope slide, and cover with a glass coverslip as in the previous exercise on protists.

  • Observe at 400× magnification. Can you observe budding? Illustrate for your lab notebook.

  • Let the slide sit for 5 minutes; observe again. What has changed?

  • Given what you know about the metabolism of fungi (see the Introduction), explain why sugar was added to the culture preparation. Identify the gas produced by the yeast.

Lichens (pronounced *LYE-kenz*) (Figure 16-6) are symbiotic combinations of a fungus, usually an ascomycote, and a green alga (often *Trebouxia*), or cyanobacterium (frequently nitrogen-fixing *Nostoc*) (Figure 16-6A). Some cases include all three. Although there are over 25,000 species, lichens do not represent a monophyletic grouping (a few are basidiomycotes and one is a glomeromycote). The species name of the lichen refers to the fungus; each alga has its own species name. The lichen body is called a **thallus**, a term that refers to the body of multicellular nonmoving organisms such as fungi, large algae, and simple nonvascular plants that lack distinct organs.

The relationship appears mutualistic because the alga obtains an agreeable site in which to grow and prosper in an otherwise unsuitable habitat, while the fungus extracts carbohydrates produced by the alga.

However, it is actually a controlled parasitism: the fungus limits and controls the alga's growth, often penetrating the algal cells with **haustoria**, as in parasitic fungi. Lichens absorb mineral nutrients from their substrates and may contribute to soil formation. They can be found in a wide range of habitats in which other macroscopic photosynthetic organisms cannot survive, including barren rocks, deserts, Antarctica, tree bark,

Image courtesy of Charles G. Messing, 2011.

FIGURE 16-6 Lichens. A. Cross-section of preserved and stained lichen showing algal cells close to upper surface. B. Crustose lichen with enlarged inset showing cuplike apothecia. C. Fruticose lichen.

and telephone poles. They can tolerate extremely dry conditions, are often the first pioneers in new habitats, such as volcanic rock and burnt out areas, and are able to suspend their metabolic activities under adverse conditions. Lichens are sensitive to air pollution and are important environmental indicators because they cannot rid themselves of toxins.

■ Examine the specimens of the three basic lichen growth forms on display in the laboratory.

• Differentiate among crustlike (**crustose**) (Figure 16-6B), leafy (**foliose**), and shrubby or branching (**fruticose**) (Figure 16-6C) lichens. Illustrate for your lab notebook.

■ Examine a prepared microscope slide of a cross section through a lichen thallus.

• Note the distribution of algal cells within the fungal mycelium. Illustrate for your lab notebook.

BASIDIOMYCOTA

These are the **club fungi**(Figures 16-1, 16-7), a group that includes the mushrooms, toadstools, puffballs, bracket fungi, chanterelles, and earth stars, as well as a variety of symbiotic and pathogenic species and some yeasts. The name derives from the Greek *basidion*, a small base or pedestal, which describes the spore-bearing structures (that may also look like little clubs). A wide variety, including the shiitakes, enoki, Portobello, and bolete, are edible, while others are highly toxic (*Amanita*) or hallucinogenic (*Psilocybe*).

The basidiomycote life cycle follows the basic fungal pattern, but shows some interesting variations as well. In some cases, hyphae within a single mycelium can fuse to form dikaryotic hyphae. In most cases, however, genetically different hyphae fuse. Because many different mating gene alleles exist, there are also more than two mating types, a situation analogous to having multiple sexes. When two hyphae fuse (**plasmogamy**), the dikaryotic mycelium that develops (also called a **dikaryon**) can survive for years, or even centuries. The tips of dikaryotic hyphae occasionally or periodically (sometimes seasonally) produce specialized club-shaped cells called **basidia** (singular: basidium) in which **karyogamy** takes place, forming a diploid cell. These cells undergo meiosis and produce four haploid nuclei that each migrate into their own cell called a **basidiospore** (Figures 16-7B) at the tip of each basidium. Variations include basidia with 1, 2, 3, 6, or 8 basidiospores. In a few cases, the entire basidium is released, instead of just the spores. The large fruiting body that most club fungi produce and that we know as a mushroom is called a **basidiocarp** and consists of a **stipe** (stalk) and **cap**. The underside of the cap is divided into thin radiating sheets called **gills** (Figures 16-4A), which bear the basidia.

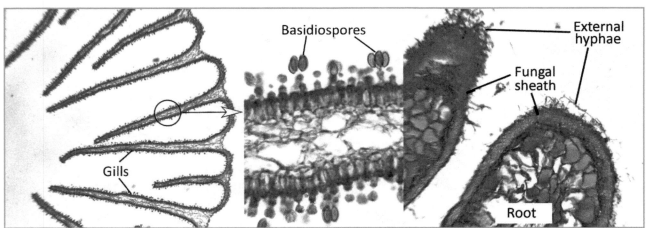

FIGURE 16-7 Basidiomycota: mushroom, *Coprinus*. A. Cross-section of mushroom cap showing gills. B. Magnified section of gill showing quartets of basidiospores perched on short, club- or knob-shaped basidia. C. Ectomycorrhizae showing fungal sheaths around root tips and external hyphae that penetrate the soil. Preserved and stained microscope slides.

Numerous variations exist on the basic mushroom basidiocarp design, including masses of gelatinous tissue (jelly fungi); branched unstalked coral fungi; spheres; woody shelves on trees or logs; and boletes with pores under the cap instead of gills.

Not all species produce a basidiocarp. **Rusts**, which include parasites of such important plants as wheat, may have as many as five different kinds of spores and require two different hosts to complete their life cycles. **Smuts** are parasitic on plants such as corn and sugarcane; they develop a distinctive thick-walled resistant spore and may also go through a yeast phase of development.

Ectomycorrhizae (Figure 16-7C) are mostly basidiomycotes that, unlike endomycorrhizae, form a sheath around the plant root, penetrating between root cells, and extending out into the soil. The extensive mycelium of a single fungus may actually connect to more than one tree or even multiple tree species, so that different trees may exchange nutrients via the fungal filaments. However, far fewer different kinds of plants are involved in the relationship, e.g., roses, pines, eucalyptus, oak, and birch.

- Examine the variety of basidiocarp (fruiting bodies) on display in the laboratory.

    • Note the variations on the basic mushroom design. Illustrate for your lab notebook.

- Examine a prepared microscope slide of a cross section through a mushroom cap (probably *Coprinus*).

    • Under increasing magnification, identify the gills, basidia, and basidiospores. Illustrate for your lab notebook.

- Examine a prepared microscope slide of ectomycorrhizae (Figure 16-7C).

    • Look for the thick sheath of hyphae around the outside of the plant root. Illustrate for your lab notebook.

Questions

1. How have groups such as the conjugating fungi, sac fungi and club fungi modified the basic fungus life cycle?

2. Apart from the lack of the standard gametes and anatomical equipment, why might basidiomycote sex be really confusing if the situation applied to animals (including us)?

References

Ferguson, B. A., Dreisbach, T. A., Parks, C. G., Filip, G. M., and Schmitt, C. L. 2003. Coarse-scale population structure of pathogenic *Armillaria* species in a mixed-conifer forest in the Blue Mountains of northeast Oregon. *Canadian Journal of Forest Research* 33 (4): 612–23.

Giovannetti, M., Avio, L., Fortuna, P., Pellegrino, E., Sbrana, C., and Strani, P. 2006. At the root of the Wood Wide Web: self-recognition and non-self incompatibility in Mycorrhizal networks. *Plant Signaling and Behavior* 1 (1): 1–5.

Helgason, T., Daniell, T. J., Husband, R., Fitter, A. H., and Young, J. P. W. 1998. Ploughing up the wood-wide web? *Nature* 394:431.

Hibbett, D.S., Binder, M., Bischoff, J.F., Blackwell, M., Cannon, P.F., Eriksson, O.E., et al. 2007. A higher level phylogenetic classification of the Fungi. Mycological Research 111 (5): 509–547. Hudler, G. 1998. *Magical Mushrooms, Mischievous Molds*. Princeton, NJ: Princeton University Press.

Human Mycoses. http://www.doctorfungus.org/mycoses/human/human_index.htm (accessed 9 Feb 2010).

Simard, S. W., Perry, D. A., Jones, M. D., Myrold, D. D., Durall, D. M., and Molina, R. 1997. Net transfer of carbon between ectomycorrhizal tree species in the field. *Nature* 388:579–82.

Tree of Life Web Project. Zygomycota. http://tolweb.org/Zygomycota (accessed 10 Feb 2010).

Wang, B., and Qiu, Y. L. 2006. Phylogenetic distribution and evolution of mycorrhizas in land plants. *Mycorrhiza* 16 (5): 299–363.

Whittaker, R. H. 1969. New concepts of kingdoms or organisms. Evolutionary relations are better represented by new classifications than by the traditional two kingdoms. *Science* 163 (3863):150–60.

Fermentation lab http://en.wikibooks.org/wiki/Biology,_Answering_the_Big_Questions_of_Life/Fermentation_student_lab#B._Observe_yeast_cultures

Materials and Supplies

Prepared Microscope Slides

Allomyces sporophyte

Allomyces gametophyte

Aspergillus mycelia with conidiophores

Coprinus (or other mushroom), cross section through cap

Ectomycorrhizae

Endomycorrhizae

Lichen, cross section

Penicillium mycelia with conidiophores

Rhizopus asexual sporangia

Rhizopus zygosporangia

Peziza apothecium (ascocarp) cross section

Whole Specimens

Morchella (morel), dried

Variety of basidiomycotes: puffball, earthstar, Portobello, shiitake, bolete, shelf fungus, or others

Amanita poisonous mushroom (in jar)

Lichen growth forms: crustose, fruticose, foliose (use fresh crustose lichen from local tree bark)

Equipment

Glass microscope slides

Glass coverslips

Disposable droppers

500-ml beaker

Supplies

10 mL sugar

Fast-rise yeast packet

Warm water

Pre-Laboratory Preparation

(Same day): Mix sugar, yeast, and water in beaker; let stand for at least 30 minutes.

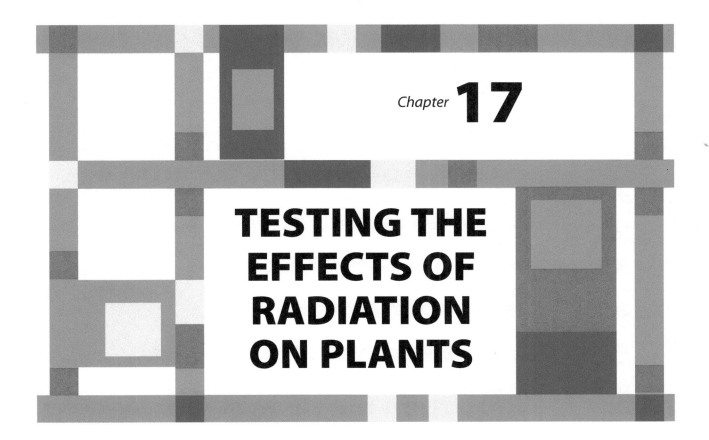

Chapter **17**

TESTING THE EFFECTS OF RADIATION ON PLANTS

Introduction

Radiation is an important environmental abiotic factor, especially for plants, because one small section of the electromagnetic radiation spectrum, called Photosynthetically Active Radiation (PAR), provides the energy to drive the light reactions of photosynthesis. PAR falls mostly within the spectrum of visible light, spanning wavelengths from 380 to 760 nm. Other segments of the electromagnetic spectrum, such as ultraviolet (UVA and UVB), X-rays, and gamma rays, have shorter wavelengths (i.e., higher frequencies) and therefore contain higher energy. Such radiation damages biological tissues by detaching electrons from the atoms that make up organic molecules. The results include radiation poisoning (with symptoms ranging from nausea to death in humans and reduced growth and loss of fertility in plants), cancer, and elevated mutation rates. By detaching electrons, such radiation produces ions; it is therefore called ionizing radiation.

Scientists use ionizing radiation to increase gene mutation rates in experimental organisms such as plants. The treated plants are then grown under selected environmental conditions in order to enrich the population with that mutant. Differences between the mutant and untreated wild type of plants may then contribute to a better understanding of the chromosomal basis and biochemistry of the differences. Such investigations form the basis of biotechnology and genetic engineering. However, the probability of generating "improved" mutants is low, and you will explore this concept in the following laboratory exercise using radish seeds exposed to various levels of high-energy gamma radiation.

In this laboratory you will investigate four questions:

1. Does exposure to high-energy electromagnetic radiation have a measurable effect on radish seed germination rates?

2. Does exposure to such radiation have a measurable effect on radish seedling growth?

3. If you can demonstrate any effect, is it dependent on the level of radiation exposure?

4. Do individuals in the population exhibit variations in their tolerance to radiation exposure?

Because increases in high-energy radiation such as UVA and UVB will occur with depletion of the ozone layer, results of this experiment may provide some insight into the potential effects of environmental degradation on crop plants.

Methods

You will use Rapid Radish™ plants for this experiment because they grow quickly, they are reasonably hardy, and they are good representatives of the types of plants used for crops.

Materials

Rapid Radish™ seeds irradiated by gamma radiation at 50, 150, and 500 mrads (millirads[1]) and control seeds (non-irradiated)

Plastic tray lined with an absorbent mat

Rapid Radish™ growing quads (Styrofoam)

Potting soil

Fertilizer pellets

Labeling tape

Fluorescent light fixture

Water

Procedure

1. Form groups of 3 to 4 students each. Each group will conduct the experiment using one replicate of each treatment and control.

2. Label each cell (control, 50, 150, 500) of your group's Styrofoam growing quad and place your group name on it. Arrange the sequence of cells so they match those of adjacent growing quads in the plastic tray. It is best to use one large plastic tray per laboratory section.

3. Place the quad in the plastic tray lined with the mat.

4. Fill each quad cell about ⅔ full with potting soil. **Note: Lightly pack the potting material, but not too much!**

5. Add one pellet of fertilizer to each cell.

6. Add more potting soil to about 5 mm below the top of the cells.

7. Set a 50-mrad radish seed on the top of the soil in its corresponding cell.

8. Set a 150-mrad radish seed on the top of the soil in its corresponding cell.

9. Set a 500-mrad radish seed on the top of the soil in its corresponding cell.

10. Set the control radish seed on the top of the soil in its corresponding cell.

11. Add more potting soil so that the soil surface is level with the top of the cells.

12. Saturate all of the growing quads with water by misting with the spray bottle. Also, make sure that the absorbent mat in the plastic tray remains saturated with water throughout the experiment.

---

[1] A rad is a unit of absorbed radiation dose of ionizing radiation. It is defined as the absorption of 0.01 joule of such radiation by 1g of matter, usually human tissue. A millirad (mrad) is one-thousandth (0.001) of a rad. Although the rad remains in common use in the United States, the International System of Units (SI) has replaced it with the Gray (Gy, named after British physicist L. H. Gray); 1 Gy = 1000 rad.

The plastic container will be placed on the counter at the back of the laboratory room under a fluorescent light. The professor and laboratory assistant will be responsible for watering the plants every other day. It is your responsibility to check on the radish seeds and measure seedling growth for each of the three weeks following the setup. Thus, you will have data for Week 1 (one week after the lab was started), Week 2, and Week 3.

Measurements, Data, and Recordkeeping

- Measure each plant's height (in centimeters to the nearest millimeter) from the soil surface to the point where the uppermost leaf stem (petiole) attaches to the main stem of the plant (Figure 17-1). **DO NOT** measure to the uppermost leaf, as petiole length is independent of plant height and may introduce a lot of variation into your data. Think about why it is important that every group measure plants in the same precise way.

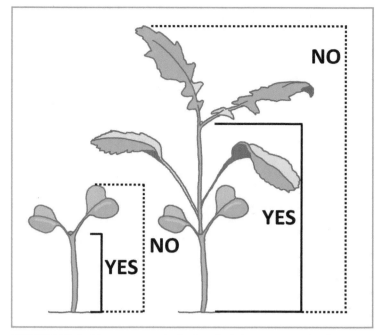

FIGURE 17-1 Measurement of plant height at two growth stages. Measure from soil surface to the point at which the uppermost petiole attaches to the main stem, NOT to the upper-

- Record anything you think is important (e.g., color, form, appearance) in the notes column next to the seed you are examining. Be sure to record when you first make each such observation, e.g., germination, flowering, death.

- All of the data, once collected, will be compiled; one statistical analysis will be performed for you on seed germination using Chi-Square analysis, and on seedling growth using a one-way Analysis of Variance. Your professor will discuss the meaning of these analyses.

Hypothesis Testing

In order to determine whether a relationship exists between two or more phenomena that we can measure, or whether a possible treatment has an effect or not, we must develop **hypotheses**, which are statements that are able to be proven false, and test them on observed data. The **null hypothesis** typically states that no significant difference exists between our measured phenomena, or that the treatment has no effect. The **alternative hypothesis** indicates that some relationship or difference does exist.

As a group, determine what effect(s) you expect the radiation may have on seed germination and seedling growth. There are a minimum of two null hypotheses and numerous alternates. It is helpful to discuss which alternates you think are most likely and why. You will discuss these alternative hypotheses formally in your report; be careful that you are clear about what the results mean. In particular, results of statistical analyses can be misinterpreted, so be sure you are clear about their meaning and interpretation.

Investigators use statistical analyses to determine the meaning of results, e.g., whether treatments have effects or not. If results are statistically significant, we reject the null hypothesis (H_o). In all statistical analyses, when the value calculated from data (e.g., Chi Square statistic or calculated F in Analysis of Variance) is larger than a critical value (selected from the correct table), we reject H_o. If the calculated value is less than the critical value, we fail to reject H_o. This is not the same as accepting the null, so be careful with your wording in your lab report. There is an important logical distinction between failing to reject something and accepting it.

In our Chi Square analysis we want to determine if our seed germination data is what we would expect if radiation has no effect. Thus, we compare our recorded values with a calculated distribution. For example, say we plant 10 seeds in the control cell and 10 in each of the three treatment cells, if radiation has no effect, we could expect similar germination rates in the control and treatments, perhaps 90% of all seeds on average, or 9 seeds in each group. Remember that some variation always exists in nature, so small differences (perhaps due to genetic variation) will often appear among groups even when the experimental treatment has no effect.

Seedling growth can be analyzed using an Analysis of Variance (ANOVA), but first it is important to determine if variances are homogenous in our samples. Variance is a measure of the spread of your data, or how far your numbers spread from the mean value. For this, an F-test is performed, and if variances are homogenous, that is, the spreads for treatments and control are all similar, we fail to reject H_0, and we can then perform an ANOVA. If we fail to reject H_0, we have found no effect of radiation on seedling growth. However, if we do reject H_0, the ANOVA has only told us that the data from one or more of our experimental groups differs significantly from the others. It does not indicate which differ. We must then perform an a posteriori test to see where the differences occur. We will use Tukey's test, which compares all the possible pairs of mean values and identifies those pairs of means that differ more than the expected standard error, another measure of how much spread exists in our data.

In summary, it is up to statistical analyses to determine whether differences are meaningful. Your professor will discuss the details.

First H_0 (relates to seed germination):

Second H_0 (relates to seedling growth):

Alternate Hypotheses (H_A) (at least two are needed here, one for each null hypothesis):

PLANT LAB REPORT GRADING RUBRIC—BIOL 1510

Name_____ **Date**_____

1. **Overall Format—10%**
   - The title of the report should be appropriate and descriptive.
   - Clear, concise writing is used throughout the report.
   - Minimal spelling and grammatical errors.
   - 12-pt Times New Roman font, 1-inch margins, double spaced (except for abstract)

2. **Abstract—5%**
   - This section is single-spaced and appears on the bottom of the title page.

3. **Introduction—20%**
   - The nature of the experiment must be stated along with why the experiment was done.
   - Important background information includes the taxonomic status (genus, species, and family) of the plant; why it is an appropriate experimental subject; general information on the type of radiation used in treating the seeds; and examples of previous experiments similar to this one. You will present the previous experiments here and use their outcomes to compare to ours in the discussion section. Be sure to be as specific as possible regarding the types and levels of radiation used in the experiments you found in the literature. You must cite this information.
   - Include the null (H_o) and alternate (H_A) hypotheses. Note that the word "hypotheses" is plural as this experiment is testing two. State them in the traditional scientific format, e.g.,

     H_o: Different levels of UV radiation have no effect on radish seed germination.

4. **Materials and Methods—10%**
   - Reference the instruction sheet for the procedure. It is not necessary to repeat it in your report
   - Be sure to describe any departures from planned procedures.

5. **Results—15%**
   - Timely submission of data (–10% if not entered into the lab computer on time)
   - Include graphs and/or tables as appropriate. Clearly label axes and units; must be large enough to read easily; independent and dependent variables must be placed on the correct axes; use Excel or similar graphing program. Each graph, chart, or figure should have a caption with the identifier (e.g., Table 1) and an explanation of what it is displaying.
   - The professor will provide results of two statistical analyses (Chi Square and ANOVA) to help interpret your results. Be sure that you understand and describe the meaning of this important part of the results in your report.
   - Narrative is required! Important results are also described here, but be careful not to enter into your discussion—this is just a report of what you found.
   - **No Raw Data** (–5% if raw data are included in your report). The purpose of this is for you to process your data into more meaningful formats such as charts, tables, and graphs as mentioned in the second bullet of this section.

6. Discussion—25%
    - Summary of the data—explain **why** you obtained the results as stated in your section above. You will need to refer to the work of others in this section (cite appropriately).
    - Be sure to interpret data with respect to the hypotheses—did you fail to reject H_o or did you reject H_o? If the latter, which H_A did you accept? Explain why!
    - Examine your methods and materials for sources of experimental error and describe them here.

7. Conclusion—10%
    - This summary clearly states the conclusion(s) of the experiment.
    - Typically, this section is limited to one paragraph.

8. Literature Cited—5%
    - Do not forget to cite your laboratory manual if you use it to provide direct information for your paper. It is required that you do outside research to support your findings. We suggest at least 3 outside references for an average grade (= C).

Total = 100%

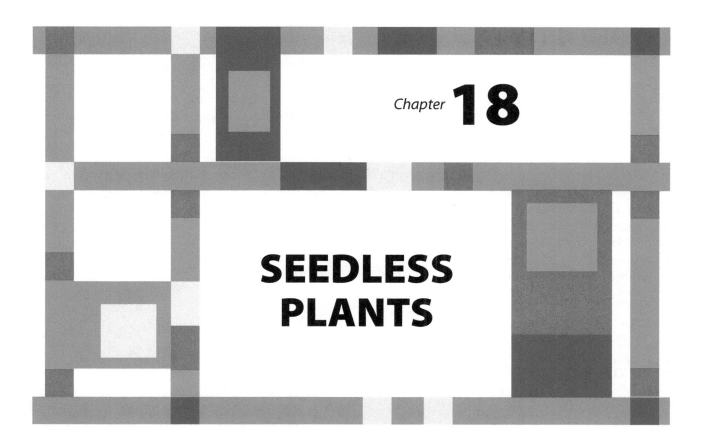

Chapter **18**

SEEDLESS PLANTS

Introduction

Unless you live in a concrete canyon or some hot deserts, on high mountaintops, glaciers, or ice caps, you are probably surrounded by plants, often in great variety. Almost all of the green growing things you encounter with the naked eye are plants, from most pondweeds to shrubs and trees. Plants are major contributors of oxygen to the atmosphere, and, of course, we use plants for everything from food to construction to medicine. But, the idea of precisely what should be called a plant has varied across history. Aristotle first divided up the living world into animals and plants, and vestiges of his classification scheme persisted for about two thousand years. It was not until the nineteenth century, for example, that both sponges and fungi were removed from the plant kingdom, where Aristotle placed them. Even today, debate

Classification summary of groups discussed in

TABLE 18-1 *this chapter.*

RHODOPHYTA (red algae)
PLANTAE
    Chlorophyta (green algae)
    Charophyta (stoneworts)
    Embryophyta (land plants)
        BRYOPHYTA (MOSSES)
        MARCHANTIOPHYTA (LIVERWORTS)
        TRACHEOPHYTA (VASCULAR PLANTS)
            Lycopodiophyta (club mosses)
            Pteridophyta (ferns, horsetails)

continues about what should and should not be considered a plant. The narrowest interpretation of **Plantae**, or the plant kingdom, includes only the land plants. Broadening the definition adds the green algae, from which land plants clearly evolved. A still broader definition includes the red algae as well, but it appears likely that such a grouping must include some single-celled "protist" algae as well to be considered monophyletic. This exercise includes the red algae, green algae and the more primitive land plants.

RHODOPHYTA

Unlike any other group of photosynthetic organisms, the **red algae** have no flagella or centrioles. Their sperm cells are drifters that cannot swim. They do have chloroplasts with chlorophyll, but their dominant pigments are **phycobiliproteins**, which give them their characteristic red to purple colors. Also, unlike green algae, plants, or brown algae, the storage product in red algae is **floridean starch**, a compound similar to glycogen. Red algae occur as single cells, filaments, tufts, bushes, and sheets and range from polar waters to the tropics. All species reproduce sexually, but details vary widely.

Some species produce important gelatinous colloidal compounds. **Agar** is the main ingredient in bacterial culture mediums and biotechnology gels (for separating and analyzing proteins and DNA) and is also used in cosmetics, bakery goods, jellies, and pharmaceutical capsules. **Carrageenan** is used as a stabilizing and thickening agent in the manufacture of ice cream, pharmaceutical products, paint, dairy products, and other emulsions. Many species, known as **coralline** (or **calcareous**) **red algae** deposit $CaCO_3$ within their cell walls and are major contributors to coral reef structure. The dark paperlike sheets called nori that are used to wrap sushi derive from the cold-temperate red alga *Porphyra* (also called "laver").

- Examine the examples of dried red algae displayed in lab.

  - Note variations among the species displayed. Illustrate for your lab notebook.

PLANTAE

The **green plants**, which include both green algae and land plants, have both chlorophyll *a* and *b*; they store the products of photosynthesis as the carbohydrate **starch**, and their cell walls contain **cellulose**. Unlike many other photoautotrophs, such as dinoflagellates, their chloroplasts are surrounded by only two membranes, suggesting that these organelles arose directly from an ancestral endosymbiotic cyanobacterium. Although green algae have sometimes been treated as protists, their close relationship to land plants is clear. The two groups together are sometimes known as Viridiplantae or Chlorobionta. The green algae (**Chlorophyta**) are the ancestral group of green plants. One group of chlorophytes gave rise to a more specialized group called the **Charophyta**, and one lineage of charophytes evolved to become the first land plants, or **Embryophyta**.

Chlorophyta

Unlike the animal kingdom, in which wide gaps exist among the most closely related living protists and simplest living animals (sponges, cnidarians), living **green algae** exhibit a wide range of forms ranging from sin-

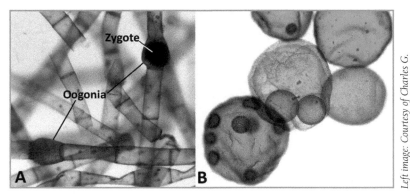

Left image: Courtesy of Charles G. Messing, 2011. Right image: Image © Jubal Harshaw, 2011. Image used under license of Shutterstock, Inc.

FIGURE 18-1 Chlorophyta. A. Filamentous green alga, *Oedogonium* showing oogonia. B. Colonial green alga, *Volvox,* showing developing new colonies inside. Preserved and stained microscope slides.

gle cells and simple colonies through filaments to complex plantlike growths. Life histories also vary widely and include both sexual and asexual phases. Single-celled green algae such as *Chlamydomonas* produce identical flagellated gametes (**isogametes**), while more complex forms have independently evolved many of the life history features of terrestrial plants. Some, such as *Oedogonium* ("*EE-do-GO-nee-um*"), which grow as filaments or threads one cell thick, have developed the distinctly different male and female gametes (**heterogametes**) that we call sperm and eggs. The thick protective cell wall of the **oogonium** cell in which the egg and fertilized zygote develop anticipates similar protective features in the life cycle of land plants (Figure 18-1A). Interestingly, *Oedogonium* also produces two kinds of spores as well as gametes: **microzoospores** derived from meiosis of the fertilized egg, and larger asexually-produced **macrozoospores**. Both are flagellated and haploid. Although microzoospores and macrozoospores are produced by photosynthetic plantlike algae, the "zoo" in each term refers to their "animal-like" swimming ability. Larger more complex forms, such as sea lettuce (*Ulva*), alternate between haploid and diploid life cycle stages, another feature convergent with land plants (see below).

Green algae occur in both marine and freshwater habitats, as well as in moist soil. One even occurs on alpine snow. Some microscopic species are symbiotic with fungi as lichens (see under Fungi), while others are symbiotic inside protists including some radiolarians and foraminiferans. Many tropical species deposit calcium carbonate ($CaCO_3$), contributing their skeletal flakes and filaments to reef sands and fine lagoonal muds.

Members of one group, the Volvocales, illustrate important transitions toward multicellularity. Colonies range from four cells to over 500. *Volvox*, which forms spherical colonies with cells imbedded in a glycoprotein matrix, exhibits the beginnings of division of labor (Figure 18-1B). Each cell has two flagella and a light-sensitive eyespot. All of the flagella beat in coordination, and the eyespots are better developed on one side of the colony, so the colony swims like an individual toward the light. Also, only some cells are capable of reproduction. Colonies may be asexual or sexual, and sexual colonies may contain either sex or both. Males release numerous sperm cells, while individual cells enlarge to become eggs in female colonies.

- ▦ Prepare and examine a wet mount from a living culture of *Volvox* following the instructions for protists such as *Euglena* and *Paramecium* from the Chapter 15 laboratory exercise.

  - Examine colony structure. Look for new developing **daughter colonies** within the *Volvox* spheres. Illustrate for your lab notebook.

  - Turn off the microscope lamp and place a small light source close to one side of the slide. Observe and describe swimming behavior.

- ▦ Examine a prepared microscope slide of *Volvox*.

  - Examine colony structure and compare with the living colonies. Look for new developing **daughter colonies** within the *Volvox* spheres. Illustrate for your lab notebook.

- ▦ Examine a prepared microscope slide of the filamentous green alga *Oedogonium*.

  - Look for swollen cells (**oogonia**) that each produces an egg. A fertilized egg (zygote) will appear dark due to its thick cell wall. Four smaller cells within a swollen oogonium are the **microzoospores** that develop via meiosis. Illustrate for your lab manual.

  - Look for a series of short disk-shaped cells (**antheridia**), each of which will release a sperm cell. Illustrate for your lab manual.

- ▦ Examine preserved dried samples of a variety of macroscopic green algae such as *Ulva*, *Caulerpa*, *Halimeda,* and *Penicillus* displayed in lab.

  - Compare and contrast thallus structure and diversity among species. Illustrate for your lab notebook.

  - Note the structure of the green algae such as *Halimeda* and *Penicillus* that deposit calcium carbonate in their cell walls. In particular, the calcified segments of *Halimeda* are important contributors to coral reef sands.

Charophyta ("*KAH-row-FYE-ta*")

Members of this group of fresh-water green algae (**stoneworts** and their allies) are the closest relatives of land plants and share numerous characteristics with them, including peroxisome enzymes, sperm with two flagella oriented asymmetrically (although not all species have sperm), flower-shaped cellulose-manufacturing enzyme complexes in the cell wall, and several features of mitosis. Their forms range from microscopic double cells called desmids that may superficially resemble diatoms, through filaments that form slimy green masses in quiet fresh waters (e.g., *Spirogyra*), to branched pondweeds such as *Chara* and *Nitella*. Some species require good water quality and so disappear at the first signs of pollution.

Chara and *Nitella* are easily mistaken for true plants. However, their "stems" are actually a series of giant multi-nucleated cells, and the narrow "leaves" are actually small branchlets that arise from **nodal cells** at intervals along the stem. The thallus represents the haploid gametophyte. The sexual reproductive structures are round male **antheridia** and oval female **oogonia**; both arise with the branchlets from the nodes.

■ Examine a living specimen of *Chara* or *Nitella* in naked eye view and under the dissecting stereomicroscope.

   • Can you detect any gritty texture? They may deposit a crust of calcium carbonate, giving them the common name **stonewort**.

   • Can you detect the smell associated with sulfur metabolism? These algae are also known as muskgrass or skunkweed.

■ Examine one or more branchlets and nodes under higher magnification.

   • Look for rapid cytoplasmic streaming. Can you determine the pattern of streaming?

   • Distinguish between male antheridia and female oogonia. Illustrate for your lab notebook.

Embryophyta

Land plants are often classified as embryophytes because they pass through an **embryo** stage, a multicellular stage of development from the zygote that remains surrounded by sterile maternal tissue and dependent upon it. The land plant life cycle is referred to as an **alternation of generations**, in which both haploid and diploid phases consist of many cells. The multicellular haploid **gametophyte** generation produces **gametes** (eggs and sperm) via mitosis. **Fertilization** produces a diploid **zygote**, which develops into a multicellular **sporophyte** generation. Some cells in the sporophyte undergo **meiosis** to produce haploid **spores**, which will germinate and develop via mitosis into the multicellular haploid gametophyte phase again. This differs from the animal life cycle, in which only the single-celled gametes (eggs and sperm) represent a haploid phase. Also, plant gametes develop from a structure that is already haploid, so meiosis does not occur at this stage in the cycle.

Functions such as gamete production and meiosis take place in specific organs. Although we normally associate the concept of an anatomical organ with animals (e.g., your stomach and lungs), they are also characteristic of plants (e.g., leaves and flowers). An organ is a structure composed of different kinds of tissues organized (get it?) to carry out a specific function. The plant gametophyte develops organs called **gametangia** that produce the gametes. Male gametangia, called **antheridia**, produce sperm. Their female, egg-producing counterparts are **archegonia**. The sporophyte phase develops organs called **sporangia** that contain specialized **spore mother cells** in which meiosis takes place to produce the haploid spores. (For all these terms, an 'a' ending indicates the plural; the singular typically ends in 'um', e.g., gametangium.) The spores contain **sporopollenin**, an extremely resistant organic polymer and one of the critical features that allowed the earliest plants to succeed on land.

Two important patterns in the way land plants grow also differ from those of their algal ancestors. Land plants have **apical meristems**: localized regions of cell division at tips of roots and shoots (the downward- and upward-growing portions of the thallus). Meristem cells differentiate into different plant tissues and, in more advanced plants, also generate the leaves. Land plants also grow as similar repeated units, each derived from a single cell and each containing the same kinds of tissues and organs (think leaves and branches).

The most primitive land plants are **nonvascular**; they lack the tubelike cells that form a **vascular system** for transporting nutrients and water. No need for such a system exists in a small plant in which absorptive and photosynthetic surfaces are close together. These plants also lack true leaves and roots. However, early Paleozoic fossils indicate that, even back then, plants had formed symbiotic mycorrhizal associations with fungi that facilitated nutrient uptake from the soil. Although they are land plants, living nonvascular species remain tied to at least periodically moist environments, because they release flagellated sperm that must swim through a film of water to reach the eggs.

As in their charophyte ancestors, primitive land plants have life cycles dominated by the haploid gametophyte. As plants evolved to become more independent of moist environments, the diploid sporophyte phase became more and more dominant until, in the great majority of living plants, the gametophyte became reduced to nothing more than a cluster of cells within and dependent upon the sporophyte phase. In this exercise, we will examine examples of nonvascular plants in which the haploid phase dominates, as well as some of the early vascular plants that still retain an independent haploid phase and so have not yet completely escaped from their aquatic ancestry.

BRYOPHYTA

Mosses are nonvascular plants that usually grow as velvety carpets in moist habitats, although some species can exceed a meter in height. The simple gametophyte thallus usually consists of a thin upright "stem" covered with narrow "leaves." We give these two terms in quotation marks because their definitions are based on structures found in more complex vascular plants. Moss leaf blades, for example, are usually only one cell thick and do not comprise different kinds of tissues. Mosses anchor and extract nutrients and water from the soil via slender filamentous **rhizoids**, which are, like the "leaves," much simpler than true roots.

A germinating moss spore first develops into branching threads one cell thick called a **protonema** (from the Greek for "first thread"). "Buds" (again, much simpler structures than the true buds of more complex plants)

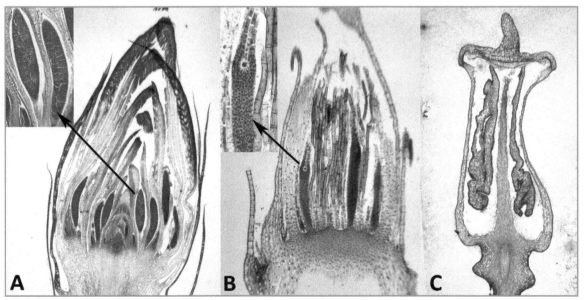

Image courtesy of Charles G. Messing, 2011.

FIGURE 18-2 Embryophyta, Bryophyta: moss *Mnium*. A. Cross section of the antheridial head of a male gametophyte with an inset showing two antheridia enlarged. B. Cross section of the archegonial head of a female gametophyte with an inset showing a single archegonium containing an egg. C. Cross section of a sporophyte capsule.

that arise from the mass of protonemata (plural) each have their own **apical meristem**. Rapid cell division in the meristem generates the typical moss gametophyte thallus. Once a moss plant matures, the apical meristem also gives rise to gametangia: male **antheridia** that will produce sperm, or female egg-producing **archegonia**. Each gametophyte is usually either male or female, although some species are bisexual. Sperm must swim through at least a film of water to the egg, which remains inside the archegonium. After fertilization, the zygote develops into a long upright slender stalk with a **capsule** at its tip. This is the diploid sporophyte phase, which remains attached to the gametophyte and dependent upon it for water and nutrients. Cells inside the capsule divide by meiosis to produce haploid spores that will be released to disperse on the wind. A single capsule may release as many as 50 million spores.

(**NOTE**: The informal term "bryophyte" refers to all nonvascular plants, including both mosses and liverworts. The formal taxon Bryophyta refers only to mosses.)

- Examine a living moss gametophyte thallus under the dissecting stereomicroscope.

  • Note the structure of "leaves" and rhizoids.

- Examine a preserved or living specimen of moss sporophyte.

  • Distinguish the stalk (also called the seta) and capsule. What process takes place in the capsule? What does the capsule release?

- Examine a microscope slide preparation of the cross section through the sporophyte capsule of the moss *Mnium* (pronounced *"NEE-um"*).

  • Identify the developing spores. How do you suppose they are released? Illustrate for your lab notebook.

- Examine prepared microscope slides of the antheridia and archegonia of the moss *Mnium*.

  • Distinguish between the male antheridia and female archegonia. What differences do you observe? Illustrate both for your lab notebook.

- Examine a microscope slide of a moss young gametophyte.

  • Identify the protonema. How does it resemble the filamentous green alga *Oedogonium*? Illustrate for your lab notebook.

MARCHANTIOPHYTA (OR HEPATOPHYTA)
(*"mar-SHON-tee-o-FYE-ta"*)

Named for the fancied resemblance of some species to the human liver (it's a stretch), **liverworts** are a group of low-growing nonvascular plants that may be leafy, scaly, or ribbonlike (Figure 18-3). Like mosses, the thallus is a haploid gametophyte, and a flagellated sperm must still swim to the egg. Unlike mosses, the rhizoids consist of single threadlike cells, and the **antheridia** and **archegonia** are borne on miniature parasol and palm-tree-shaped structures (**antheridiophores** and **archegoniophores**, respectively) on separate male and female plants (Figures 18-3, 18-4). The diploid sporophyte that develops from the fertilized egg hangs down from the underside of the "palm tree" (Figure 18-4B). Most of the sporophyte is the egg-shaped spore-producing structure, or **sporangium**. Inside its outer **capsule**, some cells become **spore mother cells** that divide by meiosis to produce haploid spores. They are accompanied by elongated cells called **elaters**. Spores and elaters together form a tangled mass exposed when the mature sporangium ruptures. The elaters absorb water, twisting as they do so, releasing the spores to be dispersed by the wind.

FIGURE 18-3 Embryophyta, Marchantiophyta: liverwort *Marchantia*.
Living thallus showing gemmae

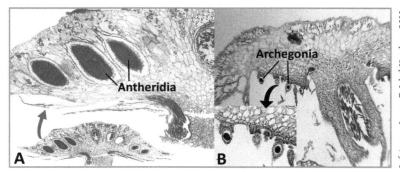

Left image: Image © Jubal Harshaw, 2011. Image used under license of Shutterstock, Inc. Right image: Courtesy of Charles G. Messing, 2011.

FIGURE 18-4 Embryophyta, Marchantiophyta: liverwort *Marchantia*. A. Antheridiophore (bottom) with enlargement above showing three antheridia. B. Archegoniophore with enlarged inset below showing two archegonia. Preserved and stained microscope slides.

Liverworts also reproduce asexually. Small masses of cells called **gemmae** develop in cups on the upper surface of the thallus and bud off to grow into new plants (Figure 18-3).

■ Examine a living *Marchantia* ("*Mar-SHON-tee-yeh*," named for the French botanist Marchant) gametophyte thallus under the dissecting stereomicroscope.

• Note the structure of leaves and rhizoids.

■ Examine prepared microscope slides of cross sections of the archegonium and antheridium of *Marchantia*. (**NOTE:** The slide label may refer to the "archegoniophore" or "antheridiophore"; these are the entire palm-tree– or parasol-shaped structures on which the archegonia or antheridia are borne. The suffix "-ophore" or "-ophora" means "to bear" or "to carry.")

• Distinguish between male and female structures. Can you identify any opening through which either sperm or spores are released? Why isn't there an opening for releasing the egg? Illustrate for your lab notebook.

TRACHEOPHYTA

Living on land placed a great adaptive advantage on species that could spread broader photosynthetic surfaces higher than their competitors. But, this created two problems. It increased the distance between food-generating photosynthetic surfaces and the source of minerals and water in the soil. Increasing height and size of photosynthetic surfaces also created greater mass and increased requirements for absorption from and anchoring in the soil. The feature that permitted plants to grow taller, separating photosynthesis from absorption, was **vascular tissue** (Figure 18-5), which allowed water, minerals, and nutrients to be conducted upward or downward. Tracheophytes (from the Greek for "rough artery," same as your trachea) are thus known as **vascular plants**. We will discuss more details in the next laboratory exercise. However, it is worth mentioning that the cell walls of some vascular cells, called **tracheids** (hence, the name tracheophyte), are strengthened by the complex organic polymer **lignin**, which allowed plants to grow taller against gravity. Lignin is a major component of wood, although many vascular plants, such as ferns, grass, and herbs, have too little to be called woody.

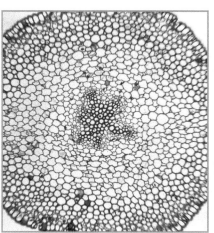

Image courtesy of Charles G. Messing, 2011.

FIGURE 18-5 Tracheophyta, Pteridophyta: whisk fern, *Psilotum nudum*. Cross section of stem showing central bundle of vascular tissue. Preserved and stained microscope slide.

The race to become taller may have been triggered as the sporophyte generation increased in importance, the advantage being that a larger, more complex, and branched sporophyte could produce more spores. Larger, more complex sporophytes tended to differentiate into an above-ground **shoot** system for support and photosynthesis, and an underground **root** system for anchoring and absorption. However, vascular plants nearest the base of the tracheophyte family tree still retain an independent gametophyte generation, and free sperm must still swim to the egg, restricting these plants to at least temporarily moist habitats. All of these plants still release spores. The next laboratory exercise will discuss plants with seeds.

Lycopodiophyta (or Lycophyta)
("*LYE-co-PO-dee-o-FYE-ta*")

Modern **club mosses** and their allies are remnants of the oldest group of vascular plants. Although now represented only by small, low-growing forms, enormous tree lycophytes reached 40 m tall in vast forests during the Carboniferous period (359–299 mya), so named because those forests eventually became coal deposits. As their name suggests, club mosses resemble mosses, with small leaves called **microphylls** (Figure 18-6). But these leaves do contain vascular tissue, if only a single central strand; true roots (though they only fork as they grow) arise from horizontal stems, and the thallus represents the sporophyte generation. The gametophyte is reduced to a tiny independent leaflet.

Image © Vitaly Raduntsev, 2011. Image used uder license of Shuttesrock, Inc.

FIGURE 18-6 Tracheophyta, Lycopodiophyta: club moss, *Selaginella.*

■ Examine a living example of the club moss *Lycopodium* or *Selaginella.*

• Compare the small simple vascular microphylls with similar structures in true mosses and larger photosynthetic organs of ferns (below). How are they similar, and how do they differ?

Pteridophyta (or Pterophyta)
("*TER-ih-do-FYE-ta*")

Most **ferns** are easily recognized from their wide use in gardens and as ornamental plants. As in lycophytes, the sporophyte generation dominates, the gametophyte is reduced to a tiny independent leaflet, and free sperm must still swim to the egg. However, ferns and their relatives have developed complex leaves (**megaphylls**) with branching vascular systems, as well as complex branching roots. Pteridophyte classification is still debated. In addition to ferns, the group now includes plants previously classified separately—the **whisk**

Image courtesy of Charles G. Messing, 2011.

FIGURE 18-7 Tracheophyta, Pteridophyta. A. Tree fern, *Cyathea cooperi,* developing fiddlehead frond. B. Two rows of sori on the underside of a fern frond.

FIGURE 18-8 Tracheophyta, Pteridophyta. A. Whisk fern, *Psilotum nudum,* with pale yellowish round sporangia. B. Royal fern, *Osmunda regalis,* showing bushy terminal sporangia. C. Horsetail, *Equisetum arvense.* D. Horsetail, *Equisetum hyemale,* showing whorl of segmented branchlets.

ferns and **horsetails**—and the ferns themselves include several distinct evolutionary lineages. For example, sporangia develop from clusters of cells in some ferns and single cells in others.

Ferns typically consist of a horizontal stem—either an underground **rhizome**, or aboveground runner—that gives rise to both roots and leaves. Fern leaves, or **fronds**, are usually divided into lobes or leaflets, and new fronds, called **fiddleheads** (Figure 18-7A), uncoil as they develop. **Tree ferns** have an erect, partially woody trunk and may reach 20 m tall.

The **whisk fern**, *Psilotum nudum* (Figures 18-5 and 18-8A), is a small, green, leafless branching plant that lacks roots (it has rhizoids instead) and bears knoblike sporangia that turn yellow as they mature. *Psilotum* so closely resembles some of the earliest fossil vascular plants that it was long considered their direct descendant, a "living fossil." Molecular evidence and anatomical details, however, place it among the ferns.

In **royal ferns** (*Osmunda*) (Figure 18-8B), some fronds terminate in bushy golden or brown sporangia (rather than sori), so they are often called "flowering ferns." Similar species are known as far back as the Triassic period.

Horsetails (*Equisetum*) (Figures 18-8C and D) grow as slender, segmented, usually erect, photosynthetic stems. Also called scouring rushes, their gritty texture, derived from silica in their cell walls, promoted their historic use in cleaning pots and pans. Tiny triangular microphyll leaves and sometimes also whorls of slender side branchlets arise around each segment. Some stems may be tipped with a swollen spore-producing "cone."

The life history of a typical fern serves as a good example of a seedless plant in which the sporophyte dominates, but the gametophyte remains independent. Although most fronds look pretty much alike, some develop clusters of sporangia, or **sori** (Figure 18-7B), on their undersides. Meiosis takes place inside the sori (singular, sorus), and the daughter cells develop into haploid **spores**, which have resistant outer coats containing **sporopollenin** and disperse on the wind. A germinating spore develops into a small heart-shaped leaflet, the gametophyte, which is photosynthetic and bears threadlike rhizoids similar to those of mosses. Gametangia, either sperm-producing **antheridia** or egg-producing **archegonia**, or both, differentiate on the gametophyte surface (Figure 18-9). Male antheridia are usually scattered on the center or toward the pointed end of the gametophyte, while female archegonia cluster in the notch of the heart. Eggs and sperm develop via mitosis, because the entire gametophyte is already haploid; meiosis took place earlier, in the development of spores. The fertilized egg grows into the sporophyte fern plant, with the first frond unrolling as a fiddlehead again.

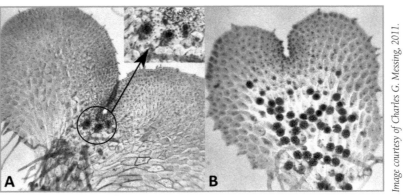

FIGURE 18-9 Tracheophyta, Pteridophyta: fern gametophytes. A. Egg-producing archegonia in the notch of the heart-shaped gametophyte, with an enlarged inset. B. Numerous globular sperm-producing antheridia on a small male-only gametophyte. Preserved and stained microscope slides.

Image courtesy of Charles G. Messing, 2011.

- East of the Parker Building, examine the following pteridophytes in the Mesozoic Garden.

  - Tree ferns. Compare the appearance of the trunk with that of a palm tree. Which appears to be woodier?

  - Horsetails (*Equisetum*). These plants often live in waterlogged soil. What might be the adaptive function of their hollow stems?

  - Whisk fern (*Psilotum*). Compare its appearance with an illustration of fossil *Cooksonia*.

  - Royal, or flowering, fern (*Osmunda*). Unlike most ferns in the Mesozoic Garden, which belong to families that arose more recently, *Osmunda* does not have horizontal stems and so cannot spread via rhizomes or runners. Look for fronds that terminate in bushy golden or brown sporangia, which give these plants the name "flowering ferns."

  - Look for sori on the underside of fern fronds. How do they differ among different ferns?

  - Identify and illustrate fern fiddleheads.

- Examine the following prepared microscope slides.

  - On a fern gametophyte, locate male antheridia and female archegonia. They may develop on the same or separate gametophytes. Locate the threadlike rhizoids that serve in place of roots for water and mineral absorption. Illustrate for your lab notebook.

  - Fern sori. Can you locate individual spores? Illustrate for your lab notebook.

Questions

1. Unlike the situation among green algae, in which a general continuum exists between single-celled and complex multi-celled living species, a substantial gap exists between living vascular plants in which the gametophyte dominates the life cycle, and those in which the sporophyte dominates. Hypothesize (describe or illustrate) what a "missing link" life cycle might look like if such a plant existed today.

References

Campbell, N. A., Reece, J. B., Urry, L. A., Cain, M. L., Wasserman, S. A., Minorsky, P. V., and Jackson, R. B. 2009. *Biology.* 8th ed. San Francisco, CA: Pearson Benjamin Cummings (1418 pp.).

Cavalier-Smith, T. 1981. Eukaryote kingdoms: seven or nine? *BioSystems* 14:461–81.

Dolphin, W. D. 2007. *Biological investigations.* 8th ed. Boston, MA: McGraw-Hill (458 pp.).

Kim, E., Graham, L. E. 2008. EEF2 Analysis Challenges the Monophyly of Archaeplastida and Chromalveolata. *PLoS ONE* 3 (7): e2621. doi:10.1371/journal.pone.0002621

Qiu, Y-L, and Palmer, J. 1999. Phylogeny of early land plants: insights from genes and genomes. *Trends in Plant Science* 4 (1): 26–30.

Materials and Supplies

Living Plants (Mesozoic Garden)

Equisetum (horsetail)

Lycopodium or *Selaginella* (club moss)

Osmunda (royal or cinnamon fern)

Psilotum nudum (whisk fern)

Tree ferns

Various ferns

Living Cultures

Volvox

Chara or *Nitella*

Marchantia

Moss with sporophyte

Fresh Specimens (from Mesozoic Garden)

Fern frond with sori

Equisetum (horsetail) stem

Prepared Microscope Slides

Fern gametophyte with archegonia and antheridia (together or on separate slides), whole mount

Fern sori, whole mount

Marchantia antheridium, cross section

Marchantia archegonium, cross section

Mnium (Moss) capsule, cross section

Mnium (Moss) antheridium, cross section

Mnium (Moss) archegonium, cross section

Mnium (Moss) young gametophyte with protonema, whole mount

Oedogonium

Volvox

Dried Specimens on Herbarium Paper

Variety of noncalcareous Rhodophyta (red algae), e.g., *Ceramium, Polysiphonia*

Variety of noncalcareous Chlorophyta (green algae), e.g., *Ulva, Caulerpa*

Variety of calcareous Chlorophyta (green algae), e.g., *Halimeda, Penicillus, Udotea*

Whole Specimens

Calcareous Rhodophyta (red algae), e.g., *Lithothamnium*

Equipment

Glass microscope slides

Glass coverslips

Disposable droppers

Laboratory tape

Permanent markers

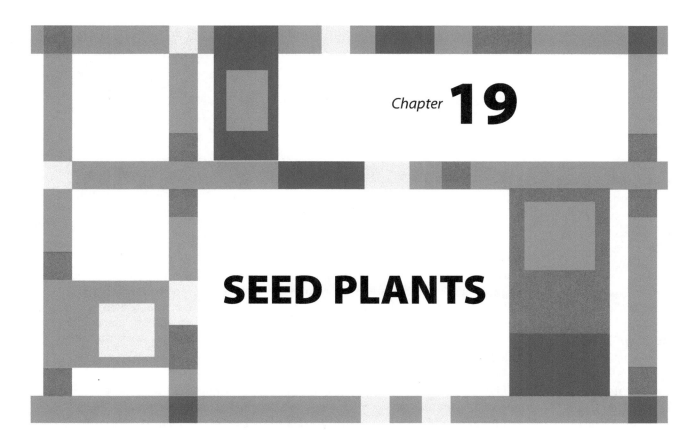

SEED PLANTS

Introduction

This exercise continues the previous one. The seed plants (Spermatopsida) represent a branch of vascular plants that arose from pteridophyte-like (fernlike) ancestors.

Spermatopsida (or Spermatophyta)

With the exception of ferns and mosses and their relatives, all modern land plants produce both seeds and pollen. That's well over 250,000 species. They arose from seedless plants during the Late Paleozoic Era. Seeds represent an alternative to spores as an evolutionary means of dispersing offspring and surviving in harsh habitats. Instead of the single spore cell, seeds consist of many cells, including multiple outer layers that provide extra protection. They also contain a supply of stored food, permitting an often longer dormant period before germination.

Seed plants are characterized by several major reproductive adaptations that eliminated reliance on dispersal via spores and flagellated sperm, which require an aquatic milieu, and offered the

TABLE 19-1	*Classification summary of groups discussed in this chapter.*

PLANTAE (continued from chap. 18)
   Embryophyta (land plants)
   (continued from chap. 18)
      TRACHEOPHYTA (VASCULAR PLANTS)
      (CONTINUED FROM CHAP. 18)
        Spermatopsida (seed plants)
        GLOSSOPTERIS
        GYMNOSPERMAE
          Ginkgophyta (Ginkgo)
          Cycadophyta (cycads)
          Pinophyta (conifers)
        ANGIOSPERMAE (flowering plants)

freedom to colonize drier habitats (Figure 19-1). These plants continued to reduce the haploid gametophyte generation. Now, the sporophyte phase dominates even more than in ferns. Spore-producing sporangia develop on a modified leaf or leaflike structure (**sporophyll**), such as a pinecone or flower, but the spores are not released. Instead, the gametophyte develops from the spore as a microscopic cluster of cells still within the sporangium, completely protected from the outside environment and completely dependent on the sporophyte for nutrition. Although greatly reduced, the gametophyte still offers advantages: it provides a store of food for the embryo developing inside it, and its haploid condition provides a screen for new allelic mutations (lethal mutations will not be passed on as recessive).

FIGURE 19-1 Spermatopsida, Angiospermae: dandelion, *Taraxacum officinale;* seed head showing dry fruits called achenes, which each contain one seed, and the "parachute" that permits dispersal via the wind.

Another feature involved differentiating two different types of spores. Although most seedless plants are **homosporous**, that is, one spore type produces both eggs and sperm, some club mosses (*Selaginella*) and some small aquatic ferns are **heterosporous**; they evolved two spore types—female **megaspores** and male **microspores**—a preadaptation critical to seed evolution. The female reproductive structure, called an **ovule**, develops on specialized sporophylls, as mentioned above. An ovule consists of one or two protective outer layers of sporophyte tissue called **integuments** that enclose the **megasporangium**, which produces a haploid **megaspore** by meiosis. (Note that "mega-" with reference to reproductive structures indicates female, and "micro-" indicates male; remember that eggs are much bigger than sperm.) The megaspore divides via mitosis to produce the haploid megagametophyte, which consists of food-storage cells and egg. Once the egg has been fertilized (see below), the entire package is called a **seed**; it consists of the diploid outer protective **seed coat** derived from the integuments, a food supply derived from some of the haploid gametophyte cells, and a diploid embryo—the sporophyte of the next generation. That's three generations in one container. Seeds may remain dormant for weeks, months, or even years.

On the male side, male reproductive structures called **microsporangia** produce haploid **microspores** via meiosis. A microspore then divides by mitosis to become the mature (but still microscopic) haploid microgametophyte that we call a **pollen grain**; it consists simply of a tough sporopollenin-containing coat and sperm nucleus. Pollen grains permit far wider dispersal of male gametes than flagellated sperm and do not require a film of water for the transfer (although pollen may disperse aquatically as well as aerially, or on insects and other animals). **Pollination** is the process of transferring the sperm-containing pollen to the ovule, which contains the egg. When a pollen grain lands in the vicinity of an ovule, it begins growing a long tube that tunnels through the female's tissues, fuses with the egg, and delivers the sperm nucleus. As with spores, seed plants must generate enormous numbers of pollen grains to ensure that some land where they can fertilize eggs.

Modern seed plants fall into two large taxonomic groups: gymnosperms ("naked seeds"), in which the mature seeds lie exposed on the surfaces of the sporophylls, and angiosperms ("container-seeds"), in which seeds are enclosed in an ovary.

GLOSSOPTERIS

The classification of this genus of fossil plants with distinctive tongue-shaped leaves (*Glossopteris* means "tongue-wing") has been debated for a long time. Its species have been included among the extinct seed ferns—a loose grouping of extinct plants with seeds but with fernlike growth—as well as among the gymnosperms (below). It is often difficult to decide how to classify plant fossils because entire plants are rarely preserved. Separate leaf, trunk, twig, root, and cone or flower fossils that may have belonged to a single species can be given different names. We include it here because it was the dominant component of the flora of the great southern supercontinent Gondwana during the Permian period and was one of the pieces of evidence that Alfred Wegener used to support his theory of continental drift. Its fossils are found in India, South America, Australia, Africa, Madagascar, and Antarctica.

- ■ Examine a fossil specimen of *Glossopteris*.

  - • This is an example of a compression fossil. Illustrate for your lab notebook.

GYMNOSPERMAE

Gymnosperm means "naked seed," because the seeds of these plants, and the unfertilized ovules from which they develop, lie exposed on the surface of typically scalelike **sporophyll** leaves clustered together as **cones**. Pollen also develops on specialized cones. Gymnosperms diversified during the Permian period as climates dried and cooled, favoring seed plants over the seedless vascular plants such as ferns and club mosses that required moister habitats. They dominated landscapes through much of the early and middle Mesozoic but declined with the diversification of flowering plants. Although gymnosperms are not a diverse group today—the group includes only about 800 species—some continue to dominate certain ecosystems, particularly northern temperate forests. We will examine representatives of three of the four groups of living gymnosperms.

Ginkgophyta

The single extant species, *Ginkgo biloba*, the maidenhair tree, is only definitely known from domesticated individuals. Its deciduous fan-shaped leaves appear identical to those of fossils from the Late Cretaceous, so it is usually thought of as a "living fossil." Male trees are resistant to insects and pollution and are widely planted in urban environments. Female trees produce fleshy seeds but are not planted as ornamentals because the decaying seed coat produces a repulsive odor.

- ■ Examine both modern and fossil leaves of *Ginkgo*.

  - • Can you recognize any obvious differences between the two? Illustrate for your lab notebook.

Cycadophyta

Cycads, with their crown of pinnate fronds and thick, starchy trunk, are often mistaken for palm trees (Figure 19-2A). Some are even called sago palms. However, unlike true palm trees, they have sporophylls aggregated into cones rather than flowers, the scars of former leaves encircle the trunk, and sperm retain flagella inside the pollen grain. Cycads were more abundant and diverse during the Mesozoic Era, which is sometimes called the "Age of Cycads." *Zamia integrifolia*, the **coontie**, is the only cycad native to Florida. It differs from many other cycads in that its trunk may be completely underground, and it loses its fronds during cold seasons. Coonties have separate male and female plants.

FIGURE 19-2 A. Cycadophyta. Cycad with male cone. B. Pinophyta. Bunya pine, *Araucaria bidwillii*.

■ Examine the variety of cycads growing in the Mesozoic Garden.

- Compare the cycads with examples of palm trees, which are flowering plants, outside the Parker Building. What are the most obvious differences that you observe? Note cones, if present.

- Observe the small coontie cycad. Note distinct male and female cones, if present. How does this plant differ from nearby ferns with similar fronds?

Pinophyta (or Coniferae; formerly Coniferophyta)

The **conifers** are the best-known and most widespread and diverse group of living gymnosperms (630 species). Most are evergreen trees with waxy, needlelike, or scalelike leaves, although the leaves do fall off after at least a couple of years. Specialized sporophyll leaves are aggregated into simple or compound **cones.** Ovules and seeds lie on the surface of the scales on female cones. The group includes pines, spruces, firs, hemlocks, yews, junipers, redwoods, sequoias, and larches. Most occur in colder temperate regions, although pines dominate many Florida upland forests and cypresses may dominate warm temperate swamps, such as the Everglades. One group of conifers, the araucarias (Figure 19-2B), are often considered living fossils, as their wood is almost identical to the fossil "petrified," or remineralized, wood of Triassic age from Petrified Forest National Park, Arizona, and elsewhere. The **resins** that many conifers produce are thick, viscous liquids that seal breaks and confer protection against many herbivores. Hardened, fossilized resin is the semiprecious **amber,** of *Jurassic Park* fame.

■ In the Mesozoic Garden, observe the large central tree, *Araucaria bidwillii*, the Bunya pine, or Bunya-Bunya tree.

- Note that the leaves are broader than the needles of pine and spruce trees. (**CAUTION:** They are particularly sharp.)

■ Examine the large log sections of "petrified wood" in the Mesozoic Garden, and a smaller piece in the laboratory.

- What plantlike features can you identify in these specimens? Vascular tissue? Bark?

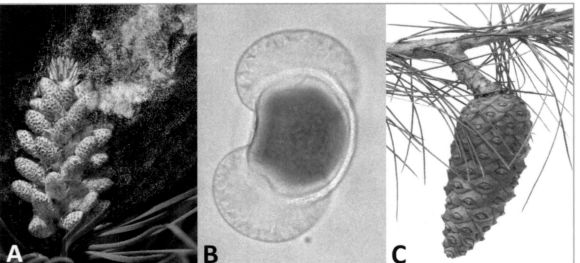

Left Image: Image © Brian Maudsley, 2011. Image used under license of Shutterstock, Inc. Middle Image: Courtesy of Charles G. Messing, 2011. Right Image: Image © Arkady, 2011. Image used under license of Shutterstock, Inc.

FIGURE 19-3 Gymnospermae, Pinophyta: Pine tree, *Pinus*. A. Staminate cone with cloud of released pollen. B. Pollen grain under high magnification. Preserved and stained microscope slide. C. Ovulate cone at state receptive to pollen.

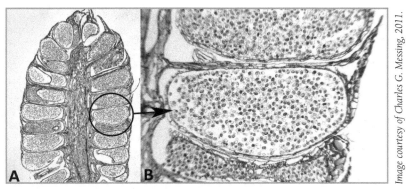

FIGURE 19-4 Gymnospermae, Pinophyta: Pine tree, *Pinus*. A. Longitudinal section of staminate cone. The circle encloses a single microsporangium. B. A microsporangium enlarged, with developing pollen grains inside.

- In the Mesozoic Garden, observe the cypress trees (*Taxodium distichum*) near the hedge behind the Cenozoic Era sign. Unlike most typical conifers, this tree is deciduous, at least in the northern part of its range. Branches will also be available in the laboratory with pine and Bunya pine branches for comparison.

  • Compare the small soft, scalelike leaves with typical pine needles and Bunya pine leaves.

- Examine a specimen of amber under the dissecting stereomicroscope.

  • Can you find a preserved insect?

A pine tree (*Pinus*) serves as an example of the life cycle of a conifer (and gymnosperm). Pine trees produce separate male and female cones. Each will produce its own kind of spore, gametophyte and gametes. Small **staminate cones** (male) grow in clusters or singly on lower branches (Figures 19-3A, 19-4). Each consists of whorls of thick sporophyll scales that each contain two **microsporangia** on its underside. Inside, **microspore mother cells** divide by meiosis to produce four haploid **microspores** that will develop into pollen grains (Figures 19-3B, 19-4B). Each pollen grain represents the mature male microgametophyte and consists of only four cells. One of these will divide to produce two sperm cells. The outer coat of the pollen grain contains resistant sporopollenin and bears a pair of round, swollen, air-filled sacs that look like disks under the microscope. When released, pollen grains initially fall before being carried away by the wind, which avoids self-pollination of the **ovulate cones** (female) (Figures 19-3C, 19-5A, C), which grow on the higher branches. Such dispersal spreads sperm far more broadly than in ferns and other seedless plants in which the flagellated sperm must swim to the egg.

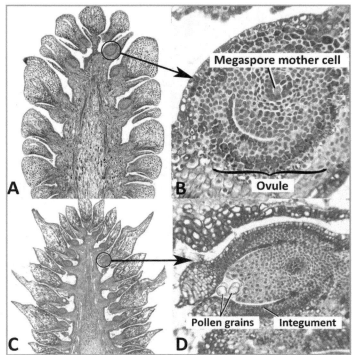

FIGURE 19-5 Gymnospermae, Pinophyta: Pine tree, *Pinus*. A. Longitudinal section of first year ovulate cone with a single ovule circled. B. Enlargement of A showing megaspore mother cell within ovule. C. Longitudinal section of older (but still young) ovulate cone with a single ovule circled. D. Enlargement of C showing pollen grains invading megasporangium. Preserved and stained microscope slides.

Each scalelike sporophyll of an ovulate cone bears a pair of egg-shaped **ovules** near the base of its upper surface (Figure 19-5). Each ovule consists of a protective integument that surrounds the **megasporangium** (also called a **nucellus**). Inside, as in male sporangia, a **megaspore mother cell** (Figure 19-5B) divides by meiosis to produce four haploid **megaspores**, but three of these degenerate. The surviving cell draws nutrition from the surrounding nucellus and repeatedly divides by mitosis to become a megagametophyte that consists of about 2,000 haploid cells. Two of these cells will mature into functional eggs. Although still quite small, with scales spaced apart and pointed upward on its branch, the female cone is now receptive to pollen.

In order to fertilize an egg, a pollen grain must land near the base of the ovule that faces the central axis of the cone. Here, a small opening in the protective integument, the **micropyle** (Figure 19-5D), leads to a narrow canal that permits access to the eggs. A drop of secreted fluid traps the pollen in the micropyle, drawing the grain inward as the fluid dries. The pollen grain now germinates, growing a fingerlike tube containing the sperm nuclei toward the eggs. Although the distance is very short, more than a year passes before fertilization takes place. Each sperm nucleus may fertilize an egg, but only one resulting zygote develops into an **embryo**. The mature **seed** now consists of three generations of pine life cycle: a surrounding protective **seed coat** derived from parental diploid sporophyte, stored nutritive material derived from the haploid female megagametophyte, and the diploid embryo that will develop into the next generation's sporophyte pine tree.

- Examine examples of mature staminate and ovulate pine cones.

  - Note differences between male and female cones in terms of shape and structure.

  - Distinguish between ovulate cones that are at the receptive stage and the familiar pine cones that fall from trees. Do the latter still retain any seeds?

- Examine a prepared microscope slide of a cross section through a staminate cone.

  - Locate the thick scalelike sporophylls that each contains a microsporangium chamber with developing pollen inside. Illustrate for your lab notebook.

- Examine a prepared microscope slide of mature pine pollen.

  - What kind of hat do the grains resemble? What purpose do the two, round, transparent air bladders likely serve? Illustrate for your lab notebook.

- Examine a prepared microscope slide of an ovulate cone.

  - Locate and illustrate the ovule, integument, and nucellus. Because not all cross sections pass through every structure, examine several ovules to find megaspore mother cells and micropyle.

- Examine a prepared microscope slide of a pine needle.

  - Distinguish the following: dense waxy **epidermis**; central **vascular bundle**; **stomata** for gas exchange, and pair of **resin ducts**.

ANGIOSPERMAE (OR MAGNOLIOPHYTA)

Flowering plants are the most widespread and diverse group of plants. Estimates of the number of species range from 223,000 to 420,000. The wide disparity results from different ways of estimating how many names are synonyms, or duplicates, of valid species names. Much of our food comes from flowering plants or through the animals that eat them: vegetables, fruits, grains, nuts, beans, herbs, and spices. So do coffee, tea, chocolate, and alcoholic beverages (e.g., beer, wine, whiskey). Linen and cotton derive from flowering plants as do many drugs: controlled, prescribed, and over-the-counter (e.g., aspirin, atropine, tobacco, cocaine, opium, and marijuana).

Flowers—The sexual reproductive structures of angiosperms, called flowers, are composed of up to four circlets of modified leaves that arise from a **receptacle**, the expanded tip of the stalk that bears the flower (Figure 19-6). The outermost consists of usually green **sepals** that enclose the developing flower before it

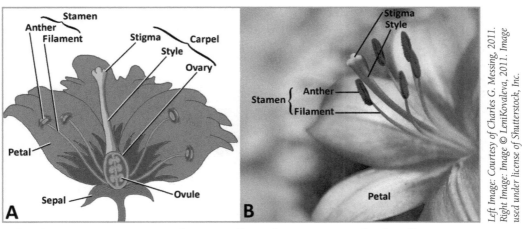

FIGURE 19-6 Angiospermae. A. Diagram of basic flower structure. B. *Lilium* flower showing basic structures.

Left Image: Courtesy of Charles G. Messing, 2011. Right Image: Image © LemiKovaleva, 2011. Image used under license of Shutterstock, Inc.

opens (bud). Next, the **petals** are usually brightly colored and aid in attracting pollinators. Wind-pollinated flowers such as those of grasses are typically small, dull, and inconspicuous. **Stamens** (male sporophylls) produce microspores that give rise to male microgametophytes and pollen; each consists of a stalk (**filament**) and terminal pollen-producing **anther**. The central **carpels** (female sporophylls) produce megaspores that give rise to female megagametophytes and ovules; each consists of one or more **ovaries**, and a stalklike **style** with pollen-receiving **stigma** at its tip. Because a flower may contain one or more carpels, the term **pistil** is often used to describe the visible female reproductive structure when the number of carpels is not clear.

Flowers come in a bewildering variety of structures, shapes, and arrangements. **Perfect flowers** have both male and female parts (bisexual), while **imperfect flowers** are either male (staminate) or female (pistillate). An individual plant may produce only perfect flowers, both male and female flowers, only one or the other, or all three: perfect, male, and female flowers. Flowers may develop singly or in clusters called **inflorescences** that range from simple groupings to highly complex structures such as the drooping **catkins** of willow trees, the parasol-like **umbels** of Queen Anne's lace, and the **spikes** of larkspur (*Delphinium*). The "flowers" of members of the Asteraceae (the largest family of flowering plants with over 20,000 species), such as sunflowers and daisies, are actually complex clusters of numerous small flowers, called **florets**, that together look like a single large flower. Flowers in the inflorescences of grasses such as wheat and oats lack petals and sepals; instead they are enclosed in modified leaves called **bracts** (the chaff that is separated and removed when grain is threshed). Bracts may also be colorful; the red "petals" of *Poinsettia*, the Christmas flower, are actually bracts.

- ▪ Examine the exterior and interior structure of a fresh *Gladiolus* or similar flower.

  - • Identify the following structures: sepals, petals, stamen, anther, filament, pistil, style, and stigma. Illustrate for your lab notebook.

  - • Split the pistil with a scalpel to expose the chambers that contain the ovules. How many can you see? Illustrate for your lab notebook.

  - • Is the *Gladiolus* a perfect or imperfect flower? How do you know?

- ▪ Examine the variety of flowers on display in the laboratory. Some will require examination under the dissecting stereomicroscope due to their small size.

  - • Determine which are perfect, imperfect, staminate, or pistillate.

- ▪ Examine a specimen of wheat, oat, or other grass flower under the dissecting stereomicroscope.

  - • Most grasses and grains are perfect. Identify the main structures: ovary, stamens, and featherlike stigma. Locate the enclosing bracts. Are there any petals or sepals? Illustrate for your lab notebook.

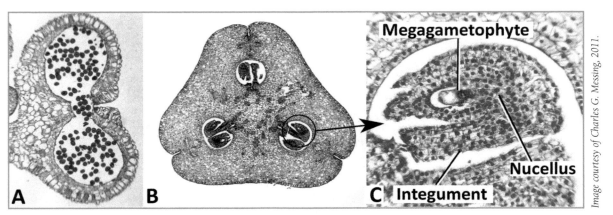

FIGURE 19-7 Angiospermae: Lily, *Lilium*. A. Cross section through an anther showing paired microsporangia (pollen sacs) containing pollen. B. Cross section through an ovary showing three pairs of ovules. C. Enlargement of an ovule. Preserved and stained microscope slides.

Life Cycles—Much of the life cycle of a flowering plant parallels that of the gymnosperm pine tree, with flowers instead of cones. The anthers contain chambers called **pollen sacs** that serve as **microsporangia** (Figure 19-7A), inside of which thousands of **microspore mother cells** divide via meiosis to produce **microspores**. Each microspore develops into a **pollen grain**—the mature microgametocyte—that consists of only three cells surrounded by a tough protective outer wall. Two of the cells are sperm, while the other will develop into the pollen tube. Pollen grains range in size from 6 to 100 μm; the outer wall is usually distinctively sculptured with one or more apertures through which the germinating pollen tube will develop.

The **ovary** lies at the base of the carpel (or pistil) (Figure 19-7B); one or more chambers inside bear one or more **ovules** attached to a central shaft. Flowers may bear one to over a thousand ovules. As in gymnosperms, each ovule consists of a diploid integument surrounding the **megasporangium** (or **nucellus**) and central megaspore mother cell. This cell divides by meiosis and, again, only one of the four resulting daughter cells survive. This is the haploid **megaspore**, which divides by mitosis to become the female megagametophyte (Figure 19-7C), which is also called the **embryo sac**. However, unlike gymnosperms, the embryo sac usually only consists of eight nuclei that segregate into seven cells. Three degenerate, two may help guide the growing pollen tube, one develops into the egg, and one large central cell contains two nuclei.

- Examine a prepared microscope slide of lily (*Lilium*) ovary.

  • Identify the ovules and surrounding megasporangia. How many ovules are there? How are they arranged? How many layers of integument can you observe?

- Examine a prepared microscope slide of lily (*Lilium*) anthers with mature pollen.

  • How do the grains differ from those of the gymnosperm *Pinus*?

When the pollen grain lands on the stigma, it develops a pollen tube that eventually reaches one of the ovules. Unlike gymnosperms, it usually takes far less time for the pollen tube to reach the egg. In corn, pollen germinates within 5 minutes after it lands. The tube can burrow 50 cm through the style at up to 1 cm hr^{-1} and reach the ovule within 24 to 36 hr, which is among the fastest growth rates of any cell. Also, the tube carries two sperm nuclei; one will fertilize the egg, while the other nucleus fuses with the two nuclei of the central cell. The resulting triploid cell becomes a unique tissue called **endosperm**, which provides nourishment for the embryo. Rich in starch (sometimes also fats or protein), endosperm is an important source of human food as well. Barley endosperm is the main ingredient in beer production. Wheat endosperm is ground for flour. Most of a corn kernel is endosperm, as is coconut meat and milk. Because two sperm nuclei fuse with two different cells, the process is called **double fertilization** and is unique to flowering plants.

- Examine a prepared microscope slide of lily (*Lilium*) pollen tubes.

■ Examine a prepared microscope slide of a mature female megagametophyte.

• Locate the surrounding integuments, micropyle and canal, egg cell, and paired central cells (future endosperm). The cells at the opposite end from the micropyle and egg will degenerate.

Seeds, fruits and vegatables—A **seed** is a mature, fertilized ovule that consists of a diploid protective **seed coat** derived from the ovule's integuments, a triploid endosperm derived from the gametophyte, and the diploid **embryo** of the next generation's sporophyte plant that develops from the fertilized egg (zygote). As the embryo grows and differentiates inside the seed, it develops the beginnings of a root, stem, shoot, and one or two **cotyledons**, or seed leaves (sometimes more than two in gymnosperms).

A **fruit** is a seed surrounded by a modified and usually thickened ovary, although it may incorporate other flower parts as well. Fruits are adaptations that promote seed dispersal, via wind (dandelions, maple trees), water (coconuts) or animals, e.g., burrs that cling to fur, or edible fruits that pass through digestive systems, leaving the seed intact and surrounded by natural fertilizer. Fruits are classified both by their structure and origin. With respect to structure, **dry fruits** include nuts, grains, peas, beans, and sunflower seeds. **Fleshy fruits** include **berries** (grape, tomato), **pomes** (apple, pear), **drupes** (cherry, peach), and **hesperidia** (orange, lemon). In each kind, the ovarian wall develops differently and may surround one (e.g., cherry) or more seeds (apple, orange, tomato). With respect to origin, **simple fruits** derive from flowers with a single pistil (peach, pea, rice). **Aggregate fruits** form from single flowers with multiple carpels (raspberry). **Multiple fruits** derive from clusters of flowers (pineapple). **Accessory fruits**, such as strawberries, apples, and **pepoes** (squash, cucumber, melon, pumpkin) include structures in addition to the ovary. As examples, the tiny sepals at the tip of a blueberry indicate that the fruit developed below the flower. In an apple, only the core is the fruit; the edible surrounding flesh derives from other flower parts such as carpels.

■ Examine the variety of fruits on display in the laboratory.

• Distinguish between dry and fleshy fruits.

The words "fruit" and "vegetable" have different meanings in different contexts. For cooking, the distinction may rest on whether the plant part is sweet (fruit) or not (vegetable). Botanically, however, fruits derive from reproductive structures, and so include peas, corn, tomatoes, eggplant, and cauliflower. We consume every plant organ, depending upon the species, of course: flowers, leaves, stems, or roots. In many cases, the organ is highly modified, often for storage of photosynthetic products. **Bulbs** are underground portions of shoots with leaves or leaf bases thickened, scalelike, and modified for storage. They enclose a bud for the following season's growth. **Tubers** are also underground storage organs. They may either derive from horizontal stems, or **rhizomes**, as in potatoes (**stem tuber**) or from modified lateral roots, as in sweet potatoes and yams (**tuberous root**). One way to distinguish them is that potatoes have eyes, which correspond to the nodes of a typical stem; each has a leaf scar and each can germinate a shoot. A **taproot** is a central, single vertical root enlarged for storage. Edible species include carrots, radishes, parsnips, and turnip. Many plants begin life with a taproot but gradually change to a **fibrous root** system that spreads horizontally as well as vertically, with no dominant central root.

■ Examine the variety of edible stem and root structures on display.

• Distinguish among bulb, stem tuber, tuberous root, taproot, and fibrous root.

Leaves—Although their primary role is photosynthetic, leaves vary tremendously in shape, structure, and even function. Their basic structure includes a single outer layer of **epidermis**, and interior **mesophyll** and vascular bundles (Figure 19-8). Epidermal cells are furnished with a waxy **cuticle** and openings called **stomata** that control water loss and gas exchange. Stomata are typically more abundant on the lower leaf surface. Mesophyll is usually divided into an upper **palisade** layer of elongated, vertically-oriented cells packed close together, and a lower **spongy mesophyll** of rounded cells with large spaces between them. Leaf veins are vascular bundles consisting of both water- and mineral-transporting **xylem**, and **phloem**, which carries the products of photosynthesis.

A leaf basically consists of a **petiole** (stem) and **blade** (broad photosynthetic structure). It arises from a stem node and bears the tiny bud of its replacement leaf at the base. In **simple leaves**, the blade may be smooth-edged or variously serrated, lobed or subdivided. In a **compound leaf**, the blade is completely divided into multiple leaflets but still has only a single petiole. Leaves may be highly modified in shape, size, margins, arrangement, and venation (arrangement of veins). Their surfaces may be smooth, hairy, sticky, wrinkled, warty, rough, scaly, or pimpled. They may be modified as spines (cacti), curling tendrils (ivy), colored bracts (*Poinsettia*), or for insect capture (Venus flytrap). Special glands may release poisons (poison ivy), aromatic oils (thyme, basil), or pheromones.

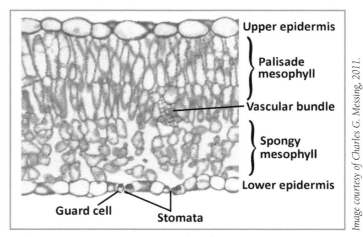

FIGURE 19-8 Angiospermae: Lily, *Lilium*. Cross section through a leaf. Preserved and stained microscope slide.

■ Examine the prepared microscope slide of a leaf cross section.

  • Identify epidermis, palisade mesophyll, spongy mesophyll, stomata, and their flanking **guard cells**. Illustrate for your lab notebook.

■ Examine the diversity of leaves on display.

  • Distinguish between simple and compound leaves. Note variations in leaf shape, structure, and surface texture.

Angiosperm Diversity—Flowering plants have traditionally been divided into two major groups, the monocots and dicots, based on leaf, flower and embryo structures. Although recent research supports monocots as a monophyletic group, the dicots are polyphyletic. Some small groups of former dicots branched off near the base of the angiosperm family tree, while another small branch containing magnolias, laurels and black pepper plants branched off separately. The remaining species—almost two-thirds of flowering plants—are the **eudicots** ("*yoo-DIE-cots*").

Monocots are characterized by one seed leaf (cotyledon, hence the name monocot), vascular bundles scattered throughout the stem (Figure 19-9A), pollen grains with one opening, and (usually) parallel leaf veins, fibrous roots, and flower parts in multiples of three. Examples include grasses, lilies, orchids, and palm trees. Eudicots have two seed leaves, pollen grains with three openings, and usually net-like leaf veins, vascular tissue in a ring around the stem (Figure 19-9B), and flower structures in multiples of four or five. Examples include daisies, oaks, roses, coffee tree, morning glory, basil, Venus flytrap, and poison ivy.

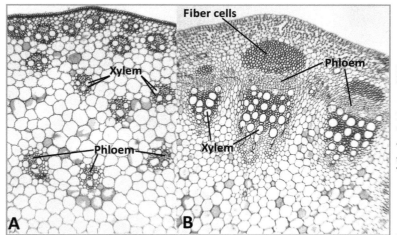

FIGURE 19-9 Angiospermae. Cross sections of portions of stems. A. Monocot: corn, *Zea,* showing scattered vascular bundles with xylem and phloem. B. Eudicot: sunflower, *Helianthus,* showing three vascular bundles along the rim of the stem with xylem and phloem. Preserved and stained microscope slides.

Vascular Tissue—As noted in the laboratory exercise on seedless plants (Chapter 18), vascular tissue was one of the primary adaptations that permitted plants to invade and diversify in fully terrestrial environments. Vascular plants have two kinds of tissue for conducting materials: **phloem** ("*FLO-um*") carries the products of photosynthesis and other organic molecules, e.g., sugars, amino acids; **xylem** ("*ZYE-lum*") moves minerals and most of the water (Figure 19-9).

- Examine the various flowers and plants on display and around the Parker building.
  - Be able to determine whether an angiosperm is a monocot or eudicot.
- Examine the prepared slides of monocot and eudicot (labeled dicot) stem cross sections.
  - Distinguish between the two forms, and illustrate for your laboratory manual.
  - Distinguish the two kinds of conducting tissue and their distributions in the two kinds of stems and illustrate for your laboratory manual.

Questions

1. Different structures may serve similar purposes. Explain the differences between a fern spore and a pollen grain. What purpose might they have in common?

2. How does the gametophyte of a seed plant differ from that of a fern?

3. If all angiosperms were pollinated by the wind, would flowers be big, bright, and colorful? Would any fruits be large and fleshy? Would insects still likely be the most diverse group in the animal kingdom?

4. Are pollination and fertilization the same events? Why or why not?

5. Explain how this laboratory exercise changed what you think of as fruits and vegetables. List some vegetables that are actually fruits, and some fruits that are actually vegetables.

References

Barnabas, B., and Fridvaiszky, L. 1984. Adhesion and germination of differently treated maize pollen grains on the stigma. *Acta Botanica Hungarica* 30:329–32.

Govarts, R. 2003. How many species of seed plants are there?—a response. *Taxon* 52:583–4.

Materials and Supplies

Living Plants (Mesozoic Garden)

Various cycads, e.g., *Dioon, Cycas, Zamia* (coontie)

Araucaria bidwillii (Bunya pine tree)

Taxodium distichum (cypress tree)

Fresh Specimens

Araucaria bidwillii (Bunya pine tree) branch and leaves (from Mesozoic Garden)

Taxodium distichum (cypress tree) branch and leaves (from Mesozoic Garden)

Gladiolus flower, or flower of similar species

Variety of fresh flowers (from local landscaping plants and weeds)

Wheat, oat, or grass flower spike

Variety of fruits sliced open to show structure (e.g., peach, orange, cherry, raspberry, strawberry, tomato, peanut, corn, squash, apple, cucumber, walnut)

Variety of edible stem and roots (e.g., potato, sweet potato, carrot, radish, turnip, parsnip, onion, scallion)

Grass with fibrous root system

Variety of leaves (including monocot and eudicot, simple and compound)

Prepared Microscope Slides

Pinus staminate cone longitudinal section

Pinus ovulate cone longitudinal section (first year)

Pinus ovulate cone longitudinal section (young)

Mature pine pollen

Monocot and eudicot (labelled dicot) stem cross sections

Lilium anthers with mature pollen cross section

Lilium pollen tube cross section

Leaf cross section

Lilium ovary cross section

Dried Specimens

Ginkgo biloba leaves

Whole Specimens

Glossopteris leaf fossil

Ginkgo leaf fossil

Araucarioxylon ("petrified wood" log) in Mesozoic Garden and small lab specimen

Amber fossil specimen with imbedded insect

Pinus staminate cone

Pinus ovulate cone

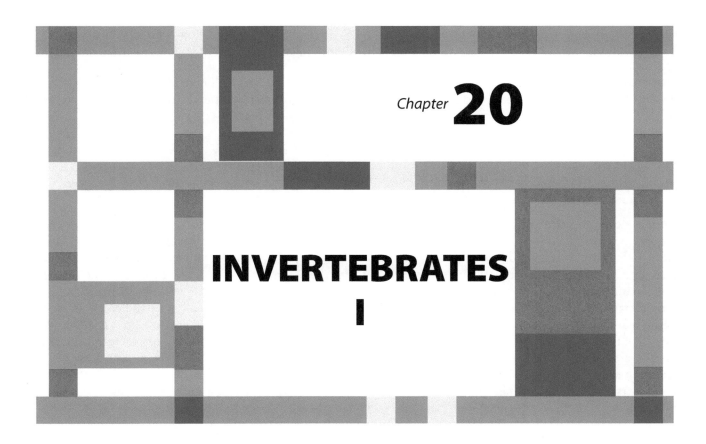

Chapter **20**

INVERTEBRATES I

Introduction

Members of the **animal kingdom** range from microscopic rotifers no bigger than *Paramecium* to blue whales. The kingdom traditionally included chiefly mobile and nonphotosynthetic single-celled protozoans such as *Paramecium* and *Amoeba,* but these have all been transferred out to many different protist groups. The division into **invertebrates** and **vertebrates**, animals without and with a backbone, respectively, has no evolutionary or taxonomic standing. It is an entirely informal split that reflects our interest in those creatures most closely related to us. Many invertebrates are more closely related to vertebrates than they are to other invertebrates. We might just as easily, and with as little justification, divide the animal kingdom into the insects and the non-insects.

Members of the animal kingdom are all **multicellular heterotrophic phagotrophs**; that is, they largely subsist on solid food. This is not a hard rule, however. Many can also absorb dissolved organic molecules, and many parasites absorb all of their nutrients from their hosts. Animals are unique in containing the glycoprotein **collagen**, which supports the extracellular matrix and is a major component of connective tissue. There are no cellulose cell walls, but there are specialized intercell junctions found in no other organisms. Unlike many plants, the diploid stage entirely dominates the life cycle. Only the gametes (eggs and sperm) are haploid.

TABLE 20-1	*Classification summary of groups discussed in this chapter.*

PORIFERA (sponges)
CNIDARIA
    Anthozoa (corals, anemones)
    Medusozoa (hydroids, medusae)
BILATERIA
    Protostomia
        PLATYHELMINTHES (FLATWORMS)
            "Turbellaria" (planarians and allies)
            Trematoda (flukes)
            Cestoda (tapeworms)
        ANNELIDA (SEGMENTED WORMS)
            Polychaeta (bristleworms)
            Clitellata (earthworms, leeches)

The animal kingdom includes more species and a greater range of body forms than any other group of organisms. To understand animal diversity and how the different groups are related to each other, we must examine the basics of both animal structure and development, as well as the features and adaptations that characterize each group. The great majority of animals are **bilaterally symmetrical**: their body parts are arranged on either side of a longitudinal axis with differentiated **anterior** and **posterior** ends and **dorsal** and **ventral** surfaces. Only one cut produces two more-or-less identical halves. This arrangement is almost always associated with **cephalization**—the anterior concentration of sensory structures, e.g., for vision and olfaction (that is, these animals have a head). A few groups exhibit **radial symmetry**, with their body parts arranged like wheel spokes. This arrangement tends to be associated with free-floating planktonic forms or attached, sessile species. It is also chiefly restricted to a few primitive groups, although the echinoderms (sea stars, sea urchins, and their relatives) originated as bilateral animals and secondarily developed radial symmetry.

Animal development exhibits a series of distinct stages, although these are variously modified, sometimes highly, in different groups. The fertilized egg (**zygote**) undergoes **cleavage**—a series of mitotic cell divisions—that results in a solid ball or hollow sphere of cells called a **blastula**. In hollow forms, the fluid-filled interior space is the **blastocoel**, which communicates with the exterior via a small **blastopore**. In the process of **gastrulation**, new cells proliferate or fold inward to form the rudiment of the digestive system and initiate the differentiation of cell layers. The **gastrula** thus consists of two cell layers, also called **germ layers**: an outer **ectoderm** and an inner **endoderm**. Most animals develop a third layer, the **mesoderm**, in between. Many but not all animals pass through a stage called a **larva** (which may begin with the blastula or gastrula) that represents a sexually immature developmental stage distinctly different from the adult. In many cases, larval anatomy must be abruptly and dramatically reorganized in order to reach the adult state, a process called **metamorphosis**. Different patterns of cleavage and early development give rise to the major subdivisions of bilaterally symmetrical animals.

PORIFERA

Sponges are the simplest of major animal groups. Although a few species are radially symmetrical, the great majority are irregular and exhibit no organizational symmetry at all (Figure 20-1A). There are no tissues or organs, only a limited number of different kinds of cells. Sponges range in size from rice grains to bathtubs, or giant ears up to 4 m across. Most sponges are built as a system of microscopic flagellated chambers and canals. Specialized cells called **choanocytes** (Figure 20-1B) line the chambers. Each cell has a central flagellum surrounded by a ring of slender fingerlike **microvilli**. The beating of the flagella draws water into the sponge through tiny inhalant openings called **ostia** (singular: ostium). Food particles, chiefly no larger than

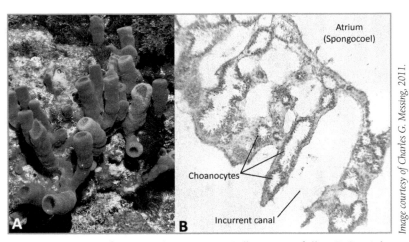

Image courtesy of Charles G. Messing, 2011.

FIGURE 20-1 Porifera. A. Tube sponge, *Callyspongia fallax*. B. Partial cross section through preserved sycon sponge, *Scypha,* showing incurrent canal and choanocytes in pouches.

bacteria, are captured by the microvilli and phagocytized. The outgoing current passes out of the chambers into canals that eventually converge on larger exhalant openings called **oscula** (singular: osculum). Much of the food captured by individual choanocytes is passed on to other cells. A few very small species consist instead chiefly of two simple cell layers: an outer layer of flattened ectodermal cells and an inner layer of choanocytes that line a large central cavity, the **atrium** (or spongocoel). There are no canals; water is drawn in through doughnut-shaped pore cells and exits through a large terminal osculum. Other small sponges increase their feeding surface by adding folds or pouches lined with choanocytes around the central cavity. The terms that describe these forms—**ascon** for the simplest tubelike construction; **sycon** (Figure 20-1B) for those with pouches or folds and a central cavity, and **leucon** for the majority with chambers and canals—have no taxonomic significance.

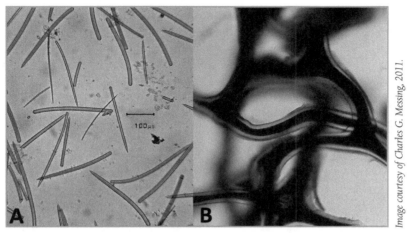

FIGURE 20-2 Porifera. A. Sponge spicules. B. Spongin fibers. Prepared microscope slides.

The volume of the sponge body between the outer ectoderm, the canals and chambers is the **mesohyl**, which consists of a matrix of polysaccharides, collagen fibers, mucus, and a variety of cells. Among these are wandering amoeboid cells that can phagocytize larger particles from the canals and differentiate into any other cell type, and cells that secrete the sponge's skeleton. Although a rigid supportive skeleton prevents locomotion, it offers support for a permanently attached organism. Rigid canals also allow maintenance of a pressure head for the feeding and respiratory current. The sponge skeleton consists of mineral **spicules**, either silica or calcium carbonate, or protein fibers called **spongin**, or a combination of both (Figure 20-2).

Most sponges are hermaphrodites, producing both eggs and sperm, but usually at different times. Choanocytes, and sometimes entire chambers of choanocytes, differentiate as sperm cells, while certain amoeboid cells become eggs.

- Examine the variety of sponge specimens on display. All exhibit leucon construction.
  - Note variations in form and consistency. Are all of the specimens "spongy"?
  - How does the cleaned, dried specimen of bath sponge (family Spongiidae) differ from the others?
- Examine a whole preserved specimen of the ascon sponge *Leucosolenia* or *Grantia*.
  - Locate the oscules and spongocoel.
- Examine a prepared microscope slide of a cross section through the sycon sponge *Grantia*.
  - Look for the tiny flagellated choanocytes that line pouches or folds that radiate from the central cavity.
- Examine a prepared whole mount microscope slide of the sponge *Grantia* or *Leucosolenia*.
  - Observe the abundant spicules that provide structure and support. Describe and illustrate individual spicule structure for your laboratory notebook.

CNIDARIA

Members of the Cnidaria (pronounced *"Nye-DAH-ree-yuh"*) are chiefly found in the ocean and range from microscopic to enormous (Figure 20-3). They occur from the intertidal zone to the deepest ocean trenches and may be bottom-dwelling (**benthic**) or planktonic, solitary or colonial. The basic form is a radially symmetrical bag, cup, or tube with a mouth surrounded by at least one ring of tentacles at one end and no anus. Rather than anterior or posterior, the opposite ends are referred to as **oral** (the mouth end) and **aboral** (the other end). There are two cell layers (**diploblastic construction**), an outer **epidermis** (= ectoderm) and inner **gastrodermis** (= endoderm), separated by a gel-like **mesoglea** that ranges

FIGURE 20-3 Cnidaria, Anthozoa: sea anemone *Metridium senile.*

from a thin sheet to thick and fibrous. The interior gastrodermis-lined space serves both in digestion and circulation and so is called a **gastrovascular cavity**. It may be a simple interior volume, divided by partitions, or give rise to few to numerous canals. Cnidarians have tissues but no organs.

Cnidarians are named for the stings that many of them cause. All species possess a unique cell called a **cnidocyte** (*"NYE-do-site"*) that produces an intracellular capsule called a **cnida** (*"NYE-duh"*; plural: cnidae; from the Greek *knide,* a nettle), which houses a coiled or folded hollow thread (Figure 20-4). When properly stimulated, either mechanically or chemically, the capsule opens and the thread, which may be many times longer than the capsule, everts outward. The commonest type of cnida is called a **nematocyst**. Cnidae serve primarily in food capture and defense. The threads of some can coil around small prey, but most are open-tipped, penetrate the prey (or would-be predator), and inject a toxin that, from a human point of view, ranges from having no effect to being lethal. In many cases, large numbers of cnidocytes cluster together as **batteries** (as in artillery, not electric).

◾ Examine a prepared microscope slide of a section through a tentacle of the Portuguese man o' war.

- Look for the small circular cnidae in a row along the very edges of the sectioned tissue. Under higher magnification, look for the coiled thread within each cnida. Illustrate for your laboratory notebook.

The cnidarian body takes one of two forms, which are basically inverted versions of each other. The benthic (bottom-dwelling) **polyp** is usually a tube, cup, or cylinder, internally lined with gastrodermis. Its blind abo-

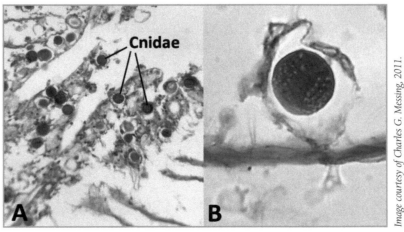

FIGURE 20-4 Cnidaria, Medusozoa, Hydrozoa: Portuguese man-o-war, *Physalia physalis.* A. Cross section of a portion of preserved tentacle showing cnidae (nematocysts). B. Cnida of same under higher magnification, with coiled thread visible within capsule. Preserved and stained microscope slides.

ral end typically attaches to the substrate, often as a broad flat pedal disk, but it may project rootlike structures or runners, or secrete a calcium carbonate ($CaCO_3$) or protein skeleton. The oral end may be conical, tubelike, or expanded as an **oral disk**. Polyps can reproduce sexually or asexually. Asexual reproduction by budding—differentiating and pinching off new polyps—is widespread. However, buds may remain attached together to form **colonies**. In some cases, all of the polyps of a colony take the same basic form. Others exhibit **polymorphism**, the specialization of polyps in a colony for feeding, reproduction, digestion, or defense.

The other cnidarian form is the **medusa**, or jellyfish (although you should avoid the latter name as there are many other unrelated jellylike organisms in the sea). Medusae are chiefly planktonic; they are composed chiefly of mesoglea and may be bowl-, cup-, saucer-, bell-, or umbrella-shaped. The mesoglea provides buoyancy, form, and a flexible skeleton. When the ring-shaped muscle fibers that run around the edge of the bell contract and force water out from under the bell, jet-propelling the medusa through the water, the elastic mesoglea restores the bell's shape for the next contraction. The tentacles typically lie along the bell margin. The mouth opens at the tip of a tube, which may be modified as frilly **oral arms**. Canals lined with gastrodermis radiate out from a distinct stomach.

Anthozoa

Cnidarians are divided into two main groups. In the Anthozoa, which includes corals and anemones, the polyp gastrovascular cavity is partitioned by radiating sheets of tissue called **mesenteries** that increase the surface area for digestion (Figure 20-5A). A sleevelike **pharynx** extends inward into the gastrovascular cavity from the mouth (Figure 20-5B). Anthozoans lack any medusa stage. The polyp produces eggs and sperm. Fertilization produces a **planula** larva, which settles out of the plankton to develop into a new polyp.

▪ Examine the variety of corals on display. These include stony corals that deposit a calcium carbonate skeleton and plantlike gorgonian corals that produce a horny, protein, supportive axis.

- On the dried stony coral colonies, locate the skeletal cups that the polyps may withdraw into. They may be quite small and require examination under the dissecting stereomicroscope. Observe that each cup has radiating skeletal partitions.

- On the branching or fanlike gorgonian corals, can you find the openings for the polyps? Note the dark brown or black supporting axis.

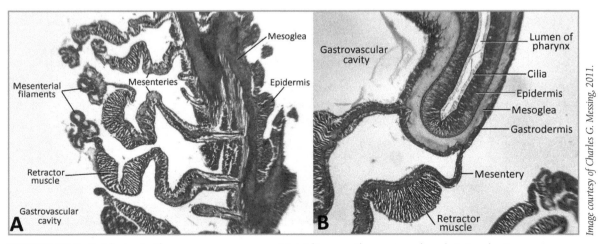

FIGURE 20-5 Cnidaria, Anthozoa: sea anemone, *Metridium senile,* prepared and stained microscope slide. A. Cross section through a portion of the body wall and mesenteries (high magnification) below the pharynx; free inner ends of mesenteries are expanded as cloverleaf-shaped mesenterial filaments composed of gastrodermis. Retractor muscle fibers lie along mesenteries. Mesoglea is stained blue. B. Cross section closer to mouth with inner ends of mesenteries attached to sleeve-like pharynx.

■ Examine the preserved specimen of the sea anemone *Metridium*.

  • In the sectioned individual, look for the numerous mesenteries and the sleevelike pharynx.

■ Examine the prepared microscope slide of a cross section through the sea anemone *Metridium*.

  • Note the radiating mesenteries and central pharynx. Illustrate for your laboratory notebook.

Medusozoa

The other group, the **Medusozoa**, has more simply constructed polyps with no interior partitions and no pharynx. A medusa stage is usually present. In the basic life history, the planula larva develops into a polyp, which reproduces asexually by budding to form a colony. Some polyps become modified and produce juvenile medusae that pinch off and take up a free existence. When mature, the freed medusae reproduce sexually by releasing eggs and sperm. Numerous variations exist on this basic pattern. In some medusozoans, the medusa stage is modified and never released, and may even be completely absent. In others, it is the polyp stage that is reduced or absent. Most meduso-

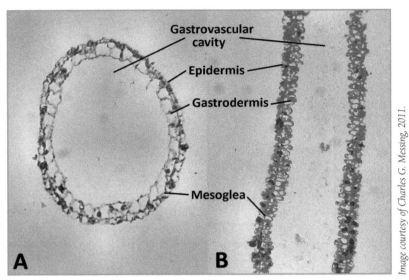

Image courtesy of Charles G. Messing, 2011.

FIGURE 20-6 Cnidaria, Medusozoa, Hydrozoa: *Hydra*. A. Cross section. B. Longitudinal section. Preserved and stained microscope slide.

zoans belong to the **Hydrozoa**, which includes *Hydra*, a simple, fresh-water polyp with no medusa stage (Figure 20-6); *Obelia*, a branching colony called a **hydroid** that looks quite plantlike (Figure 20-7A); *Polyorchis*, a medusa with a very small or absent polyp stage, and *Physalia*, the Portuguese man o' war, which is actually a floating colony of different kinds of polyps. As in many hydrozoans, the medusa of Obelia has its mouth on the end of an oral tube (Figure 20-7B). The other group of medusozoans is the **Scyphozoa**, chiefly larger medusae with the oral tube divided into multiple, often frilly oral arms (Figure 20-7C). This group includes the moon jelly, sea nettle, mauve stinger, and highly toxic box jellies, or cubomedusae.

■ Obtain a living *Hydra* from the culture jar by carefully withdrawing one with a dropper. Place the specimen with a small amount of water in a small watch glass under the dissecting stereomicroscope.

  • Allow the specimen to relax undisturbed for several minutes. Locate the mouth, tentacles, and pedal disk. Gently touch the animal with a probe or forceps. Describe its response. Can you conclude whether *Hydra* has muscles or a nervous system?

  • If available, introduce a few *Daphnia* crustaceans (water fleas) into the watch glass and observe the response of *Hydra*.

  • If a *Hydra* captures a *Daphnia*, remove the crustacean to a drop of water on a depression slide; cover with a cover slip, and examine under higher magnification with a compound microscope. Look for discharged cnidae on the crustacean's exoskeleton.

■ Examine a prepared microscope slide of a cross section of a *Hydra* under the compound microscope. This will appear as an extremely small pale pink ring.

  • Observe the two-layered (diploblastic) construction. Identify the epidermis and gastrodermis. Can you see any mesoglea?

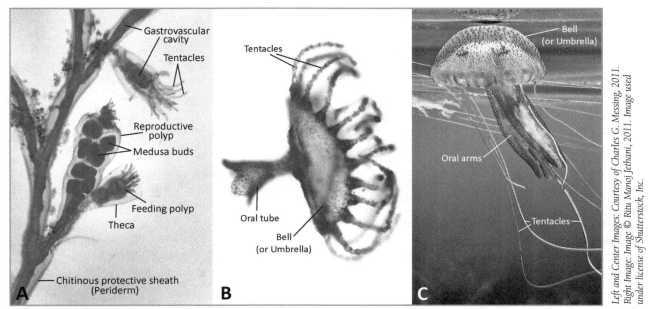

FIGURE 20-7 Cnidaria, Medusozoa. A–B. Hydrozoa, *Obelia*. A. Portion of a colony showing feeding and reproductive polyps. B. Medusa (side view with bell everted to right). C. Scyphozoa, mauve stinger, *Pelagia noctiluca*.

- Examine a prepared microscope slide of the colonial hydrozoan, or hydroid, *Obelia*.

  - Distinguish between the typical feeding polyps with tentacles and the elongated reproductive polyps, which bear several buttonlike buds that will eventually pinch off as juvenile medusae.

  - Are the polyps connected to each other? How?

  - Note how the entire colony has a translucent noncellular protective and supportive outer covering. Describe how this covering is modified around the feeding and reproductive polyps.

- Examine a prepared microscope slide of the medusa stage of *Obelia*.

  - Most will be visible in side view. If any lie flat, determine how the radially symmetrical features (e.g., radial canals) are arranged.

- Examine a specimen of *Physalia*, the Portuguese man o' war. This animal is actually a colony of numerous polyps.

  - Note the relatively short, tubelike feeding polyps and the much longer food-capturing and defensive polyps. These are little more than single tentacles armed with huge numbers of cnidae. The larva first begins to develop the gas-filled float (chiefly containing nitrogen, but also some carbon monoxide), which keeps the colony at the sea surface.

- Examine a specimen of the medusa *Polyorchis* or *Gonionemus* under the dissecting stereomicroscope.

  - Is the gastrovascular cavity a simple central space? Can you observe any radiating canals?

- Examine a preserved specimen of the scyphozoan mauve stinger, *Pelagia noctiluca*, a bioluminescent medusa found in the open ocean.

  - Locate the oral arms.

  - The small bumps scattered on the outer surface of the umbrella are batteries of cnidae. Cnidae on the tentacles are used to capture prey; suggest a reason for their presence on the umbrella.

  - Locate the sense organs, which alternate with the bases of the tentacles around the scalloped margin of the umbrella. Each contains a sensory structure receptive to light and gravity (for orientation).

BILATERIA

All remaining members of the animal kingdom discussed in this course are bilaterally symmetrical, exhibit cephalization (with one exception), and have tissues and organs derived from three embryonic germ layers (**triploblastic construction**): ectoderm, mesoderm, and endoderm. They have anterior and posterior ends and dorsal and ventral surfaces. Patterns of embryonic development divide bilaterians into two major groups: **protostomes** and **deuterostomes**. The exception mentioned above is the radially symmetrical Echinodermata (sea stars, sea urchins, and their relatives), but this is clearly a secondary modification; echinoderm larvae are bilaterally symmetrical.

One of the major anatomical features of the great majority of bilateral animals is a **body cavity**, a fluid-filled space between the digestive tract and the outer **body wall**. The body wall includes the epidermis (= ectoderm), muscle layers, and a thin sheet of fibers, proteins and extracellular matrix called the **basement membrane**. The interior body cavity may serve several purposes. In many soft-bodied invertebrates, it acts as a **hydrostatic skeleton**; the fluid (mostly water with dissolved macromolecules and a variety of cells) is incompressible (like water) and acts antagonistically to the surrounding muscle layers, permitting undulation and burrowing movements. It also serves as a space for gamete storage and enlargement of internal organs. Our own body cavity is largely filled with our internal organs.

In most major animal groups, the body cavity forms within spaces that develop within masses of mesoderm cells during early embryonic stages. The mesoderm goes on to become a thin sheet of cells that line both the inner surface of the body wall and the outer surface of the digestive tract, surrounding the body cavity. A body cavity completely lined with mesoderm is called a **coelom** (*"SEE-lum"*), and animals with such a body cavity are **coelomate** (*"SEE-luh-MATE"*). In some cases, chiefly associated with the evolution of reduced size or extremely flattened bodies, the coelom has been reduced or lost. Flatworms, for example, have lost the coelom (although one lineage of tiny species may never have had one), a condition referred to as **acoelomate** ("without a coelom"). In **pseudocoelomates**, the body cavity derives from the embryonic **blastocoel** (the space inside the blastula larva) and is not lined or only partly lined with mesoderm. In mollusks and arthropods, the coelom is reduced to small spaces around some of the organs, and its function is taken over by a series of spaces and canals, some resembling arteries, veins, and capillaries, called a **hemocoel** ("blood space"). For many years, the development of the coelom was supposed to be marked by increasing complexity, from a primitive acoelomate condition, through pseudocoelomate to coelomate, but this evolutionary scenario is no longer accepted.

We will examine the protostomes first, in this and the next laboratory exercises.

Protostomia

This vast group of invertebrates includes the mollusks, joint-legged arthropods, and a wide variety of worms and wormlike animals. Protostome means "first mouth" because the first opening to the larval gut that develops during gastrulation is the mouth. Early development is characterized by **spiral determinate cleavage**, in which the planes of the mitotic divisions lie diagonally to the vertical axis of the embryo creating a spiral arrangement of cells, and the eventual fates of cells (whether they become skin, gut, or muscle, for example) are determined as early as the four-cell stage. Here, the coelom, when present, is called a **schizocoel** (*"SKY-zo-seel"*; "split space") because it develops as a cavity within the growing masses of embryonic mesoderm cells.

Protostomes are divided into two major groups. Members of the **Lophotrochozoa** have either a **trochophore** larva, with a pair of encircling bands of cilia, or have adults with a ring of ciliated tentacles around the mouth. In this and the next laboratory exercise, we will examine representatives of the Platyhelminthes, Annelida, Mollusca, Bryozoa, and Rotifera. Members of the other major group, the **Ecdysozoa**, have a complex cuticle that is periodically molted. We will examine representatives of this group, the Nematoda and Arthropoda, in the next laboratory exercise.

PLATYHELMINTHES

The **flatworms** are often treated as the most primitive of bilateral animals. They are acoelomate, with a body cavity filled with mesoderm cells and connective tissue. The digestive system lacks an anus, and in some parasites is altogether absent. In nonparasitic species, the epidermis bears locomotory cilia at least ventrally. **Circular and longitudinal muscles** form layered sheaths beneath the epidermis. Respiratory, circulatory, and skeletal systems are all absent, a reflection of their flattened shape or small size. All of the cells are close enough to the surrounding medium or to the gut that nutrients and dissolved gases can reach them via diffusion. Yet, despite this simplicity of structure, flatworms have complex reproductive systems. Most are hermaphroditic, and fertilization is accomplished via copulation. Many species have a great capacity for regeneration.

Image © Daryl H, 2011. Used under license from Shutterstock, Inc.

FIGURE 20-8 Platyhelminthes, "Turbellaria": polyclad flatworm, *Pseudoceros ferrugineus*.

Flatworm phylogeny has recently been revised substantially. Two small lineages of acoelomate species are no longer considered true flatworms. The free-living, or nonparasitic, flatworms, traditionally called the Class Turbellaria, are a paraphyletic group (Figure 20-8). The name is therefore placed in quotation marks below. One branch of turbellarians gave rise to all of the parasitic species, which were long treated as separate equivalent classes: the Trematoda and Monogenea (flukes), and Cestoda (or Cestoidea) (tapeworms). Parasitic flatworms chiefly live in the digestive tracts of other animals. We will examine specimens of Turbellaria, Trematoda, and Cestoda.

"Turbellaria"

Planaria, or *Dugesia*, is a free-living flatworm found under sticks and rocks in freshwater ponds and streams (Figure 20-9). The gut is divided into three major branches, one directed anteriorly and two, posteriorly. The mouth lies in the middle of the ventral surface at the tip of a tubular pharynx that can be protruded outside the body for capturing small prey or feeding on carrion. Enzymes released through the pharynx begin the digestive process before the food is ingested. The two, dark comma-shaped spots near the anterior end are light-sensitive eyespots. Although there is no true brain, a cluster of nerve cells lies near the anterior end and gives rise to two nerve cords that run the length of the body on either side.

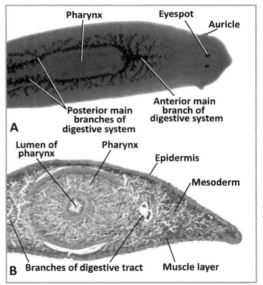

Image courtesy of Charles G. Messing, 2011.

FIGURE 20-9 Platyhelminthes, "Turbellaria": planarian flatworm, *Dugesia*. Cross section through preserved and stained microscope slide showing retracted pharynx.

- ■ Obtain a living planaria from the culture jar by carefully collecting one with a small amount of water in a dropper. Quickly but gently squirt it into a watch glass or depression slide, as it will adhere to the inside of the dropper.

  - Observe under the dissecting stereomicroscope. What symmetry do you observe? Does this animal exhibit cephalization? What features support your conclusion?

  - Touch the planaria gently with a probe or forceps. How does it react? How does the reaction compare with that of *Hydra*? How does it react when you turn it over?

- Remove the watch glass or slide from the microscope and cover partly with a piece of cardboard or other opaque material. Does the planaria appear to prefer the shaded or lit area? Why do you think so?

- Carefully confine a planaria to a glass depression slide under a coverslip and observe under higher magnification using the compound microscope. Can you observe the means by which planaria moves?

◼ Examine a prepared microscope slide of a cross section of a planaria. The slide may have multiple sections through the anterior, middle, and rear (Figure 20-9B).

- Look for the large, central doughnut-shaped pharynx that has been withdrawn into the middle part of the gut. Branches of the digestive tract should be visible on either side.

- Is there a distinct body cavity? What fills the interior of the worm between the pharynx and body wall?

- Look for both longitudinal and circular muscles just beneath the epidermis. When they contract, how do you think each changes the shape of the body?

Trematoda

Trematode **flukes** are parasitic flatworms of vertebrate digestive systems that still retain many features of nonparasitic species, including a distinct mouth and digestive system (Figure 20-10). However, they have lost external cilia and structures such as eyespots. Their complex life cycles often involve multiple phases of asexual reproduction, sometimes in multiple intermediate hosts. The Chinese liver fluke, *Clonorchis sinensis*, feeds on bile and epithelial cells in the gall bladder or bile duct (Figure 20-10A). Infections cause an inflammatory response and in some cases may lead to carcinoma. Native to eastern and southeastern Asia, it infects tens of millions of people. Fertilized eggs are released with the feces and hatch in standing fresh water such as rice fields. Such parasites are far more easily transmitted where there is no indoor plumbing; in some areas, human excrement is used as fertilizer called "night soil." The eggs hatch as ciliated larvae that burrow into a freshwater snail and undergo asexual reproduction. A microscopic tadpolelike stage, the **cercaria**, erupts out of the snail in large numbers and invades the next host, a fish, where it encysts in muscle tissue. Humans become infected by eating raw, undercooked, pickled, or salted freshwater fishes. Adult flukes attach to the digestive epithelium via an **oral sucker** that surrounds the mouth at the anterior end and via a more posterior ringlike **ventral sucker**. Behind the mouth, the gut forks and

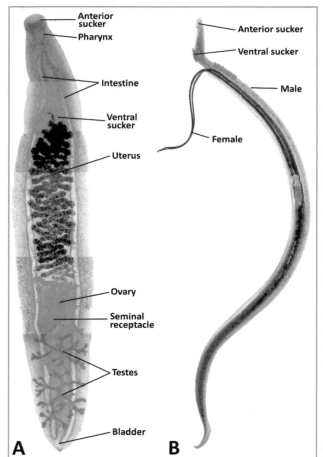

Left Image: Courtesy of Charles G. Messing, 2011. Right Image: Image © Jubal Harshaw, 2011. Image used under license of Shutterstock, Inc.

FIGURE 20-10 Platyhelmithes, Trematoda. A. Chinese liver fluke, *Clonorchis sinensis*. Composite image showing anatomical structures. B. Blood fluke, *Schistosoma mansoni*.

runs posteriorly as two long branches. As with most flatworms, *Clonorchis* is hermaphroditic. The complex reproductive system takes up much of the interior, insuring that numerous gametes can be produced. Moving from back to front, the highly branched **testes** lie at the posterior end; just in front of them are the saclike

seminal receptacle and **ovary**, followed by the large coiled **uterus** that takes up most of the middle of the worm. Both male and female systems open just in front of the ventral sucker.

Several species of blood flukes, *Schistosoma* spp., infect the liver, bladder, or intestine. Unlike most flatworms, they have separate sexes and are also unusual because the females are smaller than the males (Figure 20-10B). Mature worms remain in continuous copulation, with the smaller female snuggled in the male's ventral groove. Although not often fatal, these worms cause chronic organ damage. The disease condition, called schistosomiasis, is second only to malaria among important parasitic diseases, with tens of millions of people infected in the tropics, from the Caribbean through Africa and the Middle East to eastern Asia.

- ■ Examine a prepared microscope slide (whole mount) of *Clonorchis sinensis* (sometimes labeled *Opisthorchis sinensis*).

   - • Look for the oral sucker, ventral sucker, testes, ovary, seminal receptacle, uterus, and gut.

- ■ Examine a prepared microscope slide (whole mount) of the blood fluke *Schistosoma*.

   - • Distinguish male and female worms.

- ■ Examine a prepared microscope slide (whole mount) of cercariae (plural) from different trematode species.

   - • Illustrate at least two for your lab notebook.

Cestoda (Tapeworms)

Tapeworms are highly modified parasitic flatworms that attach to the intestinal wall of vertebrates. They completely lack a digestive system; instead, their enormous surface area permits them to survive by absorbing some of their host's digested food. The largest tapeworms may reach more than 15 m long. The tapeworm body consists of an anterior **scolex** equipped with hooks or suckers, or both, for anchoring to the gut wall (Figure 20-11A). Behind the scolex, a budding zone gives rise to a long series of repeating segments, called **proglottids** (Figure 20-11B), which make up the rest of the body like a long unwound ribbon of movie tickets, each containing both male and female reproductive tracts. The dog tapeworm, *Dipylidium caninum*, is unusual because it has two sets of reproductive organs in each proglottid. The highly branched **testes** occupy most of the segment with a grape-cluster–like **ovary** leading to a tubelike **vagina** on either side. A pouch for the male copulatory structure, called a **cirrus**, lies adjacent to each ovary. Like flukes, tapeworms may have one or more intermediate hosts.

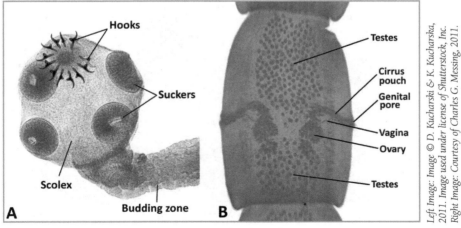

FIGURE 20-11 Platyhelmithes, Cestoda: dog tapeworm, *Dipylidium caninum*. A. Scolex and budding zone. B. Immature proglottid. Note that paired reproductive structures are labeled only on one side. Preserved and stained microscope slides.

- Examine a whole specimen of tapeworm under the dissecting stereomicroscope.

  - Identify the scolex, budding zone, and proglottids.

- Examine a prepared microscope slide (whole mount) of sections along the length of a tapeworm, such as *Dipylidium caninum* or *Taenia pisiformis*.

  - Identify the scolex, budding zone, testes, ovary, vagina, and cirrus pouch.

ANNELIDA

Segmented worms are perhaps the most diverse of the wormlike animal phyla, ranging from tiny bristle-worms a few hundred micrometers long that live between sand grains, to the giant tube worms of deep-sea volcanic hot vents that may reach 4 meters in length. The body is divided into three developmental sections. The anteriormost unit, the **prostomium**, lies above and in front of the mouth. It contains the brain and may also bear **eyes, antennae,** and **chemosensory palps** (Figure 20-12A), although these are usually not present in burrowing species. The antennae range from simple slender filaments to the elaborate, branched, feeding and respiratory crown of feather duster worms (Figure 20-12B). The posteriormost unit, the **pygidium,** contains the anus and a segment-producing growth zone. Between these two units, annelids exhibit **metamery** (or metamerism), the production of a longitudinal series of numerous repeated segments that make up most of the body. This form of segmentation involves both mesoderm and ectoderm, but not endoderm; the annelid gut passes through all of the segments unaffected by the process, although it may be modified in different sections along the way (see below). New segments form in the growth zone of the pygidium, and each contains a pair of schizocoelomic compartments and other repeated structures such as muscle blocks, nerves, blood vessels, excretory metanephridia, and gonads. As a result, the youngest segments are just in front of the pygidium, while the oldest are just behind the prostomium. No annelid has uniformly identical segments. Some segments and associated structures are usually differentiated for different functions. Some structures, such as gonads or gills, may be restricted to one or a few segments. One or more anterior segments are often fused, leading to more sophisticated cephalization with additional sensory structures. Most segments, except near the very front and hind ends, have outer circular and inner longitudinal muscle layers. Acting antagonistically to each other and to the incompressible fluid within each coelomic compartment (the **hydrostatic skeleton**), these muscles generate crawling, burrowing, and swimming movements. Burrowers move via **peristalsis,** successive waves of contraction of the two different muscle layers that alternately widen and lengthen segments.

Left image courtesy Greg Rouse, 2011. Center image courtesy Charles G. Messing, 2011. Right image courtesy Joshua Feingold, 2012.

FIGURE 20-12 Annelida, Polychaeta. A. Ragworm, *Nereis;* anterior end. B. Featherduster worm, *Anamobaea oerstedi,* showing crown of suspension-feeding appendages. C. Parchment tube worm, *Chaetopterus variopedatus* in opened tube.

The annelid epidermis produces **chaetae** (pronounced *"KEE-tee"*) (or setae), which are chitinous bristles that develop from pouches and vary from long, thin filaments to stout multi-pronged hooks. Some species, known as fire worms, have long, fragile, toxic chaetae. A **closed circulatory system** in which capillaries connect arterial and venous vessels is usually present. This is the first group we have discussed that has a **complete digestive system**, with both mouth and anus. As a result, digestion can be carried out in a series of steps, rather like an assembly (or disassembly) line, permitting different parts along the gut to be specialized for different functions, such as grinding, storage, and absorption.

Most annelids belong to the Polychaeta, which means "many bristles." One evolutionary branch of polychaetes, the Clitellata, is treated as a distinct subgroup of annelids and includes the earthworms and leeches.

Polychaeta

Polychaetes are chiefly marine and include bristle worms, ragworms, blood worms, feather duster worms, fan worms, sand worms, lugworms, tubeworms, fire worms, and giant hot vent worms. The group includes crawlers, burrowers, tube-dwellers, plankton, and commensals; carnivores, grazers, deposit-feeders, and suspension-feeders. They are often the most diverse and abundant macrofauna (>0.5 mm) in muddy and sandy bottoms. Most polychaetes have paired, paddlelike, unsegmented, fleshy appendages called **parapodia,** which may be modified for crawling, swimming, moving back and forth inside a tube, or as gills. Interestingly, gills are not homologous among all polychaetes; they may develop from different structures along different parts of the body. At the anterior end, several segments may be united as a single functional unit, the **peristomium,** which may bear a variety of feeding structures, such as an eversible pharynx with powerful jaws; numerous spaghettilike ciliated feeding tentacles, or complex, branching, ciliated featherlike structures for suspension-feeding and gas exchange (Figure 20-12B).

- Examine the variety of polychaete specimens on display under the dissecting stereomicroscope.

  - Note the differences in body proportions, chaetae, and anterior feeding appendages. How do the parapodia and their chaetae vary along the body length in the different species on display?

- Examine the feather-like appendages of a feather duster worm. Cilia generate a feeding and respiratory current and transport captured food particles down a groove that lies along the "feather's" axis to the central mouth.

  - Find the food groove. See if you can also find the groove that runs down each side branch of the feather to the main groove.

  - Locate the small eyespots that also lie along the axis.

- The parchment tube worm manufactures and lives inside its own papery tube. One pair of large wing-like parapodia secrete and hold open a mucous bag for capturing suspending food particles brought into the tube by the pumping action of three segments modified as bellows.

  - Locate the winglike parapodia and the three segments modified as bellows.

  - In addition to bringing in food, the pumping action of the bellows serves what other purpose?

- Fireworms have tufts of brittle, hollow, toxic chaetae on each segment.

  - Locate the gills, which are paired tufts on each segment.

  - The feather duster worm has respiratory structures restricted to its head end, and the fireworm has gills all along its body; which one do you think lives in a tube, and which is a free crawler?

Clitellata

Members of this group, which include the earthworms (**Oligochaeta**: "few bristles") and leeches (**Hirudinea**), all have a **clitellum**, a series of thickened segments closer to the anterior end of the worm (Figure 20-13). The clitellum produces mucus for copulation, a **cocoon** into which the eggs are deposited, and albumin for embryo nourishment. Permanent gonads are restricted to a few segments. Most species live in freshwater or moist terrestrial environments, although there are also numerous small marine species.

All clitellates are hermaphrodites with no parapodia. The prostomium is a small lobe that overhangs the mouth and bears no sensory appendages. Earthworms have a few simple chaetae, but most leeches lack them entirely.

With the exception of the clitellum, all of an earthworm's segments look alike on the outside except as they become smaller near the anterior and posterior ends. However, the internal anatomy demonstrates substantial regional specializations.

■ Obtain a preserved earthworm (*Lumbricus*), dissecting tray, two forceps, scalpel, scissors, and pins. Follow the directions below to dissect the worm and examine its internal anatomy. This requires four hands (two people) for best results.

1. Lay the worm on the dissecting tray with its dorsal side up (the mouth will be hidden under the overhanging prostomium) closer to one side of the tray than the other to permit you to observe the specimen under the dissecting stereomicroscope. Pin it in place through both the prostomium and pygidium.

2. Pinch the worm gently behind the clitellum and make an incision with the scissors at the posterior end of the clitellum, taking care to orient the scissor points almost horizontally to avoid cutting into the internal organs. Holding the sides of the incision apart with the forceps, begin to cut the body wall towards the rear end, cutting just to the side of the dorsal midline to avoid cutting up the dorsal artery. (Orient by finding the tiny prostomium at the anterior end of the worm, which lies dorsal to the mouth.) Secure the body open with pins on each side every several segments; insert the pins at about 45° angles outward so as not to interfere with your work.

3. Follow the posterior incision by cutting and pinning forward from the rear of the clitellum to the head end, taking special care in the anteriormost segments to avoid destroying the pharynx and associated structures.

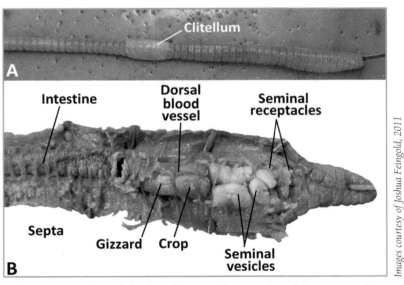

FIGURE 20-13 Annelida, Clitellata: earthworm, *Lumbricus terrestris*. A. Anterior end of preserved specimen showing clitellum. B. Anterior end of preserved specimen dissected, showing selected internal organs.

Images courtesy of Joshua Feingold, 2011

4. When the incisions are complete and the worm is secured with pins, add enough water to cover the specimen, which prevents drying and buoys the internal organs for easier observation.

- Observe the tube-within-a-tube body plan, the anterior concentration of internal organs, and the delicate sheetlike membranes called **septa** (singular: septum) that separate the successive coelomic compartments that define each segment.

- For each of the following systems, begin anteriorly, and identify as many of the structures indicated below as you can.

  1. *Digestive system*

     a. The muscular **pharynx** lies immediately behind the mouth. **Dilator muscles** that run from the body wall make the pharynx appear hairy or fuzzy. Contraction of these muscles expands the pharynx, sucking in soil particles, microorganisms, and organic material.

     b. A short **esophagus** leads to an enlarged **crop** with thin walls where food is temporarily stored.

     c. A thick muscular **gizzard** grinds the food up for absorption.

     d. The **intestine** occupies much of the middle and posterior length of the worm.

  2. *Circulatory system*

     a. Blood flows anteriorly through the **dorsal blood vessel**, which lies above the digestive tract.

     b. Five pairs of muscular pumping vessels, commonly called "**hearts**," curve around the esophagus, sending blood into the **ventral blood vessel**, in which blood flows posteriorly. Smaller vessels, too small to observe easily, return the blood from the ventral to dorsal vessels.

  3. *Reproductive system*

     a. Sperm are released from the two pairs of tiny **testes** into three pairs of large **seminal vesicles** that lie along the esophagus from segments 9 to 13. Here, the sperm mature before being released via tiny ducts through openings (**male gonopores**) in segment 15.

     b. A pair of small **ovaries** lies ventrally on the septum that separates segments 12 and 13. A short oviduct leads to the **female gonopores** on segment 14. But, sperm do not go directly into the oviduct. Instead, they enter and are stored in two pairs of **seminal receptacles** that appear as small ventral sacs on segments 9 and 10. When the eggs are released into the cocoon produced by the clitellum, the sperm are released as well and fertilization takes place outside the body.

  4. *Nervous system*

     a. The primary nerve cord in protostomes is ventral. Gently lift and remove the posterior portion of the intestine, and look for the **ventral nerve** beneath. Each segment should have a swelling along the nerve, each a cluster of nerve cell bodies called a **ganglion**.

     b. The **cerebral ganglion** appears as a pair of small swellings above the pharynx. It is connected to the ventral nerve by nerve tracts that run around the pharynx, but these may not be easily visible. Although it is a concentration of nerve cells that serve the pharynx and anterior tactile and chemosensory organs, the cerebral ganglion is not a true brain.

- Examine a prepared microscope slide of a cross section of the earthworm *Lumbricus*.

  - Observe the following structures: digestive tract with **typhlosole**—a ridge that hangs down within the interior of the gut and increases the surface area for absorption; dorsal and ventral blood vessels just above and below the gut; ventral nerve cord just below the ventral vessel; spacious coelom; **circular muscle layer** just inside the epidermis, and thicker fibrous **longitudinal muscle layer** inside the circular layer.

  - The muscle layers of each segment can contract and relax independently. How will the shape of a segment change if the circular muscles contract? If the longitudinal muscles contract?

Leeches are a group of clitellates specialized as parasites and carnivores. Like earthworms, leeches are hermaphrodites with gonads restricted to few segments. Almost all species lack both chaetae and separated coelomic compartments. They are dorsoventrally flattened, usually tapered at both ends and have the anterior and posterior segments modified as suckers. Most have three large bladelike jaws in a triangle inside the mouth surrounded by the anterior sucker. The muscular pharynx pumps in blood and body fluids. However, some are predators that ingest their small prey (e.g., worms, snails, crustaceans, insect larvae) whole.

- Examine a preserved leech.

  - Identify the anterior and posterior suckers.

  - Leeches may go long periods without feeding. How do you think their body shape changes after a full blood meal?

Questions

1. Cnidarians such as sea anemones typically have a large interior space. Why is this space not considered a coelom?

2. How do invertebrates such as *Dugesia* and tapeworms survive with neither a circulatory system nor a coelom?

References

Anderson, D. T. 2001. *Invertebrate zoology*. 2nd ed. Oxford ENGL: Oxford University Press (476 pp.).

Ruppert, E. E., Fox, R. S., and Barnes, R. D. 2004. *Invertebrate zoology: a functional evolutionary approach*. 7th ed. Belmont, CA: Brooks/Cole—Thomson Learning (989 pp.).

Materials and Supplies

Living Cultures

Hydra

Planaria (*Dugesia*)

Daphnia (water fleas)

Prepared Microscope Slides

Grantia cross section

Grantia whole mount

Leucosolenia whole mount

Physalia tentacle cross section

Metridium cross section

Hydra cross section

Obelia whole mount

Obelia medusa whole mount

Planaria (*Dugesia*) cross section

Clonorchis (or *Opisthorchis*) *sinensis* whole mount

Schistosoma male and female in copula whole mount

Cercariae different types, whole mount

Dipylidium or *Taenia* series of segments whole mount

Lumbricus cross section

Dried Specimens

Various sponges (e.g., *Callyspongia, Ircinia, Spongia, Hippospongia*)

Various stony corals (e.g., *Acropora, Pocillopora, Porites*)

Various octocorals (e.g., *Gorgonia, Eunicea, Pseudopterogorgia*)

Whole Preserved Specimens

Leucosolenia (ethanol)

Metridium (ethanol)

Physalia (formalin)

Hydrozoan medusa (e.g., *Polyorchis* or *Gonionemus*) (formalin)

Pelagia noctiluca (formalin)

Tapeworm (formalin)

Variety of polychaetes including, e.g., *Nereis, Hermodice, Sabella* or *Sabellastarte, Loimia, Chaetopterus, Aphrodita* (ethanol)

Earthworm *Lumbricus* for dissection (Carosafe)

Leech (ethanol)

Supplies

Ethanol

Formalin

Equipment

Dissecting stereomicroscopes

Compound microscopes

Fine forceps

Probes

Dissecting trays

Scalpels

Scissors

Dissecting pins

Glass microscope slides

Glass microscope depression slides

Watch glasses or small petri dishes

Glass coverslips

Disposable droppers

Large, medium, and small glass bowls for specimen display

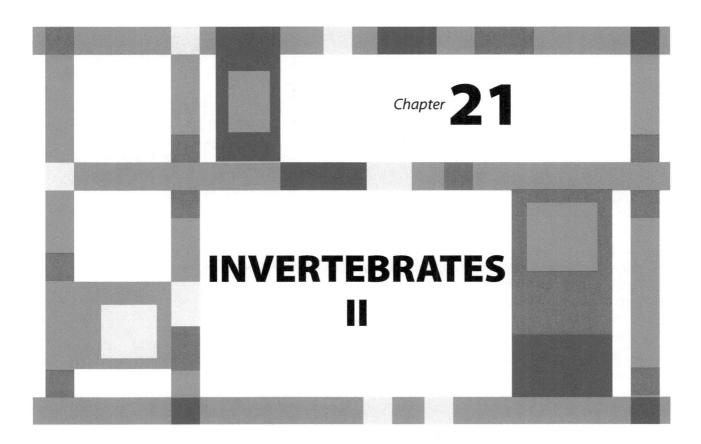

Introduction

In this exercise, we continue our examination of bilaterally symmetrical, protostome animals, beginning with the Mollusca and including the Rotifera and Bryozoa, all within the **Lophotrochozoa**. The exercise also includes two members of the other protostome lineage, the **Ecdysozoa**. As noted in the previous laboratory exercise (page 204), members of the Lophotrochozoa have either a trochophore larva with a pair of encircling bands of cilia, or adults have a ring of ciliated tentacles (lophophore) around the mouth. Ecdysozoans have a complex cuticle that is periodically molted.

MOLLUSCA

At first glance, the animals identified as mollusks appear to be so dissimilar in so many ways that it seems unlikely that they could be related. What characters might gather snails, slugs, clams, mussels, squids, and octopuses together

Classification summary of groups discussed in this chapter.

TABLE 21-1

BILATERIA (continued from chap. 20)
    Protostomia (continued from chap. 20)
        MOLLUSCA
                Polyplacophora (chitons)
                Gastropoda (snails, slugs)
                Bivalvia (clams, oysters)
                Cephalopoda (squid, octopus)
        ROTIFERA
        BRYOZOA (MOSS ANIMALS)
        NEMATODA (ROUNDWORMS)
        ARTHROPODA (JOINT-LEGGED ANIMALS)
            Cheliceriformes
                XIPHOSURA (horseshoe crabs)
                ARACHNIDA (spiders, scorpions)
            Mandibulata
                CRUSTACEA
                MYRIAPODA (millipedes, centipedes)
                HEXAPODA (insects)

as a single evolutionary lineage? The body of all mollusks consists of three major components. The central **visceral mass** constitutes most of the molluscan body and contains the digestive, excretory, and reproductive systems as well as the central components of the circulatory and nervous systems. The **foot** is a muscular elaboration of the ventral surface for locomotion and can be modified for crawling (via cilia or muscular undulation), digging, swimming, or leaping. The dorsal body wall, called the **mantle**, typically secretes a protective calcium carbonate **shell** and usually extends as a posterior fold of tissue that encloses a chamber called the **mantle cavity**—which contains gills, anus, and openings to excretory and reproductive systems. The **radula** (Figure 21-1) is a uniquely molluscan feeding structure that consists of a membranous ribbon bearing numerous chitinous teeth, rather like a flexible file. It arises from a sac at the rear of a cavity inside the mouth and can be protruded outside the mouth to scrape food. It is important to remember, however, that most of these features can be highly modified, reduced, or even absent in some groups. Octopuses have lost the shell, slugs have lost both shell and mantle cavity, and suspension-feeding clams, oysters, and their relatives have lost the radula. Radular teeth range from numerous and fine for rasping diatom films, to coarse and fanglike for tearing flesh. Cone snails use a single radular tooth for harpooning prey and injecting toxins.

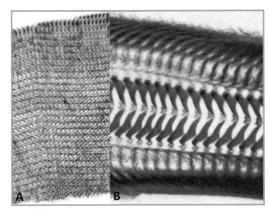

Left image courtesy Charles G. Messing, 2011.
Right image courtesy Kelly Parks, 2012.

FIGURE 21-1 Mollusca, Gastropoda. Portions of the radulas of two snails. Prepared microscope slides.

Like annelids, mollusks produce a trochophore larva. Unlike annelids, mollusks are not segmented (although repeated structures develop in a few groups), and the coelom is reduced to small chambers surrounding the heart and gonads. Instead, they have a **hemocoel**, an open circulatory system of channels and sinuses not lined by mesoderm.

In addition to muscle layers of the body wall, mollusks have a variety of discrete muscles for different functions, such as closing the shell, pulling the shell down against the substrate, withdrawing into the shell, swimming, or burrowing.

Mollusks are found on land, and in freshwaters and the sea. Estimates of the number of species range upwards of 100,000. There are eight traditional classes, of which we will examine four. The Gastropoda includes the snails, whelks, cowries, conchs, and slugs. The Bivalvia includes clams, mussels, oysters, scallops, cockles, and shipworms. Octopuses, squids, cuttlefish, and nautilus belong to the Cephalopoda. The Polyplacophora includes the chitons, or coats-of-mail.

Polyplacophora

Chitons (*"KYE-tinz"*) are chiefly shallow-water, rocky bottom algae grazers. The oval flattened body is covered by a shell divided into eight overlapping **valves**. The thickened, tough mantle margin, called the **girdle**, surrounds the shell and overhangs the sides of the body, forming a groovelike mantle cavity that houses numerous pairs of gills. Many chitons live in wave-swept habitats. The low profile of the body dissipates wave energy. Pressing the girdle against the substrate and raising its interior edge creates a partial vacuum in the mantle cavity, allowing the chiton to cling tightly to the rocks. Chitons use the radula for scraping algae. In some, the teeth are reinforced with the iron-containing mineral magnetite.

- Examine the specimens of Polyplacophora ("many-shell-bearer") on display.

  - Locate and identify the multiple valves, girdle, foot, mantle cavity, and anterior ventral mouth.

Gastropoda

Unlike the flattened chitons, the gastropod body became elongated along the dorsal-ventral axis, which converted the shell from a flat shield to a tall conical retreat that became coiled (Figure 21-2). Separate

FIGURE 21-2 Mollusca, Gastropoda. A. Land snail, *Liguus fasciatus*. B. Fighting conch, *Strombus alatus*; shell

from the coiling of the shell, gastropods undergo **torsion** during their early development, a 180° rotation of the visceral mass that moves the mantle cavity with its gills and anus from posterior to anterior and twists the digestive tract and several major nerves. Sensory organs usually include eyes and a pair of sensory tentacles. Gastropods move via muscular undulations or cilia, but the foot is also modified in some species for digging or swimming. The rasping radula is often modified for boring holes, or tearing or harpooning prey. The anterior end of the mantle may be extended and rolled up as a snorkel-like siphon that directs the inflow of water and permits the snail to burrow without getting its gills clogged. In land snails, the mantle cavity has become modified as a lung, while the shell was independently reduced or lost in sea slugs, sea hares, and terrestrial slugs.

- Examine the variety of gastropod shells on display.
  - Note variations in overall shell shape and how the proportions of the coiled spire and the opening, or aperture, contribute to shell form.
  - The tip of the shell's coiled spire tends to orient dorsally or posteriorly. Which shells likely belong to gastropods that have the mantle extended as a long anterior tube-like siphon?
- Examine prepared microscope slides of at least two different kinds of snail radulas (Figure 21-1).
  - Describe how the two radulas differ in terms of (approximate) numbers of tooth rows and tooth shape. Which one is most likely adapted for herbivorous grazing and which for carnivorous tearing?
- Examine the whole preserved specimens of land snail.
  - Locate and identify the shell, foot, mouth, and antennae.

Bivalvia

Bivalves differ from other mollusks in having their body compressed laterally and no distinctive head. The shell consists of two valves hinged together dorsally by ligaments or teeth, or both (Figure 21-3). Contraction of one or two adductor muscles closes the valves together for protection. A large mantle cavity encloses extensive gills on both sides of the body. Cilia on the gills generate both respiratory and feeding currents. Specialized gill cilia trap suspended particles and convey them to the mouth. There is no radula. The posterior part of the mantle may be fused to form inhalant and exhalant **siphons**, which allows many bivalves to burrow in sand or mud and not get clogged. The large foot is usually hatchet-shaped and muscular for burrowing. Bivalves burrow by forcing fluid into their foot to extend and then broaden the tip as an anchor. Muscle contractions then pull the shell down to the foot anchor. However, in mussels and some other species, the foot is reduced and fingerlike;

a gland at its base secretes a mass of adhesive threads called a **byssus** that these bivalves use to attach to hard substrates. In other variations, oysters have asymmetric valves; the larger one cements to a hard substrate while the smaller one opens like a lid. Scallops are swimmers that have a reduced foot and live unattached; their single large adductor muscle claps the two valves together, generating a water jet directed by the muscular mantle. Shipworms are wormlike bivalves that bore into wood, destroying boats and docks.

- ■ Examine the variety of bivalve shells on display.

  - • Although even rapid burrowing is far slower than swimming, it can require a streamlined shape for movement through a dense medium. Which shell(s) do you think are best suited for rapid burrowing in sand? Which appear least likely? Why?

- ■ Examine the preserved specimens of edible steamer clams.

  - • Locate and identify the long fleshy siphons that permit these clams to continue feeding and respiring while buried in the mud.

- ■ Examine the prepared microscope slide of the vertical section through a clam.

  - • Locate and identify the central visceral mass, ventral foot, and, on either side, the sheetlike mantle, mantle cavity, and gills.

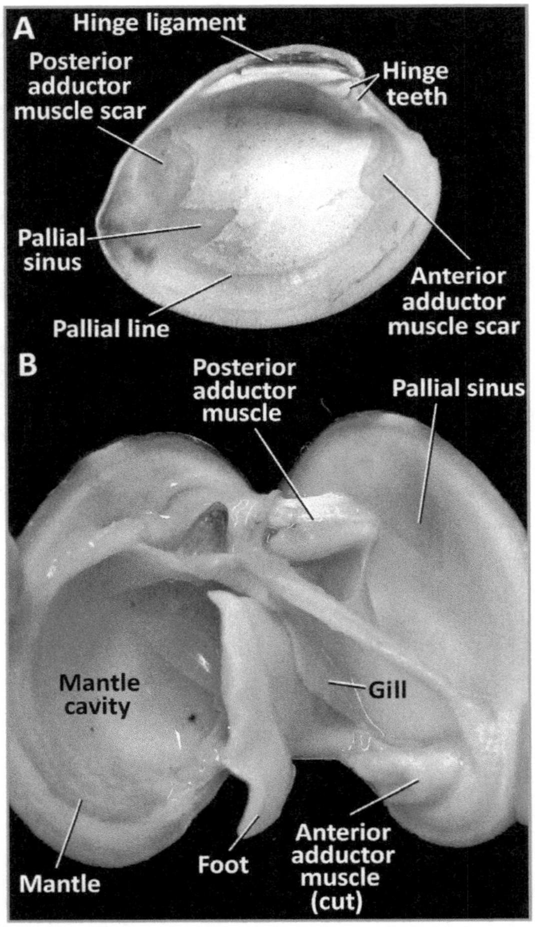

Cephalopoda

Cephalopods include the largest noncolonial invertebrates and the most intelligent ones. The foot is modified as a ring of **arms** and a muscular **funnel** (or siphon). Two of the arms may be modified as longer **tentacles**. Locomotion is via jet propulsion (although octopuses also crawl with their arms). Contractions of the muscular mantle force water out of the mantle cavity through the funnel. Giant nerve cell axons permit uniform simultaneous contraction. The radula is accompanied by a pair of horny **beaks** for tearing food. Unlike other mollusks, cephalopods have a well developed **closed circulatory system**. Their sophisticated predatory behavioral patterns reflect a complex brain and nervous system. Pigment-containing **chromatophores** in the skin permit rapid and complex color changes associated with camouflage, courtship, and territoriality.

The primitive *Nautilus* retains an external, chambered shell, a simple eye, and about 38 arms that have no suckers. The animal occupies the last and largest chamber and has a leathery hood that closes over its head for protection when it withdraws. Earlier chambers are sealed off, but a strand of tissue runs through all of them, filling them with air to achieve neutral buoyancy.

- ■ Examine the preserved specimen of *Nautilus* and the shell that has been cut in half.

  - • Locate and identify the numerous arms, the hood, and the simple eye. Note the internal shell structure with its multiple chambers.

FIGURE 21-3 Mollusca, Bivalvia: hardshell clam, *Venus mercenaria*. A. Inner surface of one valve. B. Ventral view. The narrow diagonal strip of tissue is the edge of the mantle that has pulled away from the right valve. The pallial line indicates where the mantle attaches to the shell. The pallial sinus accommodates the siphons when they withdraw into the shell.

Image courtesy of Charles G. Messing, 2011.

All other cephalopods have an internal shell or none, and arms (and tentacles) with **suckers**. Cuttlefish have an internal calcium carbonate shell called a **cuttlebone**, eight arms, and two retractile tentacles. Squids have an internal chitinous shell called a **pen**, eight arms, and two nonretractile tentacles. Many open ocean squid species are bioluminescent, producing light via **photophores**. Octopuses have a baglike mantle, eight arms, and no tentacles or shell (Figure 21-4). These cephalopods have far more complex eyes than those of *Nautilus*. These eyes are functionally similar to those of vertebrates, but they arose via convergent evolution. The receptor cells face the eye opening (**direct retina**), and muscles move the rigid lens back and forth for focusing. In the vertebrate eye,

Image © lavigne herve, 2010. Used under license from Shutterstock, Inc.

FIGURE 21-4 Mollusca, Cephalopoda: *Octopus.*

the retinal cells face rearward and light must pass through them before stimulating the receptors (indirect retina), and the muscles change the shape of the flexible lens for focusing.

Squids are streamlined for rapid swimming. The elongated, tapering tubelike body is actually the muscular mantle. Inside, the visceral mass hangs from the dorsal body wall within a spacious mantle cavity. The anterior end of the mantle forms a **collar** surrounding the base of the head where it attaches to the visceral mass. The funnel lies on the ventral side of the head. When the muscles of the mantle relax, water enters the mantle cavity around the sides of the head and funnel. To swim, powerful **retractor muscles** pull the head back against the collar; **circular mantle muscles** contract, first around the collar to prevent water from escaping, and then simultaneously along the rest of the mantle, forcing water out through the funnel and jetting the squid through the water. The flow of water also aerates the gills, which hang in the mantle cavity as well. Although squids typically swim backward, the funnel can also be curled so the squid can move in any direction. The triangular fins at the rear end of the mantle act as steering planes.

The digestive tract is U-shaped. The mouth opens inside a tough, muscular buccal mass that houses both the radula and enclosing chitinous beaks. The thin esophagus passes through a yellowish liver and then the pancreas before reaching the muscular stomach. Food passes from the stomach for temporary storage in a large blind digestive caecum that extends all the way to the hind end.

Although squids and other cephalopods appear to have distinct anterior, posterior, dorsal, and ventral surfaces, these are not the true orientations homologous with other mollusks. Squids evolved from primitive snail-like ancestors in which the body had become elongated along the dorsal-ventral axis. Standing a squid on its head gives you the correct orientation. The head end is ventral; remember that the arms and funnel derive from the ventral foot. This means the apparent dorsal surface is actually anterior, the apparent ventral surface is the original posterior side, and the pointed hind end is originally dorsal. Confused? We hope not. Cephalopods have separate sexes and one gonad.

■ Obtain a preserved squid specimen (probably *Loligo*), dissecting tray, forceps, scalpel, scissors, and pins. Follow the directions below to dissect the squid and examine both its external and internal anatomy.

1. Lay the squid on the dissecting tray posterior side up (with the funnel visible). Examine the external anatomy first.

   • Locate the mantle, head, funnel, eyes, fins, arms, and tentacles. Distinguish the eight arms and two tentacles. How do they differ?

   • Remove a sucker from one of the arms and observe under the dissecting stereomicroscope. Squid suckers are stalked. Note the ring of chitinous teeth on the rim of the sucker.

2. Slit the funnel open.

   - Locate the tongue-shaped valve that regulates water flow.

3. Remove the eye.

   - Cut the lens free to examine it.

4. Cut the mantle from the collar to the pointed end, beginning your incision to the side of the funnel. Pin the thick muscular mantle body wall back on either side as you did with the earthworm. For each of the following systems, identify as many of the structures indicated below as you can. We do not separate the organ systems because different parts of different systems are visible as one works inward.

   - On the inside of the collar and outside of the funnel, locate and identify the corresponding narrow ridges and grooves that keep the head, funnel, and mantle oriented during muscular contractions.

   - Dissect out the buccal mass and slit it open. Extract the chitinous brown beaks. Look for the transparent radula at the front inside the mass and beaks. Examine the radula under the dissecting stereomicroscope. Describe the form of the teeth. How do they differ from the teeth of the snail radula? Illustrate the radula and beaks for your laboratory notebook.

   - Locate the two long **retractor muscles** that run back from the rear of the head.

   - Identify the two long feathery gills, which lie in the mantle cavity along either side of the visceral mass.

   - The visceral mass is covered by a thin membrane that you will have to remove to see the internal organs. If you have a female, locate and then remove the pair of large elongated **nidamental glands** that lie on top of the visceral mass. They release a gelatinous material that surrounds the eggs as they are released.

   - The anus opens just behind the funnel and is accompanied by the black elongated **ink sac**, which opens inside the rectum.

   - Locate the two small, round **branchial hearts** that lie at the base of the gills. They pump deoxygenated blood returning from the body to the gills. A larger **systemic heart** lies on the midline between the branchial hearts and pumps oxygenated blood from the gills to the rest of the body.

   - The large elongated testis or ovary may occupy much of the hind end of the mantle cavity. In males, the slender penis may be found protruding to one side of the intestine.

   - Locate and identify the liver, stomach, large posterior caecum, and intestine.

■ Examine a preserved specimen of *Octopus*.

   - Observe the baglike mantle, funnel, and eight arms.

   - How do the suckers differ from those of the squid? Illustrate for your laboratory notebook.

ROTIFERA

Rotifers are one of several major groups of animals that exhibit an extraordinary level of miniaturization. Most species range between 0.1 and 1.0 mm in length. As a result, they lack many organ systems such as circulatory and respiratory, because nutrients and dissolved gases can diffuse to all of their cells. The body is divided into a cylindrical-, sac-, globe-, or funnel-shaped **trunk**; a narrower posterior **foot** with adhesive glands (not homologous with the molluscan foot); and a **head** that bears a **crown** of cilia for suspension-feeding and swimming. The beating cilia often appear like a pair of rotating wheels; rotifer means "wheel bearer." The body cavity is a pseudocoelom. Rotifers and several other groups of chiefly tiny animals exhibit **eutely**; each individual has a specific number of cells. Most rotifers are found as plankton in freshwater, where they may be enormously abundant, feeding on bacteria, algae, and detritus. Some are crawlers or sessile; a few form colonylike aggregations. They may also be abundant in moist soil.

Many species produce two kinds of eggs depending upon environmental conditions. Diploid eggs develop without fertilization into females, a process called **parthenogenesis**. Haploid eggs develop into dwarf, short-lived males, although some species lack males entirely. Some rotifer species also exhibit **cryptobiosis**, a dormant "suspended animation" state in which they lose water and suspend metabolic activity for months or even years when environmental conditions deteriorate.

■ Obtain a sample of rotifers from a culture jar by pipetting up a few drops and placing them on a clean glass microscope slide under a coverslip, following the procedure for *Euglena* or *Paramecium* in the Protista laboratory exercise.

- Describe locomotion in the rotifers you observe. How does it compare with any ciliates in the culture?

- Compare the sizes of rotifers with those of the single-celled ciliates in the culture and with those with which you are familiar (see the Protista laboratory exercise). Each rotifer is composed of about 1000 cells. How does their cell size compare with that of *Paramecium* and *Stentor*?

- Is it likely that rotifers and ciliates such as *Paramecium* or *Vorticella* compete for the same food resources? Why or why not?

- Using the 10× and 40× objective lenses on the compound microscope, look for the activity of the **mastax**, the complex jaw apparatus, which lies in the head just inside the mouth.

BRYOZOA

Although bryozoans may appear as an obscure, minor group of animals, there are actually over 5,000 marine species throughout the ocean and a few freshwater species as well. We include them here as representatives of the other major lineage of Lophotrochozoa. Unlike mollusks and annelids, they lack a trochophore larva. Instead, they have a horseshoe-shaped ridge around the mouth, the **lophophore**, which bears numerous

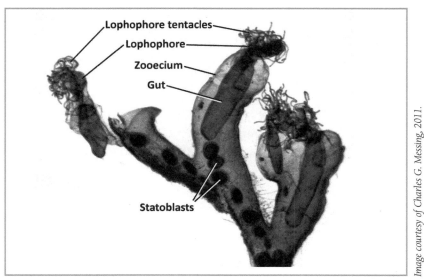

Image courtesy of Charles G. Messing, 2011.

FIGURE 21-5 Bryozoa: freshwater bryozoan, *Plumatella repens.* Four zooids showing basic structures. The zooecium is the secreted organic "exoskeleton." A statoblast is an asexually produced resting body that can develop into new colony following a period of unfavorable environmental conditions. Preserved and stained microscope slide.

fingerlike tentacles for feeding and gas exchange (Figure 21-5). Much of bryozoan structure is associated with their small size (miniaturization, again) coloniality (like hydroids), and skeleton. They are chiefly permanently attached (**sessile**) and often grow on other organisms such as sponges and algae. Colonies may be encrusting, leafy or treelike. Individuals, called **zooids**, resemble hydroid polyps but have completely different anatomies and patterns of development. Each zooid is box-shaped, oval, or tubular. Cilia on the tentacles carry bacteria, protists, and detritus to the mouth. The ring of tentacles surrounds the mouth, which leads to a U-shaped gut, divided (as in many larger invertebrates) into a pharynx, grinding section, stomach, caecum, and intestine. The anus opens just outside the tentacular ring; bryozoans are also called **ectoprocts** ("outside anus"). Bryozoan means **moss animal**, from the fuzzy mosslike appearance of many colonies when the zooids and their tentacles are extended. Retractor muscles can withdraw the anterior end of the zooid and tentacles inside the protective skeletal casing, which may be made of protein and chitin, or calcium carbonate. Freshwater species have a thick gelatinous protective covering. Colonies are hermaphroditic, but individual zooids are either male or female.

■ Examine a prepared microscope slide of the bryozoan *Plumatella* or similar species using the compound microscope at low magnification.

• Compare and contrast zooid structure and the arrangement of zooids in the colony with the hydroid *Obelia*. How does feeding differ in these two animals?

• Compare and contrast the feeding structure in this bryozoan with that in rotifers. Both are suspension feeders. What do they both have to do in order to obtain enough food to survive?

NEMATODA

The **roundworms** are our first representatives of the other major protostome lineage, the **Ecdysozoa** ("*EK-dih-suh-ZO-uh*"). The various groups of ecdysozoans are characterized by a three-layered external **cuticle** composed of the protein collagen, produced by the epidermis and repeatedly **molted**, or shed. **Ecdysis** ("*ek-DYE-sis*") is a formal term for shedding.

Nematodes are among the most abundant animals on earth, occurring in enormous numbers in soil, marine sediment, and as parasites in both plants and animals. Over fifty different species parasitize humans alone, including the pinworm, hookworm, guinea worm, mosquito-borne filarial worms that can cause elephantiasis, and *Trichinella spiralis*, which causes **trichinosis**. They range in size from less than a millimeter to over a meter in length.

Nematodes have a complete, tubular gut with little differentiation along its length, but no distinct circulatory system. Dissolved gases and nutrients circulate via a spacious **hemocoel** that was formerly called a pseudocoelom. The body wall contains only longitudinal muscles, which limits these worms to S-shaped wriggling motions.

■ Examine the nonparasitic vinegar eel, *Turbatrix aceti* (formerly *Anguillula aceti*), which can occur in unfiltered vinegar. This species is viviparous and transparent. Adult females, which are larger than males, may contain all embryonic stages, from egg to juvenile worm, lined up in the reproductive tract.

• With a pipette, remove a drop of vinegar eel culture to a glass microscope slide and cover with a cover slip. Observe under the compound microscope. Note the characteristic smooth shape tapered at both ends. Can you determine which end is anterior?

• Describe the pattern of locomotion in this roundworm. How do longitudinal muscle bands alone generate such movement?

• Under higher magnification, distinguish between males and females, and look for developing embryos.

■ Obtain a preserved specimen of the roundworm *Ascaris*, which lives in the small intestine in both humans and swine, where it causes malnutrition and abdominal pain. *Ascaris* reaches a much larger size, almost a foot in length, than free-living nematodes. Follow the instructions below to dissect your specimen.

1. Place a specimen in a dissecting tray closer to one side of the tray so that you can later view the animal under the dissecting stereomicroscope.

    •   Identify the mouth and anus. Males have a distinctly hooked posterior end. Identify the sex of your specimen.

2. Pin the specimen at both ends and cut longitudinally as you did for the earthworm, pinning as you go and taking care to make the cut superficial enough that you do not destroy the internal organs. Flood the tray with water enough to buoy up and separate the internal organs.

    •   Note that the internal structure appears chiefly as fine spaghettilike threads within a spacious body cavity, the pseudocoelom. The visible internal organs consist of the straight tubular digestive tract and reproductive system. *Ascaris* is quite large. Suggest a reason that it might not have any gills.

    •   Locate and identify the pharynx at the anterior end of the gut. It is a thicker structure that sucks in food and pumps it into the long nonmuscular intestine.

    •   In a male specimen, the reproductive tract begins with a threadlike **testis**, which becomes a longer, slightly thicker coiled tube, the **vas deferens**, which passes sperm to the still slightly thicker, posterior **seminal vesicle** for storage. Look for and identify the two posterior pronglike **spicules** that the male inserts into the female during copulation. Interestingly, nematode sperm are amoeboid and lack a flagellum.

    •   In a female, the coiled **ovary** is again the thinnest threadlike part of the reproductive system and lies most anteriorly. It passes posteriorly into a slightly thicker irregularly coiled **oviduct**, which forks to become a pair of still thicker **uteruses** that run forward and eventually join as a short **vagina**.

■ Examine a prepared microscope slide of a cross section of both male and female *Ascaris* (Figure 21-6), and identify as many of the structures indicated below as you can. Illustrate for your laboratory notebook.

    •   Locate and identify the central digestive tract. How many cells thick is it? Is the gastroderm (= endoderm) surrounded by mesoderm? What does this tell you about the body cavity, the space around the gut?

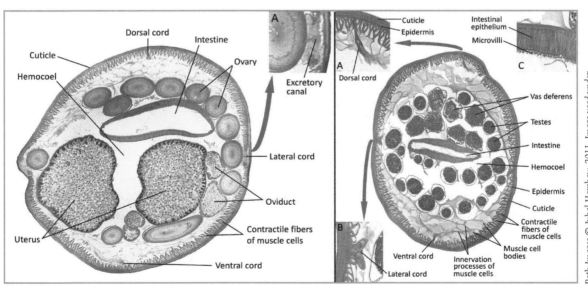

FIGURE 21-6 Nematoda: human roundworm, *Ascaris lumbricoides*. Cross sections of preserved and stained microscope slides with insets showing details at higher magnification. (Left) Female. Inset A shows excretory canal in lateral cord. (Right) Male. Inset A shows dorsal cord containing dorsal nerve; inset B shows lateral cord (excretory canal not distinct); inset C shows a portion of the intestinal wall.

- Locate and identify the noncellular exterior cuticle, epidermis, and underlying **longitudinal muscle layer**. Nematodes lack circular muscles. Because of this, what might locomotion look like in a nematode?

- Locate and identify the multiple cross sections of the reproductive tract. The location of the cross section will determine which parts of the system you can see. In the male, look for testes or vas deferens, or both. In the female, look for the small egg-filled ovary, the numerous solid dark circular sections of oviduct, and the two larger, thicker-walled, egg-filled uteruses.

ARTHROPODA

The arthropods, the joint-legged animals, are the largest major group in the animal kingdom, with well over a million species. Some scientists speculate that more than ten times that number may exist. Like annelids, arthropods have a metameric body divided into a linear series of segments. However, molecular and developmental evidence indicates that metamery evolved independently in the two groups, and they are not closely related. Arthropod body segments tend to differentiate and fuse as functional groups in different evolutionary lines, e.g., the head/thorax/abdomen of insects and the cephalothorax/abdomen of spiders. In the primitive condition, each segment had one pair of jointed appendages, but they have usually been lost from at least some segments. The appendages exhibit a vast diversity of modification and adaptations for different functions, including walking/running, swimming, burrowing, feeding, sensing, defense, and reproduction. As in nematodes, the epidermis secretes a noncellular cuticle that is molted at intervals, but in arthropods it is developed as a far more complex **exoskeleton** composed of protein, lipid, and chitin, often with calcium carbonate. Instead of muscle layers, a complex system of individual muscles and muscle bundles attaches to the inside of the exoskeleton. Arthropods have **compound eyes**, **simple eyes**, or both. There are no cilia, and the reduced coelom is replaced by a **hemocoel**, an open circulatory system with a dorsal artery and contractile **heart**. As in mollusks, the circulatory fluid in a hemocoel is referred to as **hemolymph** rather than blood. The sexes are usually separate, and development often includes **metamorphosis** from a larval stage to the adult.

FIGURE 21-7 Arthropoda, Chelicerata, Arachnida, Araneae: wolf spider.

Arthropods live virtually everywhere, from the deepest ocean trenches to high in the atmosphere; from the tropics to polar habitats; on land, in freshwater, and in the sea. They are essentially the most successful of all animal groups and include carnivores, scavengers, filterers, symbionts, and parasites of both animals and plants, although most are herbivores. They are disease carriers, poisonous species, major agricultural pests, and pest controllers. Some are critical to pollination and soil ecology; others are major components of marine food webs and sources of seafood. Fruit flies are critical to the study of genetics, and bees produce honey.

Recent research has both confirmed some of the traditional taxonomy of major arthropod groups and recognized new relationships as well. The **Trilobitomorpha**, commonly called **trilobites**, arose at the beginning of the Cambrian diversification of life and remained the dominant arthropod group throughout much of the Paleozoic Era. They disappeared during the mass extinction at the end of the Permian period. A typical trilobite has several anterior segments fused together and covered by a semicircular exoskeletal shield with compound eyes, followed by a thorax of numerous similar segments.

- Examine a fossil specimen of trilobite.

  - Locate and identify the anterior shield and the two longitudinal grooves that divide the thorax into three side-by-side lobes (hence, the name "trilobite").

Living arthropods are divided into two major evolutionary lineages. The Cheliceriformes includes horseshoe crabs, spiders, and scorpions and their allies. The Mandibulata includes the crustaceans, myriapods, and insects. The most recent data confirms that insects arose from crustacean ancestors.

Cheliceriformes

Cheliceriforms are distinguished from other arthropods by having six pairs of appendages. The food-handling **chelicerae** are the only appendages anterior of the mouth and may be modified as small claws, fangs, or piercing structures. **Pedipalps**, the second pair of appendages, may be claws, grasping or sensory. The following four pairs are usually **walking legs**, though one pair may be modified for sensory functions. There are no antennae or mandibles. The body is divided into an anterior **cephalothorax** and posterior **abdomen**, though the two are sometimes fused together.

XIPHOSURA

Horseshoe crabs (Figure 21-8) are among the most primitive cheliceriforms, with a fossil record dating to the Cambrian. The body is divided into a **cephalothorax** (head + thorax) of 7 segments covered dorsally by a shieldlike **carapace**, an **abdomen** of 12 segments also fused together, and a terminal spikelike **telson**. The carapace bears two simple eyes (**ocelli**) along the midline, and a pair of larger lateral compound eyes. Ventrally, the cephalothorax bears six similar appendages. The chelicerae, pedipalps, and first three walking legs are all similar and end in claws. The fourth pair terminates in a cluster of flat tonguelike structures for pushing the animal through the mud. **Gnathobases** ("jaw-bases"), clusters of stiff spines at the base of each appendage, tear up food (small invertebrates, plant material, and carrion) and force it into the mouth. The flattened platelike abdominal appendages bear **book gills** on their undersides, so named because each is divided into lamellae that resemble the pages of a book. The **genital pores** open on the underside of the first abdominal appendage.

■ Examine a specimen of horseshoe crab.

- Locate and identify the major body divisions, the two different kinds of eyes, and the various appendages and their gnathobases.

- Can you locate the anus? What purpose do you think the telson serves?

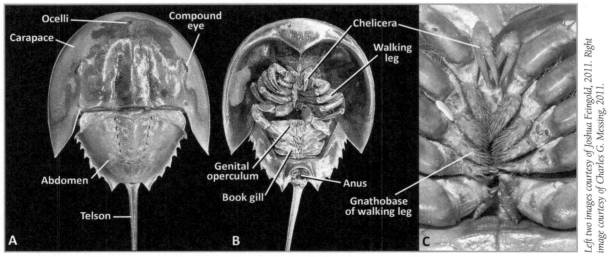

FIGURE 21-8 Arthropoda, Cheliceriformes, Xiphosura: horseshoe crab, *Limulus polyphemus*. A. Dorsal view. B. Ventral view. C. Close-up ventral view showing chelicerae and bases of walking legs.

ARACHNIDA

Most living cheliceriforms are arachnids. Unlike the horseshoe crabs, arachnids lack compound eyes. Abdominal appendages are either absent or highly modified and reduced. The abdominal segments may be fused or separate. Most arachnids have a dorsal cluster of **ocelli** at or toward the anterior end of the cephalothorax.

SCORPIONES (scorpions) Probably the most primitive of living arachnids. They are chiefly tropical and their venom ranges from mild to fatal. Scorpions have a short **cephalothorax**, a long **abdomen,** and a tail-like **postabdomen** with a **stinger** in the last segment. The chelicerae are tiny jawlike claws at the anterior end between the bases of the large pedipalp claws.

■ Examine a specimen of scorpion.

- Locate and identify the main body sections, stinger, and different appendages. The underside bears a pair of comblike sensory **pectines**.

ARANEAE (spiders) (Figures 21-7, 21-9) The cephalothorax and abdomen are joined by a narrow, waistlike **pedicel** (Figure 21-7). The chelicerae are modified as **fangs** that deliver venom from glands at their base to immobilize and kill prey. In primitive spiders such as tarantulas, the fangs articulate front to back; in most spiders they articulate side to side (Figure 21-9). Prey tissues are then liquefied with regurgitated digestive juices, and the resulting slurry is sucked in by the muscular pharynx. Some spiders can crush and chew their prey with teeth at the bases of the chelicerae. The short leglike pedipalps help manipulate food and serve a sensory function. In males, they are modified to deliver the sperm packet during copulation. On the ventral surface of the abdomen, a pair of slit-shaped **spiracles** opens into the **book lungs**, named after their multiple sheetlike lamellae that increase the surface area for gas exchange. Near or between the spiracles is a flat plate, the **epigynum**, which covers the reproductive opening in females. Additional paired spiracles open into a system of respiratory tubules called **tracheae** that also contribute to gas exchange. At the posterior end, a cluster of small knoblike **spinnerets**, which are highly modified appendages, release strands of silk produced by internal glands.

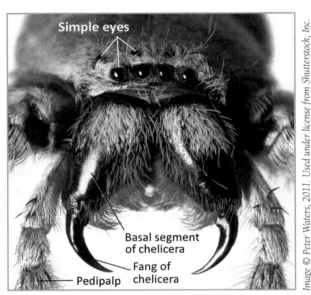

FIGURE 21-9 Arthropoda, Chelicerata, Arachnida, Araneae: spider. Anterior view showing double row of simple eyes, and articulated chelicerae with the terminal segment modified as a fang.

■ Examine the specimens of spiders on display, which may include a large tarantula, orb-weaving spiders, wolf spider, and jumping spider.

- Locate and identify the structures mentioned above, including body sections, pedicel, simple eyes, appendages, spinnerets, and ventral abdominal openings.

- Compare and contrast the proportions of eyes and appendages among the different spider species.

- Compare the structure of the chelicerae in the tarantula and orb-weaver spiders.

■ If available, observe a live spider under the dissecting stereomicroscope.

- Can you observe the beating of the heart through the exoskeleton? Where is the heart located?

- If possible, observe the release of silk from the spinnerets.

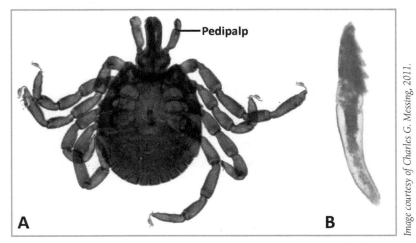

FIGURE 21-10 Arthropoda, Chelicerata, Arachnida, Acari. A. Tick showing finely toothed piercing mouthparts between the pedipalps. B. Follicle mite, *Demodex folliculorum*, showing reduced walking legs. Preserved microscope slides.

Other arachnids exhibit a variety of modifications to body form and appendages.

OPILIONES (harvestmen) Spiderlike, with incredibly slender legs, but with the cephalothorax and abdomen fused into a single egg-shaped unit and the chelicerae long and clawed.

THELYPHONIDA (or UROPYGI) (whip scorpions) Uses its heavy pedipalps to capture prey, but they do not end in true claws. The chelicerae are small claws. The first walking legs are long, slender, and function as antennae, and the slender, whiplike post-abdomen releases acetic acid as a defensive mechanism. Whip scorpions are also called vinegaroons. They lack venom.

ACARI (mites and ticks) (Figure 21-10) No visible segmentation; the chelicerae and pedipalps exhibit a wide range of modifications for chewing, tearing, piercing, and sucking. Although mites occur in a wide range of terrestrial and aquatic environments, they are most familiar as parasites. Half of adult humans carry the tiny, elongated follicle mites (*Demodex folliculorum*) in hair follicles and sebaceous glands, chiefly around the eyes and nose. They feed on sebum and dead skin cells and are usually harmless and unnoticed. Larger blood-sucking ticks may carry a variety of diseases, including Lyme disease.

- Examine the various arachnid specimens on display.

  - Compare and contrast body structures, appendages, and their functions among spiders, scorpions, harvestmen, whip scorpions, and Acari.

- Examine prepared microscope slides of the follicle mite, and a mite and tick.

  - How do they differ? Do all of them have the same appendages?

Mandibulata

All other arthropod groups belong here. Primitively, mandibulates have six anterior segments fused as a head with five pairs of appendages: two pairs of sensory **antennae**, one pair of chewing **mandibles**, and two pairs of food handling **maxillae**. Crustaceans still have all of these, but the others have only one pair of antennae, and the myriapods lack maxillae.

FIGURE 21-11 Arthropoda, Mandibulata, Crustacea, Decapoda: ghost crab, *Ocypode gaudichaudii* on a beach in the Galapagos Islands.

CRUSTACEA

Crustaceans are the only chiefly aquatic group of living arthropods, although some have invaded the land to varying degrees (Figure 21-11). They also span the widest range of sizes, from tiny copepods less than a millimeter in length, to the giant Japanese spider crab (*Macrocheira kaempferi*) that reaches 19 kg with a claw spread of up to almost 4 meters. Crustaceans have the complete mandibulate complement of head appendages: two pairs of antennae, a pair of mandibles, and two pairs of maxillae. The most primitive species retain one pair of two-branched appendages per segment, but these have been variously reduced or modified for walking, swimming, feeding, or burrowing. Feeding habits are usually reflected in the form of the anterior appendages; crustaceans include predators, scavengers, filterers, and herbivores; a few are parasitic. The number of segments varies from up to 60 in primitive species to almost completely fused. Many species have a **carapace** (Figure 21-12), a posterior extension of the head exoskeleton that may enclose only a few segments, a large gill chamber, or the entire body. Feathery **gills**, when present, are usually attached to the bases of the legs and sides of the body. Appendages, or parts of appendages, may also be modified as gills. Compound or simple eyes are usually present. The sexes are usually separate, and many species develop through an unsegmented **nauplius** larva, which has only two antennae and mandibles.

This exercise includes only a small representation of the diversity of crustaceans.

CLADOCERA (water fleas) Most live in freshwater, swim with enlarged second antennae and have a large bivalved carapace that encloses the trunk. Eggs and juveniles may be brooded under the carapace. Segmentation is reduced. The *Daphnia* that we fed to *Hydra* belongs to this group.

COPEPODA (copepods) Sometimes referred to as "insects of the sea" because of their enormous numbers in the plankton. Most range from less than 1 to about 5 mm. They are typically oval or bullet-shaped, with a narrower

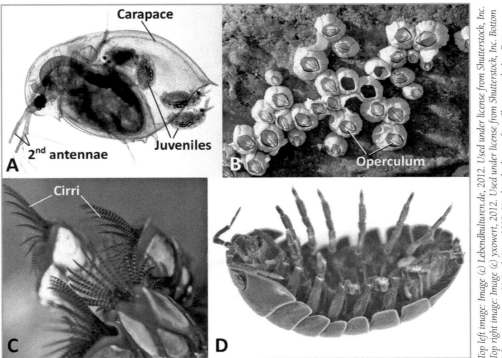

Top left image: Image (c) Lebendkulturen.de, 2012. Used under license from Shutterstock, Inc. Top right image: Image (c) yxowert, 2012. Used under license from Shutterstock, Inc. Bottom left image: Image (c) Paul Yates, 2012. Used under license from Shutterstock, Inc. Bottom right image: Image (c) Henrik Larsson, 2012. Used under license from Shutterstock, Inc.

FIGURE 21-12 Arthropoda, Mandibulata, Crustacea: A. Cladocera, Daphnia pulex, water flea, showing juveniles escaping from brood chamber under carapace. B. Cirripedia, acorn barnacles, showing operculum: movable plates that close when the barnacles are exposed as the tide goes out. C. Cirripedia, gooseneck barnacles, showing cirri: feathery, thoracic feeding appendages. D. Isopoda, pill bug, or wood louse.

segmented posterior end that lacks appendages. The first antenna is usually the longest by far, and the remaining appendages are modified for food handling (though there are no claws) and swimming. A single simple eye sits at the front end.

CIRRIPEDIA (barnacles) Highly modified crustaceans in which the swimming nauplius larva develops into a sessile, shelled adult that looks little like a crustacean. The carapace develops into a rigid calcium carbonate shell composed of several overlapping or interlocking pieces that grow and thicken without molting. Most of the appendages are flexible, feathery, and extend out of the shell for capturing small planktonic food. **Acorn barnacles** cement directly to the substrate; **gooseneck barnacles** have a flexible stalk. Barnacles are hermaphroditic and some are highly modified parasites of other crustaceans.

ISOPODA (pill bugs, sow bugs, roly-poly) These include the most terrestrial of crustaceans, although many species are marine. Land-dwelling isopods, also known as pill bugs or wood lice, lack a carapace, and have a series of similar thoracic segments and appendages; some can roll up into a ball for protection.

◼ Examine the specimens of Cladocera, Copepoda (both prepared microscope slides), Cirripedia, and Isopoda.

• Note differences in general structure and modifications of body segmentation and appendages.

DECAPODA (true shrimps, lobsters, crayfish, crabs) (Figures 21-11, 21-13) The decapod body is divided into a cephalothorax and abdomen. A carapace extends from the rear of the head to cover the entire rest of the cephalothorax and encloses a spacious gill chamber. Several groups of decapods, notably the hermit crabs, king crabs, and true crabs, exhibit a trend toward reduction of the abdomen. In addition to the standard complement of head appendages, the first three thoracic appendages are modified as food handling **maxillipeds** (Figure 21-13B). The third maxilliped is most posterior and resembles a typical thoracic walking leg, although it is held forward and has tearing teeth along its base. Moving anteriorly, the second and first maxillipeds become smaller and progressively more similar to the food-handling maxillae. Posterior to the maxillipeds are the five pairs of thoracic walking legs. The first of these is often an enlarged, clawed **cheliped** (although additional legs may bear a claw in some species). The segmented abdomen bears up to five pairs of two-branched, flattened appendages called **pleopods** that function in swimming, ventilating, or carrying the eggs. The posteriormost abdominal segment is fused with the telson and bears a pair of flattened **uropods** that together form a **tail fan** (except in those species, such as true crabs, in which the abdomen is reduced).

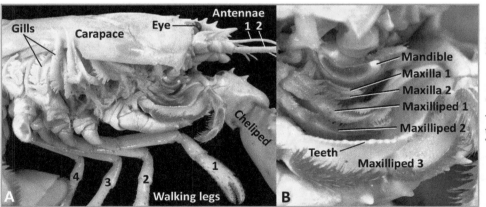

FIGURE 21-13 Arthropoda, Mandibulata, Crustacea, Decapoda: American lobster, *Homarus americanus*. A. Side view of cephalothorax with one of each pair of mouthparts and legs removed and with carapace partly cut away to reveal gills. B. Close-up of A showing one set of mouthparts.

◼ Examine the variety of crab specimens.

• Compare claw structure. Speculate about which kinds of claws may be associated with different diets, such as algae-picking, tearing prey, or crushing shells.

■ Examine the specimens of shrimps and crayfish (or lobster, as available)

- On what points of body structure, proportions, and appendages are they similar or different?

- Obtain a preserved crayfish, dissecting tray, probe, forceps, scalpel, and scissors. Follow the instructions below, noting, in particular, variations in the structure of the different appendages and their functions. This exercise will focus on external rather than internal anatomy. Figure 21-12 shows a lobster, which is larger than a crayfish. However, the arrangement and structure of the mouthparts and appendages are similar in the two species.

  1. Place the crayfish on the dissecting tray. Using the scissors, carefully cut away the carapace on one side of the body, following the groove that runs from the lower anterior margin near the base of the cheliped to the dorsal midline and back to the posterior edge of the carapace. Remove this section of exoskeleton.

     - Observe the numerous feathery gills now exposed.

  2. Lay the crayfish on its back and review the visible appendages described above. Beginning at the hind end, use a forceps to remove one set of appendages along one side of the body and lay them in a line in the tray for comparison. Most appendages are strongly attached to the inside of the body's exoskeleton by muscles and ligaments. To remove an appendage, grasp it with the forceps as close to the base as possible, rotating the forceps gently but firmly back and forth to loosen and remove the appendage. Some muscle fibers may remain attached.

     - Compare the abdominal pleopods and uropods. What function do you think the uropods and tail fan serve?

     - Removing the walking legs from rear to front, including the cheliped, note the attachment of gills to the leg bases.

     - The successively smaller and more delicate maxillipeds require gentler handling for removal. Which is the most anterior gill-bearing appendage?

     - Observe how the successively smaller and more delicate second and first maxillipeds and second and first maxillae are arranged like curved pages of a book. What structures appear to serve for food handling at the tips of these appendages? Are any of them modified for chewing? Do these appendages have one or two branches?

     - Locate and identify the elongated, transparent, boat-shaped structure attached to the second maxilla. This structure is the **gill bailer**; by undulating up and down beneath the carapace, it generates a respiratory flow of water that enters the gill chamber above the bases of the walking legs, passes up and across the gills, and exits anteriorly past the mouthparts.

     - Remove the heavy, strongly calcified mandible. As crustaceans do not have rows of separate teeth as in humans, can you identify different parts of the mandible that might serve different feeding functions, e.g., cutting versus grinding?

     - Observe the differences between the first and second antennae.

MYRIAPODA

These are the "many-leggers," the centipedes and millipedes. All are terrestrial, chiefly in humid environments. These animals range from almost microscopic to 30 cm long and have fewer than ten to almost 200 segments. Appendages include one pair of antennae and one pair of mandibles, and each appendage has one branch (like those of insects). Many possess defensive **repugnatorial** glands that secrete foul-tasting compounds. Respiration takes place as in insects and some spiders, via **tracheae**—canals that branch throughout body.

CHILOPODA (centipedes) (Figure 21-14) Active predators with flattened bodies of up to 177 segments. Each segment (except one behind the head and the last two) bears one pair of appendages. The first pair of trunk appendages is modified as large **poison claws**.

DIPLOPODA (millipedes) Chiefly cylindrical bodies with 25–100 segments. The body segments are fused in pairs, so each apparent segment usually has two pairs of legs. Diplopoda means "double footed." They are chiefly herbivorous or feed on decaying vegetation. Females build a nest in which they guard their eggs.

- ▦ Examine specimens of millipede and centipede.

  - • Observe the apparent differences in the distribution of appendages.

  - • Locate and identify the poison claws in the centipede.

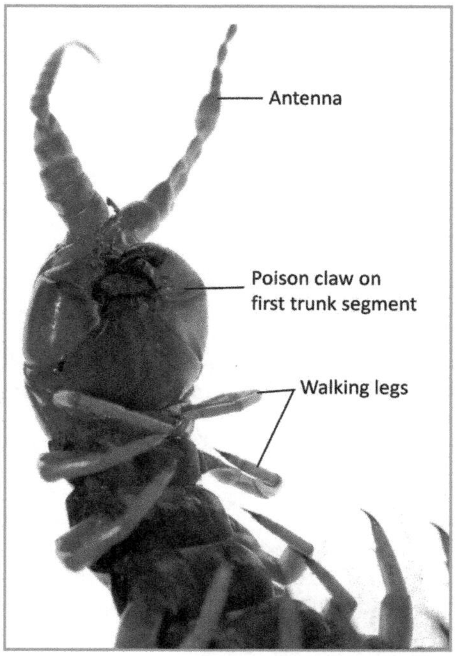

HEXAPODA

Hexapods include the insects and their nearest insectlike relatives. The name derives from their six legs. The most recent research suggests that hexapods evolved from crustaceans. The body is divided into **head**, **thorax**, and **abdomen** (Figure 21-15). The head bears one pair of antennae, compound eyes (and often simple ocelli as well), and a pair of mandibles and maxillae. Extensions of the head form an upper and lower lip, the **labrum** and **labium**, respectively, and both may be incorporated into feeding structures. Both the maxilla and labium each typically bear a slender segmented sensory **palp**. As we'll see below in discussing the different groups of insects, mouthpart structure clearly reflects diet. The thorax bears three pairs of legs and often two pairs of wings. The legs are variously modified for walking, jumping, digging, swimming, clinging, or grasping. Insects are distinguished from several more primitive insectlike hexapods by the **ovipositor**, an abdominal tubelike egg-laying structure in females.

Hexapods are the most successful arthropods, with more than a million described species. Flight, small size, and well-protected eggs all allow long distance transport. The **wings** are extensions of the exoskeletal cuticle and are not homologous with bird or bat wings. Most winged insects have two pairs; however, flies, mosquitoes, and their allies have the second pair reduced to club-shaped **halteres** that control equilibrium in flight. In beetles, the first pair of wings are thick, horny protective covers; in grasshoppers and roaches, they are papery; and in moths and butterflies, they are covered with scales. Ants and termites only bear wings during part of their life cycles.

Most hexapods are herbivorous on plant tissue and juices (e.g., locusts, aphids, cicadas), and many feed specifically on certain plant species (e.g., the cotton boll weevil). Others are scavengers (dung beetles), predators (mantises), and parasites (fleas and lice). As mentioned above, the mouthparts exhibit a wide range of adaptations associated with different diets. They also include numerous examples of convergent evolution in which mouthparts in different insect groups have become modified independently for similar diets, sometimes

Image © Pan Xunbin, 2011. Used under license from Shutterstock, Inc.

FIGURE 21-14 Arthropoda, Mandibulata, Myriapoda: centipede, *Scolopendra*. Oblique ventral view of anterior end.

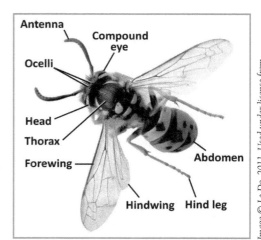

Image © Le Do, 2011. Used under license from Shutterstock, Inc.

FIGURE 21-15 Arthropoda, Mandibulata, Hexapoda, Hymenoptera: wasp. Basic hexapod structures.

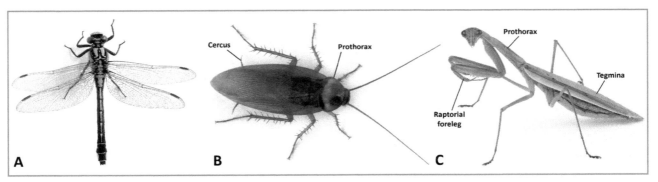

FIGURE 21-16 Arthropoda, Mandibulata, Hexapoda. A. Odonata: dragonfly, *Gomphus*. B. Blattodea: cockroach, *Periplaneta americana*. C. Mantodea, praying mantis.

Left Image: Image © alslutsky, 2011. Image used under license of Shutterstock, Inc. Middle Image: Image © James Steidl, 2011. Image used under license of Shutterstock, Inc. Right Image: Image © JIANG HONGYAN, 2011. Image used under license of Shutterstock, Inc.

using different mouthparts. The basic and least modified mouthparts are used for biting and chewing, as in dragonflies, grasshoppers, and roaches. Piercing and sucking mouthparts have evolved in several different groups, including fleas, true bugs, mosquitoes, and some flies. In houseflies, mouthparts are modified for sponging up fluids via capillary action, while horseflies first pierce the flesh with a cluster of bladelike mouthparts and then sponge up the blood that oozes out. Both honeybees and butterflies and moths have a tubelike proboscis; but the bees take in nectar with a labial pumping tongue, while butterflies and moths use a pumping pharynx, and their tubelike proboscis is much longer and coils up when not in use.

Embryonic development is highly modified so that the typical protostome spiral development has been obscured. For example, cleavage of the fertilized egg is restricted to the surface of the developing embryo; the dividing cells surround a central undivided mass of yolk. Hexapods exhibit two patterns of development following hatching. In the primitive version, called **incomplete**, or **hemimetabolous**, development, a series of growth stages, called **nymphs**, which look like small adults without wings, gradually reaches the adult stage following a series of molts. This pattern is characteristic of grasshoppers, crickets, roaches, dragonflies, true bugs, and mantises. More specialized **holometabolous**, or **complete**, development has three distinct stages. The initial **larva** is a wingless feeding stage (e.g., caterpillar, grub, maggot) that may have very different mouthparts from those of the adult, which may allow the two stages to depend on different food resources. A nonfeeding quiescent **pupa** stage (e.g., chrysalis, cocoon) follows the larval stage, during which internal anatomy reorganizes and adult features develop from embryonic rudiments. The wings, which seem to appear suddenly in the adult, have been developing internally. **Adults** do not molt. Only about a third of the major groups of insects are holometabolous, but they include 80% of species.

Hexapods occur in virtually all terrestrial and freshwater habits, but very few have invaded the marine environment (chiefly in the intertidal zone and on the sea surface). Their adaptations to successful life on land include a waxy waterproof cuticle, and the abilities to close the spiracles (respiratory openings to the tracheae), retain metabolic water, and go into a dormant state.

The vast majority of hexapods are insects. We will examine just a few of the more than two dozen major groups, traditionally called orders.

ODONATA (**dragonflies, damselflies**) (Figure 21-16A). Adults and larvae are carnivorous and have chewing mouthparts. The large head with large compound eyes sits on a flexible neck. The abdomen is long, slender, flexible, and has terminal copulatory clasping organs in both sexes. The wings are equal or subequal, narrow, and net-veined, and cannot be folded over the body at rest.

ORTHOPTERA (**grasshoppers, locusts, katydids, crickets**). Adults and larvae have chewing mouthparts. The hind legs are enlarged for jumping in most species, and the forewings are toughened as leathery or papery **tegmina** and cover the folded hind wings. The group includes important plant-eating pests. Males produce sounds.

The next three groups are linked by obscure anatomical features and molecular evidence, as the Dictyoptera. All retain chewing mouthparts.

ISOPTERA. Termites are **eusocial, polymorphic** insects; only certain individuals reproduce. Nonreproductive forms include workers and soldiers. The forewings and hind wings, when present, are of equal size and held horizontally over the body. Some soldiers have bizarre large mandibles or snout.

BLATTODEA. Roaches (Figure 21-16B) are dorsoventrally flattened. The first section of the thorax (prothorax) is enlarged and shieldlike and may cover the head. The forewings are **tegmina** and cover the membranous hind wings, which fold like fans beneath.

MANTODEA. Mantids (Figure 21-16C) are predatory, with males generally smaller than females. The head is small, mobile, and triangular, with large widely separated eyes. The prothorax is narrow and elongated, the forewings form leathery tegmina, the forelimbs are spined and raptorial, and the middle and hind legs are elongated for walking.

PHTHIRAPTERA (*"fthih-RAP-teh-rah"*) (Figure 21-17A). **Lice** are wingless ectoparasites on birds and mammals that may exhibit great host specificity. They have chewing or sucking mouthparts.

HEMIPTERA (true bugs—aphids, cicadas, leafhoppers, water striders, and allies) (Figure 21-17B). The mandibles and maxillae are modified as a piercing **stylet** with separate canals for sucking and injecting saliva, inside a beaklike labium. The bases of the forewings are often thickened. True bugs include many important plant pests.

The remaining groups all exhibit holometabolous development.

COLEOPTERA (beetles, fireflies, weevils) (Figure 21-17C). The rear wings fold under hardened forewings called **elytra**. Most have chewing mouthparts and may be herbivorous or carnivorous. There are more species of beetles (>350,000) than any other single group of animals.

LEPIDOPTERA. Butterflies and moths have membranous wings covered with **scales**. Larvae have chewing mouthparts, while the maxillae form a coiled sucking tube in adults.

DIPTERA (flies, gnats, mosquitoes, midges) (Figure 21-18A, B). The hind wings are reduced as organs of equilibrium called **halteres**. The larvae (maggots) lack true legs. Mouthparts for piercing and sucking often have fleshy pads for sponging and lapping. Dipterans include important vectors of diseases including sleeping sickness, malaria, yellow fever, encephalitis, and filariasis. There are over 250,000 species.

SIPHONAPTERA (Figure 21-18C). **Fleas** are laterally compressed, wingless ectoparasites with a piercing stylet. Mandibles and compound eyes are absent. The hind legs are enlarged for jumping. This group also includes important disease vectors, e.g., plague.

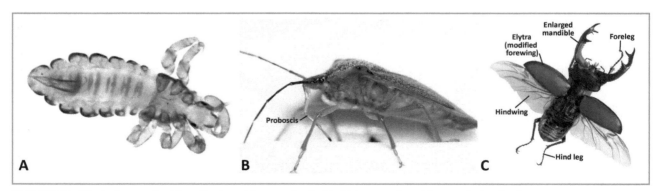

FIGURE 21-17 Arthropoda, Mandibulata, Hexapoda. A. Phthiraptera: head louse, *Pediculus humanus capitis*. Preserved microscope slide. B. Hemiptera: Hawthorn shield bug, *Acanthosoma haemorrhoidale*. C. Coleoptera: stag beetle, *Lucanus swinhoei*.

Left image: Courtesy of Charles G. Messing, 2011. Middle image: Image © Andre Mueller, 2011. Image used under license of Shutterstock, Inc. Right image: Image © alslutsky, 2011. Image used under license of Shutterstock, Inc.

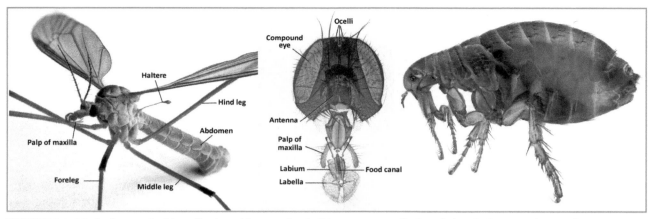

FIGURE 21-18 Arthropoda, Mandibulata, Hexapoda. A. Diptera: crane fly, Tipulidae. B. Diptera: house fly, *Musca domestica*, close-up of head showing mouthparts. Preserved microscope slide. C. Siphonaptera: flea, *Pulex irritans*.

Left Image: Image © Mark Rosteck, 2011. Image used under license of Shutterstock, Inc. Middle Image: Image © Jubal Harshaw, 2011. Image used under license of Shutterstock, Inc. Right Image: Image © Cosmin Manci, 2011. Image used under license of Shutterstock, Inc.

HYMENOPTERA (wasps, bees, ants) (Figure 21-15). The wings, when present, have distinctly fewer veins than most other insects; the hind wings are smaller and have a row of hooks along the front edge that engage the forewing. Males are haploid. The maxillae and labium are fused as a flexible lapping "tongue." The ovipositor is sometimes modified as a stinger. The group includes both social and solitary species. Social species may look all the same (wasps) or include polymorphic castes (workers, drones, queen).

■ Examine the representatives of the different insect groups on display.

• Your instructor will pin examples of different insect groups to corks for examination under the dissecting stereomicroscope. Compare and contrast the structure and modifications of limbs, wings, mouthparts, and other structures, e.g., compound eyes, ocelli. As examples, compare and contrast wing veins in a dragonfly vs. a wasp; halteres in flies; wing scales in moths and butterflies; mouthparts in a hemipteran, bee, moth, ant, and grasshopper or mantid..

Questions

1. Are the gills of crayfishes, lobsters and crabs inside or outside of the animal's body? Explain your answer.

2. Describe the foot in a chiton, land snail, clam and squid, and discuss how their different forms represent adaptations for different modes of locomotion and, when appropriate, food capture.

3. You observed rotifers under high magnification (x400) using the compound microscope. If no one told you that rotifers were multicelled animals, what features of these animals might lead you to conclude that they are indeed multicellular (despite that they may be the same size as single-celled *Paramecium*)?

4. Species of roundworms and tapeworms (chapter 20) of similar sizes may live in the human intestine. Explain how their means of feeding and nutrition differ.

References

Behringer, M. 1967. Use of the Vinegar Eel in the Laboratory. The American Biology Teacher 29(7): 515-522.

Regier, J. C., Shultz, J. W., Zwick, A., Hussey, A., Ball, B., Wetzer, R., Martin, J. W., and Cunningham, C. W. 2010. Arthropod relationships revealed by phylogenomic analysis of nuclear protein-coding sequences. *Nature* 463:1079–83.

Ruppert, E. E., Fox, R. S., Barnes, R. D. 2003. *Invertebrate zoology: a functional evolutionary approach.* 7th ed. Belmont, CA: Brooks Cole Thomson (963 pp.).

Materials and Supplies

Living Cultures

Rotifers

Daphnia

Turbatrix (or *Anguillula*) *aceti*

Live Specimens

Small spiders as locally available (e.g., orchard spider, jumping spider, *Gasteracantha*)

Insects as locally available

Prepared Microscope Slides

Snail radula

Clam vertical section

Plumatella or similar bryozoans, whole mount

Ascaris male and female cross sections

Demodex follicle mite whole mount

Mite and tick whole mount

Copepod whole mount

Cladocera (*Daphnia*) whole mount

Flea whole mount

Body, head, or crab louse whole mount

Dried Specimens

Various gastropod shells, e.g., *Strombus, Cypraea, Busycotypus, Littorina, Nerita, Natica, Oliva, Conus, Melongena, Cerithium, Turbo, Terebra, Haliotis, Acmaea*

Various bivalve shells, e.g., *Venus, Spisula, Mercenaria, Tridacna, Pecten, Atrina, Tellina, Codakia, Dinocardium, Ostrea, Pinctada, Spondylus*

Cuttlebone (*Sepia*)

Half *Nautilus* shell

Trilobite fossil

Variety of pinned insects, including representatives of Odonata, Orthoptera, Blattodea, Mantodea, Hemiptera, Coleoptera, Diptera, Lepidoptera, Hymenoptera. The faculty instructor should remove at least one example of each of the different groups listed above from the storage boxes, pin them to corks, and place them on the side bench with dissecting microscopes for examination by students.

Whole Preserved Specimens

Polyplacophora (chitons), e.g., *Chiton, Katharina, Acanthopleura* (ethanol)

Land snails (ethanol)

Mya (steamer clam) (ethanol)

Nautilus with shell (ethanol)

Squid (probably *Loligo*) for dissection (Carosafe)

Octopus (ethanol)

Marine nematodes (ethanol)

Ascaris roundworms male and female for dissection (Carosafe)

Limulus (horseshoe crab) (ethanol)

Scorpion (ethanol)

Variety of spiders, including orb weaver (*Nephila* or *Argiope*), tarantula, jumping spider, wolf spider (ethanol)

Whip scorpion (ethanol)

Harvestman (ethanol)

Shrimps (ethanol)

Variety of crabs, including e.g., hermit crab, Portunidae, Grapsidae, Ocypodidae, Xanthidae, Majidae (ethanol)

Crayfish (*Cambarus*) for dissection (ethanol)

Millipede (ethanol)

Centipede (ethanol)

Termites (ethanol)

Supplies

Ethanol

Equipment

Dissecting stereomicroscopes

Compound microscopes

Fine forceps

Probes

Dissecting trays

Scalpels

Scissors

Dissecting pins

Glass microscope slides

Glass microscope depression slides

Watch glasses or small petri dishes

Glass coverslips

Disposable droppers

Large, medium, and small glass bowls for specimen display

Small corks for individual pinned insects

Small transparent lidded boxes for capturing and displaying small live spiders and insects

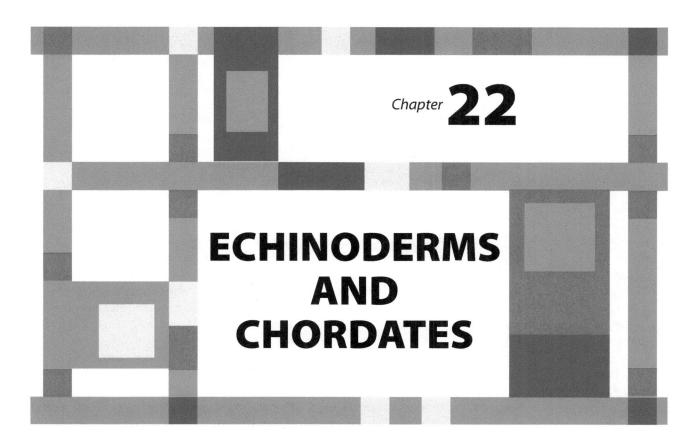

Introduction

The previous two laboratory exercises introduced the animal kingdom and one of its two main branches, the protostomes. This exercise introduces its other major evolutionary lineage, the deuterostomes, to which we belong.

Deuterostomia

Unlike the situation in protostomes, early embryonic development in deuterostomes is characterized chiefly by radial, indeterminate cleavage, in which the planes of the mitotic divisions lie at right angles to the vertical axis of the embryo and the eventual fates of cells are determined later. Separate the cells of a sea urchin embryo at the four-cell stage, and each one will develop into a complete (although smaller) larva. Deuterostome means "second mouth" because the first opening that develops in the larva during gastrulation is the anus; the mouth appears later. In addition, the mesoderm initially develops as two pouches that pinch off from the embryonic gut to form the beginning of the coelom, which is called an **enterocoel** ("gut space"). Deuterostome mesoderm is often called **endomesoderm** because of its derivation from the endoderm.

TABLE 22-1	*Classification summary of groups discussed in this chapter.*

BILATERIA (continued from chap. 21)
  Deuterostomia
    ECHINODERMATA
      Crinoidea (sea lilies, feather stars)
      Asteroidea (sea stars)
      Ophiuroidea (brittle stars)
      Echinoidea (sea urchins, sand dollars)
      Holothuroidea (sea cucumbers)
    CHORDATA
      Cephalochordata (lancelets)
      Urochordata (sea squirts)
      Vertebrata
        MYXINIFORMES (hagfishes)
        PETROMYZONTIFORMES (lampreys)
        GNATHOSTOMATA
          Chondrichthyes (sharks, rays)
          Osteichthyes (bony fishes)

Deuterostomes include only three major traditional phyla. We will examine two of them: the Echinodermata and Chordata.

ECHINODERMATA

Echinoderms, the spiny-skinned animals, are among the most bizarre members of the animal kingdom. Lacking a head or brain, and displaying a unique five-sided radial symmetry, they appear at first sight to be unrelated to any other organisms. Indeed, they also have several other unique features, but their early development places them squarely among the deuterostomes. The bilaterally symmetrical larvae undergo a drastic metamorphosis and reorganization to produce their secondary radial symmetry.

Body form varies widely among echinoderms and includes disk-, egg-, star-, flower-, and worm-shaped forms. Because they lack obvious anterior or posterior ends, we view echinoderms as having oral (mouth-bearing) and aboral (away from the mouth) surfaces. Echinoderms have a calcium carbonate skeleton composed of many pieces called **ossicles**. Unlike arthropods, this is an endoskeleton; its components are produced within cells, and the ossicles are covered in life with tissue. The skeleton ranges from the articulated ossicles of sea stars and sea lilies, through the rigid **test** of sea urchins, to the microscopic **spicules** of sea cucumbers. Other uniquely echinoderm features include **mutable collagenous connective tissue**, which connects many of the skeletal ossicles and can change from stiff to flaccid like muscle (but without requiring energy in the rigid state), and the **water vascular system**, a closed system of ciliated canals. The basic system consists of five **radial canals** that extend outward from a central **ring canal**. Branches from the radial canals end in fleshy, fingerlike or sucker-tipped **podia** (tube feet) that function in locomotion, respiration, and food-gathering. The system usually connects to the exterior via one or more pores or sievelike ossicles (**madreporite**). Because of their radial symmetry, the echinoderm body plan is divided into **radial** structures associated with each radial canal and **interradial** structures between them. Each zone or groove associated with a radial canal and its tube feet is called an **ambulacrum**. Echinoderms lack any cephalization, ganglia, or specialized sense organs. They have a simple reproductive system and do not copulate, although some species brood their young.

Living echinoderms fall into five groups traditionally treated as classes. All are exclusively marine and almost all are bottom-dwelling (**benthic**), and they occur in all seas at all depths.

Crinoidea

The **sea lilies** and **feather stars** are the most ancient and primitive of living echinoderms and include the only living species with a stalk (Figure 22-1A). The **stalk** is a series of articulated ossicles, which arises from the aboral surface and may anchor the animal via a cemented plate, rootlets, or hooklike **cirri**. Most living species, called **feather stars**, shed the stalk as juveniles and attach via cirri. The **crown** consists of a visceral mass with five long **rays** that usually branch one or more times near the base, producing up to 200 arms that have featherlike side branches called **pinnules**. All

Left image: Image © David Clague, 2011. Image used under license of Shutterstock, Inc. Right image: Courtesy of Charles G. Messing, 2011.

FIGURE 22-1 Echinodermata, Crinoidea. A. Sea lily, *Hyocrinus.* B. Feather star, *Stephanometra;* portion of arm showing pinnules and fine, threadlike podia (tube feet).

crinoids are suspension feeders. Their tiny fingerlike podia (Figure 22-1B) transfer planktonic food to a ciliated groove that runs down each pinnule to the arm and then to the central mouth. The anus and mouth are both on the upper oral surface.

- ■ Examine the preserved specimens of crinoids on display.
  - • Distinguish between the stalked sea lily and "unstalked" feather star.
- ■ Place a small section of detached arm under the dissecting stereomicroscope.
  - • Look for and identify the fine fingerlike podia that line the pinnules.

All other living echinoderms appear to have arisen from a single evolutionary lineage, but their interrelationships are still the subject of considerable debate.

Asteroidea

Sea stars (Figure 22-2) have a flattened, flexible pentagonal or stellate disk continuous with 5 or up to 40 arms (also called rays). They range in size from 1 centimeter to 1 meter from arm tip to arm tip. The mouth lies at the center of the oral surface and is surrounded by jawlike ossicles. The skeleton consists of thousands of skeletal pieces, including plates, spines, and struts. The surface may be rough, warty, tuberculate, or spiny and bears both **pedicellariae**, tiny spines modified as defensive pincers, and numerous soft finger- or bubblelike extensions of the body wall called papulae that serve in gas exchange. Sea stars have no distinct gills. The aboral surface of the central disk bears the **madreporite**, which appears as a small flat plate. An **ambulacral groove** with a double row of tube feet runs along the oral surface of each arm. The tube feet of most sea stars terminate in a suction disk, although sand-dwelling species have fingerlike podia. (It's difficult to adhere to sand.) The terminal tube foot on each arm is modified as a **sensory tentacle** and is accompanied by a tiny light-sensitive **eyespot**.

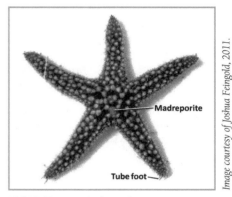

FIGURE 22-2 Echinodermata, Asteroidea: conical-spined sea star, *Echinaster sentus*.

Image courtesy of Joshua Feingold, 2011.

Internally, the sea star water vascular system fits the description given above. Each short canal that leads from the radial canal to a tube foot also gives rise to a bulblike **ampulla**, which acts as a compensation sac. Contractions of muscles on the ampulla force water-vascular fluid into the tube foot, extending it downward. To retract, muscles in the tube foot contract, shortening the tube foot and forcing the fluid back into the ampulla. Contraction of small muscles at the tip of the tube foot pull the terminal disk inward, creating suction and allowing the tube foot to adhere to the substrate. The simple reproductive system consists chiefly of **gonads** that fill much of the hollow arms when mature. Tiny **gonoducts** connect to pores on the aboral surface of the disk. The separate sexes look alike and are best distinguishable by microscopic examination of the gonads.

The mouth is surrounded by a membrane called the **peristome**. A short **esophagus** leads to the **cardiac stomach**, which is separated by a constriction from the **pyloric stomach**. Digestive glands known as **pyloric caeca** ("SEE-kuh"; singular: caecum, "SEE-cum") extend outward and fill much of the aboral volume of the arms, which are hollow. A short intestine leads to the small **anus** on the aboral surface. Sea stars are chiefly predatory, although some are mud swallowers, scavengers, detritus and algae feeders, and suspension feeders. Some extrude the cardiac stomach out of the mouth and engulf their prey, releasing enzymes so that digestion begins outside the body. Sea stars that feed on oysters and mussels actually pull the bivalve's shell apart quite quickly, insert the cardiac stomach, and let the valves close again until the digestive enzymes begin their work and the shell gapes. The crown-of-thorns sea star everts its cardiac stomach to erode tissue from sponges and Cnidaria. Population explosions can devastate coral reefs in the tropical Pacific Ocean.

■ Obtain a preserved sea star, dissecting tray, forceps, scissors, and scalpel. Place the sea star oral side down in the tray.

1. Remove the terminal 1–2 cm of an arm with a scissors. Cut carefully along one side and then the other side of the arm toward the disk; connect the two cuts by cutting across the base of the disk. Remove the aboral body wall to expose the main coelomic cavity.

   • Locate and identify the pair of pyloric caeca, which may fill most of the arm.

2. Cut around the margin of the disk. Before removing it, make a cut toward and then around the madreporite. Lift off the aboral body wall of the disk, noting the connection of the intestine to the anus as you do so.

   • Locate and identify the pyloric stomach and its connection to the radiating pyloric caeca.

   • Look for the delicate **stone canal** that runs orally from the madreporite. It connects to the ring canal that runs around the esophagus.

   • Remove the pyloric stomach and caeca to expose the gonad in the arms. The cardiac stomach may or may not be recognizable in preserved specimens.

   • Remove the gonads. Locate and identify the double row of small bubblelike ampullae that run along the interior of the ambulacral groove. Skeletal ossicles of the groove form a ridge between the two rows of ampullae.

3. Cut another arm off in the middle and make a second cut about 1 cm toward the disk, so you have a short cylindrical section of arm. Place this section in a small dish so you can see the interior, and cover with water. Observe under the dissecting stereomicroscope.

   • Locate and identify the pyloric caeca, gonads, ampulla, tube feet, and skeletal ossicles. Attempt to identify the radial canal beneath the central skeletal ossicle. If your incision is in the right plane, you may see the short canal that connects the base of the tube foot and ampulla to the radial canal. A small radial nerve lies below the radial canal.

Ophiuroidea

Brittle or serpent stars (Figure 22-3) are also star-shaped but have slender arms (or rays) distinct from the central disk. Most have five unbranched arms, although species called basket stars have branched arms. Unlike sea stars, each arm is built around an articulated series of solid ossicles. There is no external open ambulacral groove, no pedicellariae, papulae, or ampullae. The tube feet are small and fingerlike, with no terminal sucker. The digestive system is a blind sac with no anus. Brittle stars may occur in enormous abundance in many marine habitats and include detritus feeders, carnivores on small invertebrates, and suspension-feeders. Basketstars use hooked spines to snare larger zooplankton.

Image courtesy of Charles G. Messing, 2009.

FIGURE 22-3 Echinodermata, Ophiuroidea: spiny deep-sea brittle star, Ophiacanthidae.

■ Examine the specimens of brittle stars on display.

   • Compare and contrast their appearance and structure with sea stars.

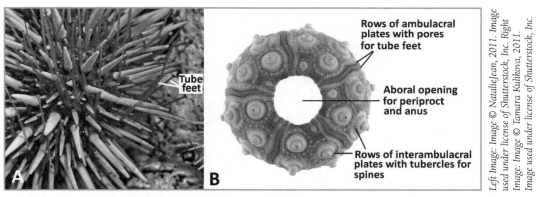

FIGURE 22-4 Echinodermata, Echinoidea. A. Purple sea urchin, *Strongylocentrotus*, showing long tube feet. B. Test of pencil urchin.

Echinoidea

Sea urchins (Figure 22-4) are more-or-less globe-shaped echinoderms in which the ossicles form a typically inflexible **test** of closely fitted plates. Twenty rows of plates encircle the test like lines of longitude. Five pairs of **ambulacral plates** form rows aligned with the internal radial water vascular canals; these plates are pierced with paired pores that connect the canals with the tube feet. Between these rows are five pairs of rows of wider **interambulacral plates**. Spines of different sizes attach to tubercles on the plates and are held in place by rings of muscle and connective tissue. The muscles move the spines, and the connective tissue can lock them in place. Urchins have stalked **pedicellariae**. On the aboral side, five small plates surround the **periproct**, the membrane that surrounds the anus. Each of these five plates has a **genital pore**, and one is modified as a sievelike **madreporite**. On the oral side, the mouth is surrounded by the **peristomial membrane**, which may be bordered by feathery **gills**. Protruding from the mouth is the complex chewing apparatus composed of many ossicles called **Aristotle's lantern**.

Sand dollars and sea biscuits are urchins that have developed a secondary bilateral symmetry. In flattened, disk-shaped sand dollars, the anus has shifted to the oral surface next to the mouth. In egg-shaped sea biscuits, the mouth and anus lie at opposite ends.

- Examine the variety of preserved and dry echinoid specimens on display.

  - Note the variously sized tubercles and the arrangement of the tube foot pores in the clean test. Can you distinguish ambulacral and interambulacral plates?

  - Submerge a preserved sea urchin in a bowl of alcohol under the dissecting stereomicroscope. Look for tiny stalked pedicellariae with jaws at their tips among the larger spines.

  - Locate and identify the genital openings and madreporite.

- Examine a specimen of sand dollar.

  - Locate the mouth and anus. Specialized respiratory tube feet are restricted to five petal-shaped areas on the aboral surface.

Holothuroidea

The **sea cucumbers** (Figure 22-5) are highly modified, chiefly sausage- or worm-shaped, soft-bodied echinoderms. Imagine a sea urchin that has been stretched along its oral-aboral axis, softened, and laid on its side. The skeleton has been reduced to microscopic calcium carbonate **spicules** in the body wall. The tube feet may be arranged in five fields along the body, scattered over the surface, or concentrated on one side as a creeping sole. Some may be modified as warts or papillae. Ten to thirty tube feet around the mouth, the buccal podia,

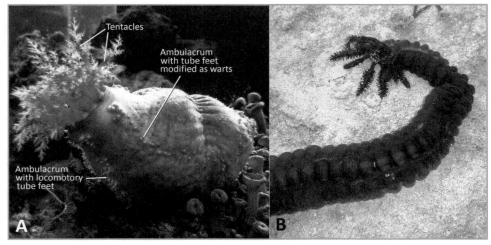

Left Image: Image © Nikita Tiunov, 2011. Image used under license of Shutterstock, Inc. Right Image: Courtesy of Charles G. Messing, 2011.

FIGURE 22-5 Echinodermata, Holothuroidea. A. Suspension-feeding sea cucumber with finely branched tentacles. B. Detritus-feeding sea cucumber with pinnate tentacles.

are modified as feeding tentacles, for consuming sediment, detritus, or for suspension feeding. The tentacles trap food particles on adhesive papillae, stuff the particles into the pharynx and them wipe off. The skeleton and tube feet (except for the tentacles) may be completely absent. Most of the digestive system is a long intestine that loops through the spacious coelom. In most species, the body wall is thick and tough, so gas exchange via diffusion through the skin is not an option. Many species have **respiratory trees**, a highly branched, paired system of internal tubules for gas exchange. For defense, some species burrow; others can eject the respiratory trees and parts of the intestine through mouth or anus, a process called **evisceration**. Some species have **Cuvierian tubules**, which are masses of slender blind tubules ejected at an attacker through the anus that become incredibly sticky.

■ Examine a preserved specimen of sea cucumber.

  • Locate and identify the mouth, anus, rows of tube feet, and feeding tentacles.

CHORDATA

Although the chordates (*"COR-dates"*) include the backboned verte-brates (Figure 22-6), including ourselves, not all are vertebrates. Two of the three main subdivisions lack a backbone and are considered invertebrates. All chordates share the following features, although some are often restricted to early embryonic developmental stages. The **notochord** is a flexible, internal dorsal rod that extends the length of the body and serves as an axis for muscle attachment; it can bend without shortening and permits undulation. The notochord is the first part of the endoskeleton to appear in the embryo but is replaced by the backbone (vertebral column) in vertebrates. A **dorsal tubular nerve cord** (neural tube) first appears as a hollow ecto-dermal groove dorsal to the gut (unlike many invertebrates in which the main nerve is ventral). Its anterior end gives rise to the brain. **Pharyngeal slits** are narrow openings that connect the anterior pharynx to the exterior. Together, these slits and the pharynx form an elaborate filtering basket in primitive chordates. They are modi-

Image courtesy of Charles G. Messing, 2011.

FIGURE 22-6 Chordata, Amphibia: tree frog.

fied as gills in fishes but never develop beyond embryonic grooves in terrestrial vertebrates. All traces disap-pear in adults. A **post-anal tail** functions in propulsion with notochord and muscles in more primitive chordates. It may be reduced or eliminated in adult stages. The **body-wall musculature** is divided into segments, although the body itself is not segmented. All chordates have a **ventral heart** (or at least a ventral contractile blood vessel).

Cephalochordata

Recent research places these slender, laterally compressed, more or less fish-shaped animals, called **lancelets**, at the base of the chordate evolutionary tree. All chordate features are present: notochord, dorsal nerve, gill slits, and tail (Figures 22-7 and 22-8). They reach 5–7 cm long and occur on shallow, sandy coastal sea floors. There are about 25 species worldwide. Lancelets are suspension feeders that lie buried tail-down in the sand with the mouth exposed. The mouth opens ventrally near the anterior end and is surrounded by a fringe of ciliated **oral cirri**. Bands of cilia, together called a "**wheel organ**" inside the oral (buccal) cavity generate a feeding/respiratory current. The flow passes through the large basketlike **pharynx** where mucus traps suspended particles. Water passes

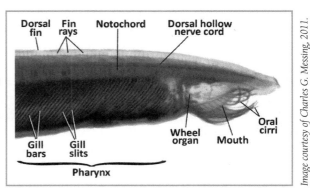

FIGURE 22-7 Chordata, Cephalochordata: lancelet, *Branchiostoma;* anterior end. Preserved and stained microscope slide, whole mount.

Image courtesy of Charles G. Messing, 2011.

out through the **gill slits** (also called pharyngeal slits) into an outer chamber (**atrium**) and exits to the exterior through the ventral **atriopore**, which lies in front of the anus. The gill slits are supported and separated by gill bars. Although the pharynx and its slits resemble gills and are homologous with them, most gas exchange appears to take place through the body surface. A pair of **gonads** lies ventrally and to the sides of the posterior pharynx and intestine.

Several characteristics foreshadow structures of more advanced vertebrate chordates. Branches of the digestive tract anticipate the liver and pancreas. The segmented trunk musculature permits undulatory swimming and is composed of V-shaped **myomeres** similar to the body-wall muscles visible in any fish filet. The posterior end is expanded as a small **caudal fin** that may extend anteriorly as **dorsal** and **ventral fins**. There are no paired fins. The circulatory system is complex and exhibits a flow pattern similar to that of primitive fishes. Unlike protostome invertebrates, the primary pumping structure is a **ventral aorta**. Fossils resembling cephalochordates are known from the Cambrian Period (Burgess Shale).

- ▬ Examine both an entire preserved specimen and a prepared and stained microscope slide of the lancelet **amphioxus** (*Branchiostoma*).

  - • Locate and identify the mouth, oral cirri, pharynx, pharyngeal slits, myomeres, atriopore, anus, and fins.

- ▬ Examine a prepared microscope slide of a cross section through a lancelet.

  - • Locate and identify the following features. The large circular or oval notochord is more or less in the middle, with the dorsal nerve cord above it. Both are surrounded by pink myomeres. In an anterior section, the pharynx appears as an oval

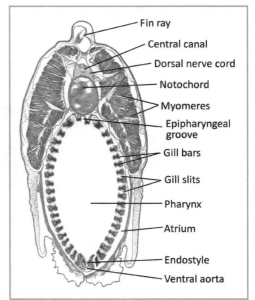

FIGURE 22-8 Chordata, Cephalochordata: lancelet, *Branchiostoma;* anterior cross section. Preserved and stained microscope slide.

Image © Jubal Harshaw, 2011. Used under license from Shutterstock, Inc.

series of short pieces (like two dotted lines), each representing a supportive gill bar that separates the pharyngeal slits between them. The atrium is the space surrounding the pharynx. In a posterior cross section, the intestine lies below the notochord. A pair of large ventral gonads may be present.

Urochordata

The urochordates are chordates highly modified for either sessile or planktonic lifestyles. **Sea squirts** (also called **tunicates** or **ascidians**) (Figure 22-9) are sessile as adults, range from microscopic to potato-sized, and may be solitary or colonial. Each individual (or colony member) is surrounded by a complex living **tunic** that contains cellulose, muscles, and circulatory vessels. Two openings, the siphons, lie opposite the attached base of the animal. The **inhalant siphon** opens into the large basketlike **pharynx**, which may constitute most of the tunicate's body. The **exhalant siphon** (or atrial siphon) opens into the **atrium**, the chamber that surrounds the pharynx. Cilia on the inside of the pharynx generate the feeding and respiratory current, drawing small food particles into the pharynx. Cilia also carry a mucus sheet across the basket that traps incoming food. Other cilia wrap the mucus sheet and trapped food into a string that is carried farther down the digestive tract to the stomach, which lies beneath the pharynx. The water passes through slits in the pharynx into the surrounding atrium and out through the exhalant siphon. Both the anus and reproductive ducts open into the atrium so that feces and gametes are carried out with the flow.

Tunicates are hermaphroditic and have a simple open circulatory system in which blood flows first in one direction and then in the other. In addition to bottom-dwelling sea squirts, urochordates also include gelatinous barrel-shaped planktonic **salps**, tube-shaped planktonic colonial **pyrosomes** ("fire-bodies" from their brilliant bioluminescence) and tadpolelike planktonic **larvaceans** that retain the larval form as adults and build temporary mucous "houses" that trap planktonic food.

Although the sea squirt **tadpole larva** (named for its shape) (Figure 22-10) has all the chordate features, i.e., notochord, dorsal nerve, segmented muscles, and tail, adults only retain the pharynx and slits.

■ Examine a preserved specimen of sea squirt that has been opened up.

  • Locate and identify the inhalant and exhalant siphons, the basketlike pharynx, and the surrounding atrium.

■ Examine a preserved microscope slide of a tunicate tadpole larva.

  • Locate and identify the pharynx, post-anal tail, notochord, and nerve cord.

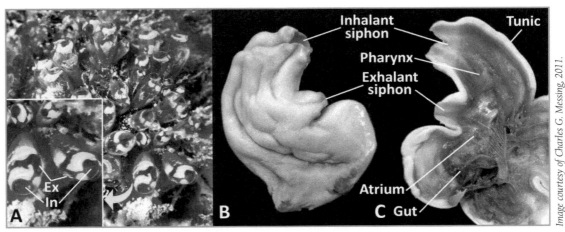

FIGURE 22-9 Chordata, Urochordata. A. Colonial tunicate, *Clavelina;* insert shows two colony members (zooids) enlarged indicating inhalant (In) and exhalant (Ex) siphons. B–C. Solitary tunicate, *Polycarpa aurata.* B. Entire preserved specimen. C. Dissected specimen showing internal anatomy.

Vertebrata

Vertebrates are the most complex and diverse of chordates. The basic chordate features, e.g., notochord, pharynx, dorsal nerve, and tail, appear at least in larvae or embryos. Additional traits specific to vertebrates include a **neural crest**, two bands of cells that arise in the early embryo on either side of the dorsal nerve and give rise to parts of the skull; much more advanced **cephalization** than in nonvertebrate chordates, including a brain and anterior concentration of sensory organ; and a two-layered integument that consists of an outer **epidermis** and inner **dermis**. Vertebrates have an **endoskeleton** of cartilage or bone, or both. Unlike the arthropod exoskeleton, this is a living tissue that exhibits continuous growth; molting is

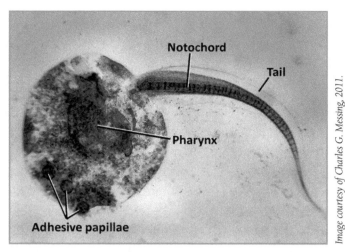

FIGURE 22-10 Chordata, Urochordata: ascidian tadpole larva. Preserved and stained microscope slide.

Image courtesy of Charles G. Messing, 2011.

not required. Most species replace the notochord with a **backbone**, or vertebral column, a series of vertebrae that surround the dorsal spinal cord. The skeleton is divisible into an **axial skeleton**, consisting of the cranium, vertebral column and ribs, and an **appendicular skeleton** composed of the paired limbs and limb girdles, which attach the limbs to the axial skeleton. The segmental myomeres have been modified into a complex system of muscles attached to the skeleton. The ventral heart has two to four chambers and serves a closed circulatory system. Other features include a pair of excretory kidneys and endocrine system. The body is usually divided into a head, trunk, and tail.

Fishes constitute the majority of vertebrate species, but do not represent a formal taxonomic group. They are basically those vertebrates that primitively lack walking limbs. As a group, then, they are **paraphyletic**: fishes include the common vertebrate ancestor but not all of its descendants; we traditionally treat the tetrapods (four-legged vertebrates) separately. "Fish" has as much taxonomic standing as "invertebrate."

Fishes owe their success to their marvelous adaptations to life in a dense medium: hydrodynamic streamlining, swimming ability, buoyancy maintenance, excellent visual and olfactory senses, and a **lateral line system**, a system of canals along the sides of the body and on the head for sensing vibrations. Within these canals, **neuromast** cells sense changes in water pressure. Fishes also have well-developed osmoregulatory capability for surviving in both freshwater and marine habitats, and they have evolved complex behaviors, many associated with reproduction.

The earliest fishlike invertebrates lacked jaws. Two groups still survive and are informally referred to as **Agnatha** ("without jaws"). They also lack bony skeletons, scales, and paired fins. Both have porelike gill openings and eel-like bodies.

MYXINIFORMES *("Mix-EYE-nih-FOR-meez")*

The **hagfishes** are marine scavengers that feed on dead and dying fishes and marine mammals. Their posteriorly displaced gill pores permit breathing while they burrow into prey, rasping away at the flesh with numerous teeth. The head bears several pairs of sensory feelers. They occur chiefly in cold and deep water and are the only vertebrates isotonic to seawater like invertebrates. Hagfishes produce enormous amounts of mucus, which dissuades other fish from feeding on their prey.

- Examine a preserved specimen of hagfish.

  - Locate and identify the posteriorly displaced gill pores.

PETROMYZONTIFORMES
("PEH-tro-my-ZON-tih-FOR-meez")

Lampreys (Figure 22-11) occur in both marine and fresh-waters and include important parasites that attach to other fish via a suckerlike mouth. Numerous horny teeth rasp flesh and suck out blood. Lampreys invaded the Great Lakes between 1913 and 1918 via the Welland Canal, which was deepened around Niagara Falls to promote shipping. By the 1950s, the multi-million-dollar lake trout industry was destroyed. Some of those stocks are now finally recovering.

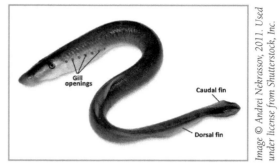

- Examine a preserved specimen of lamprey. The specimen has been cut most of the way through in front of the caudal fin.

  - Note in particular the circular oral disk covered with rows of conical spinelike teeth and the row of porelike gill openings.

  - In the cross section, locate and identify the notochord. Lampreys are among the few vertebrates in which the notochord persists in the adult.

FIGURE 22-11 Chordata, Vertebrata, Petromyzontiformes: Lamprey, *Petromyzon marinus.*

GNATHOSTOMATA ("NAH-tho-sto-MA-tuh")

All remaining vertebrates constitute a monophyletic group characterized by the possession of jaws. Jaws derive from anterior **gill arches,** the struts that support the gills. As with most evolutionary novelties, this important "new" trait is a modification of an existing character. Jaws dramatically expanded ecological opportunities for vertebrates, offering opportunities to exploit carnivory and efficient herbivory, and permitting increases in size by allowing more efficient and diversified feeding. Jaws are in many ways responsible for the great diversity and success of vertebrates. Jawed fishes also include the first vertebrates with paired fins and their associated supporting girdles that attach them to the axial skeleton. The standard complement of fins now includes the posterior **caudal fin,** the main source of propulsive swimming power; unpaired **dorsal fin** and ventral **anal fin** for stabilization, and paired anterior **pectoral fins** and posterior **pelvic fins** for sculling, braking, and maneuvering (Figure 22-12).

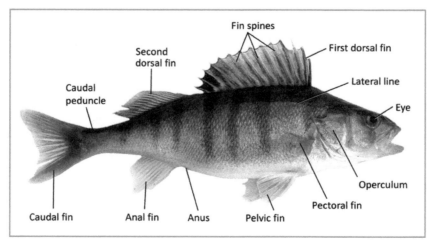

FIGURE 22-12 Vertebrata, Gnathostomata, Osteichthyes: perch, *Perca.* Side view showing basic external structure.

Chondrichthyes (*"kon-DRICK-theez"*)

The **sharks**, **skates**, **rays**, and **chimeras** are the cartilaginous fishes (Figure 22-13). True bone is absent, although the **cartilage skeleton** may include calcareous deposits. Interestingly, they evolved from ancestors that had a bony skeleton and lost it. The mouth is ventral and equipped with powerful jaws and replaceable teeth. The skin is covered with tiny toothlike **placoid** scales, each with its own enamel, dentin, and pulp cavity. Cartilaginous fishes are generally well streamlined but lack a swim bladder and are heavier than water; they must swim to remain in the water column or they sink to the bottom, although a few have an enlarged oily liver that contributes to buoyancy.

Image © JRich Carey, 2011. Used under license from Shutterstock, Inc.

FIGURE 22-13 Vertebrata, Gnathostomata, Chondrichthyes: Grey Reef Shark, *Carcharhinus amblyrhynchos.*

The heart has two chambers, and the olfactory lobe is the largest part of the brain, reflecting their highly developed sense of smell. Electrosensitive **organs of Lorenzini** in the head detect bioelectric fields.

Reproduction is via internal fertilization. The male inserts elongated **claspers** on the pelvic fins into the female **cloaca**. Offspring develop in three different ways in different species. In **oviparity**, eggs are released and hatch outside the mother's body. In **ovoviviparity**, fertilized eggs are nourished by yolk and hatch inside the oviduct. In **viviparity**, embryos are nourished in the uterus via a placenta and are born alive.

Two groups of cartilaginous fishes survive in modern seas. The **Holocephali** (**chimaeras**, or **rabbitfishes**) are bizarre, chiefly deep-water species in which the gill opening is covered by an **operculum** and the notochord persists in the adult. There are no scales except for toothlike placoid scales on a knob atop the head of males that may be involved in courtship. The teeth are fused into a beaklike row for crushing hard-shelled prey. The **Elasmobranchii** includes the sharks, skates, and rays. The skin is covered with placoid scales, and there are five to seven exposed separate gill slits as well as an additional porelike opening called the spiracle. In sharks, the fins are nonmovable; the dorsal fin provides stability, while the paired pectorals, pelvics, and asymmetrical tail provide lift. Some sharks can rest on the seafloor and pump water over their gills, while most must swim to breathe. **Skates**, **rays**, and **sawfishes** are flattened with large pectoral fins. The gills are located ventrally and the respiratory current is drawn in via the spiracle on top of the head. Many skates and rays have broad grinding molars for a hard-shelled diet (mollusks, crustaceans).

- ▪ Examine a preserved specimen of chimaera.

  - • Locate and identify the following structures: caudal, dorsal, pelvic and pectoral fins (which ones are paired?), and gill operculum. Identify the sex of the specimen. Are claspers or the toothy head knob present? Examine the teeth.

- ▪ Examine a preserved specimen of shark.

  - • Locate and identify the different fins, gill slits (how many?), and spiracle. What sex is the specimen? How do you know?

  - • Rub your finger gently along the side or back of the specimen. Describe the different sensations. To what do you attribute the difference? Observe the skin under the dissecting stereomicroscope; describe and illustrate what you see.

- ▪ Examine a preserved specimen of skate or ray.

  - • Locate and identify the gill slits and spiracle. How do the fins differ from those of the shark? Are they all present?

Osteichthyes ("os-tee-ICK-theez")

The **bony fishes** (Figures 22-12, 22-14) live in virtually every aquatic habitat and display wide variations in body form, food-obtaining apparatus, and diet. They are the most species-rich vertebrate group (>20,000 species). The bones contain calcium phosphate. Primitive forms, such as sturgeons and gars, have bony, armorlike **ganoid** scales. Most moderns species have reduced, thin scales that arise from skin pockets and produce concentric growth rings. A pouch that arises from the esophagus forms the swim bladder, which may be modified as a lung. The swim bladder retains its connection to the esophagus in more primitive forms and becomes isolated in more derived species. Gas volume is adjusted via gulping air or exchanging gas with the blood. The gills are supported on bony **gill arches** and covered by an **operculum**. Muscular expansion of the gill chamber permits breathing while not moving.

Bony fishes have the same complement of fins as sharks, but they are constructed differently. Fins are supported by radiating flexible **fin rays** of cartilage or bone. Some may be modified as more rigid **fin spines** (Figures 22-12, 22-14B). Although fins are used in propulsion as well as stabilization, the chief propulsive force derives from trunk and tail muscles. The segmental muscles are more complex than those of lancelets and are composed of W-shaped, zigzag bands called **myotomes**.

Fin structure, distribution, and swimming movements vary widely depending upon lifestyles and taxonomic group. The undulatory movement of eels is efficient only at low speeds (Figure 22-14A). Rapidly swimming fishes such as tunas and mackerels channel the energy of their body muscles into powerful tail sweeps. Much of the body remains relatively rigid. Slower, maneuverable reef fishes, such as butterflyfishes, wrasses, and parrotfishes row with their pectoral fins. Rigid-bodied species such as sea horses (Figure 22-14C), trunkfishes, and porcupinefishes scull with their dorsal and anal fins. High-speed swimmers have a streamlined fusiform body, narrow fins, a symmetrical lunate (crescent moon) tail, and often small dorsal and ventral finlets in front of the tail that reduce turbulence (Figure 22-14D). Slow moving ambush predators such as groupers have broad tails for short quick attacks. Lionfishes (Figure 22-14B) and bottom-dwelling predators such as toadfishes lunge for-

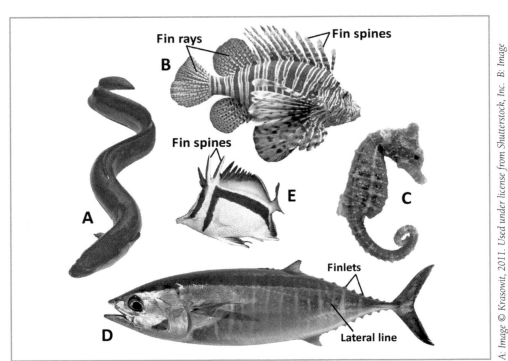

A: Image © Krasowit, 2011. Used under license from Shutterstock, Inc. B: Image © cynoclub, 2011. Used under license from Shutterstock, Inc. C: Image courtesy of Charles G. Messing, 2011. D: Image © holbox, 2011. Used under license from Shutterstock, Inc. E. Image courtesy Joshua Feingold, 2012.

FIGURE 22-14 Chordata, Vertebrata, Osteichthyes. A. Eel, *Anguilla*. B. Red lionfish, *Pterois volitans*. C. Sea horse, *Hippocampus zosterae* (preserved). D. Bluefin tuna, *Thunnus thynnus*. E. Southern scythe butterflyfish, *Prognathodes carlhubbsi*.

ward (the latter using its large pectoral fins) and engulf their food by rapidly expanding their enormous gill chamber. Pelvic fins have moved anteriorly and essentially function as legs in many bottom dwellers, e.g., batfishes and toadfishes, or even as feelers for sensing prey buried in the sediment. Flatfishes begin life as normal fish larvae; but during the course of their development, one eye migrates to the other side of the body, so these fishes lie on the seafloor on one side, often burying themselves in the sediment.

Teeth range from the sharp fangs of barracudas to the crushing molars of boxfishes. **Gill rakers** are structures that project forward from the V-shaped gill arches and also may reflect the fish's diet. Predators may have coarse, toothlike gill rakers, while herrings, sardines, and anchovies have a fine comblike row of gill rakers on each arch, with which they filter plankton from the water.

The sexes are usually separate, although some **sequential hermaphroditism** exists. In some cases, males become females (clownfishes), while in others, females turn into males (parrotfishes). Most species are **oviparous** with external fertilization.

Two major groups of bony fishes arose in freshwater during the Devonian period. The **ray-finned fishes** (**Actinopterygii**, *"ak-tih-nop-teh-REE-gee-eye"*) have fins supported by flexible rays. Small, armored ancestral forms had both gills and a lung. The sturgeons and paddlefish are the most primitive modern forms. The **lobe-finned fishes** (**Sarcopterygii**, *"sar-cop-teh-REE-gee-eye"*) have fins supported by a central bony axis with numerous muscles, and the esophageal pouch developed as lung. This group includes three surviving groups. The **coelacanth** is the survivor of a Mesozoic lineage that has both gills and lungs. **Lungfishes** can actually drown; they survive in stagnant water by gulping air into their lung. They have a separate pulmonary circulation and teeth with an enamel covering. The last group of lobe-finned fishes is the **tetrapods**, which are basically sarcopterygians with pectoral and pelvic fins modified as walking limbs. This group includes the amphibians through mammals and will be treated in the next laboratory exercise.

■ Examine the various preserved fishes on display.

  • Compare and contrast their body forms, fin structures and distributions, teeth, and mouths. Attempt to identify diet and life habits from these structures. Match the following fishes with their likeliest diet or lifestyle. You can use a diet or lifestyle more than once.

Barracuda _____	A. Camouflaged bottom ambusher
Tuna or mackerel____	B. Slow-swimming plankton picker
Flatfish____	C. High-speed long-distance swimmer
Batfish____	D. Mid-water ambusher
Seahorse____	E. Slow swimming; feeds on hard-shelled prey
Butterflyfish____	F. Plankton filterer
Porcupinefish____	G. Maneuverable reef-dweller; feeds on small prey
Toadfish____	
Trunkfish____	
Sardine or herring____	

■ Examine the different types of fish scales on display.

  • Distinguish among bony ganoid scales and thin dermal scales. Dermal scales may be **cycloid**—with a smooth outer rim—or **ctenoid**—with a toothy outer rim. Cycloid scales are typical of fishes with soft fin rays, such as trout and goldfish, while ctenoid scales are common on fishes with spiny fin rays, such as groupers and perch.

■ Obtain a preserved perch, dissecting tray, forceps, blunt probe, scissors, and scalpel. **CAUTION: This fish has sharp fin spines that can puncture your skin. Handle carefully.** Wash the specimen with tap water to remove excess preservative. Pat damp dry with a paper towel and place the fish in the tray.

1. Examine the external anatomy of the perch.

   • Locate the main body regions. The **head** extends from the tip of the snout to the rear of the operculum. The **trunk** extends posteriorly to the ventral anus. The rest of the body represents the **tail**. Is there a neck?

   • Locate the dorsal, anal, pectoral, pelvic, anal and caudal fins. Distinguish between the bony, sharp, fin spines and the softer segmented fin rays. Which fins have which? Where are the spines located on those fins that have them?

   • Locate the lateral line that begins above and behind the operculum and runs down each side of the body to the tail. Place the fish under the dissecting stereomicroscope and observe the pore in the lateral line scales that leads to the vibration-sensing neuromasts.

   • Locate both the external nares and eyes. Like the mammalian nose, the nares lead to chemosensory cells, but they are simple blind sacs. Are eyelids present?

2. Examine the mouth and gill structure of the perch.

   • Pry open the mouth and look inside from the front end. Are there teeth on both upper and lower jaws? In the rear of the mouth cavity, observe the arrangement and orientation of the gill arches. Find the **branchiostegal membrane**, which runs along the ventral and posterior edges of the operculum and controls the flow of water out of the gill chamber.

   • With the fish lying on its left side, remove the right operculum by cutting with a scissors from the anterior ventral corner to the upper posterior corner. Observe the V-shaped gill arches. Cut the uppermost gill arch free at the tips of the "V." Place the arch in a small shallow dish with enough water to cover the arch. Examine under the dissecting stereomicroscope. Observe the feathery gills along the outer posterior margin, and the toothlike gill rakers along the inner margin of the arch. How are these similar or different from those of a plankton-feeding fish such as a herring or sardine? Illustrate the differences for your lab notebook.

3. Examine the internal anatomy of the perch.

   • Insert the tip of your scissors just in front of the base of the anus (in front of the anal fin) and make an incision along the ventral midline to just in front of the pectoral fin. **Note: Make your cut shallow to avoid destroying internal organs.** Begin a second incision where the first began, but cut upward and then forward, dorsal to the lateral line, ending behind the operculum. Connect the two incisions at their anterior ends. Gently lift up the body wall, carefully separate it from the tissues beneath, and remove it.

   • First note how the interior of the perch is divided by a sheet of tissue called a **septum**, or false diaphragm, into a large **abdominal cavity** and a much smaller, anterior, **pericardial cavity** ventral to the gills. Thin membranes called **mesenteries** (not homologous with those of annelids or anemones) connect the organs to each other and to the body wall.

   • Find the shiny, tough, sausagelike swim bladder, which runs almost the entire length of the body cavity from behind the gills to above the anus. The long, thin, dark pair of **kidneys** lie dorsal to the swim bladder, just ventral to the backbone. The urinary ducts from each kidney join to form a single duct that leads to the ventral opening just behind the anus. A slender **urinary bladder** arises from this duct next to its end.

   • Insert a blunt probe into the mouth, down the esophagus and into the pouchlike **stomach**. Note that the tubular **intestine** arises near the anterior end of the stomach and loops once or twice before running posteriorly and ventrally to the anus. This allows the stomach to expand greatly when large prey are eaten; perch are predatory. Locate the multiple fingerlike **pyloric caeca** that arise from the anterior end of the intestine adjacent to the stomach; they likely serve in temporary food storage.

- Locate the brownish liver, which lies just anterior and ventral to the stomach, and the spleen, which lies between the stomach pouch and the anterior coils of the intestine.

- Cut the intestine 1 cm anterior to the anus, and cut the esophagus just anterior to the stomach. Gently lift the digestive tract out of the body cavity. (You may also have to slice the mesenteries that hold much of the intestine in place.)

- Much of the posterior volume of the body cavity will most likely be filled with the gonads. In females, a pair of **ovaries** in immature fishes fuse with growth to become single large organ that lies between the swim bladder and the intestine. The ovary tapers posteriorly to form the **oviduct.** When the eggs mature, they are released through a temporary opening between the anus and the urinary pore. In males, a pair of **testes** lies posterior to the stomach. The **vas deferens** (sperm duct) from each testis fuse together to form a single duct that opens via a urogenital pore behind the anus.

- The small heart lies ventrally, anterior to the liver, in the pericardial cavity. It consists of two chambers: a thin-walled **auricle** (or atrium) that lies posterior and slightly dorsal to the muscular **ventricle**. The ventricle pumps blood anteriorly into the ventral aorta, which sends branches to the gills. From the gills, oxygenated blood passes into the dorsal aorta and then to the rest of the body, before returning via veins to the auricle.

- Using a scalpel, carefully shave the top of the skull from the anterior head above the eyes to expose the brain, which will appear as a series of bulbs or lobes. From front to back, they are: the paired **olfactory lobes**, **cerebrum**, large paired **optic lobes**, and **cerebellum**.

Questions

1. Explain why sea lilies (stalked crinoids) were formerly classified as plants.

2. How do tube feet differ among the different classes of echinoderms? How do these different forms reflect different functions?

3. How does segmentation in amphioxus differ from that in an annelid or arthropod?

4. Given that toadfishes and batfishes are not closely related, what feature(s) about them would you describe as convergent?

References

Dolphin, W. D. 2008. *Biological Investigations: Form, Function, Diversity, & Process.* 8th ed. McGraw-Hill College Division (458 pp.)

Hagerman, H. Perch dissection. https://www.msu.edu/course/lbs/158h/manual/Perchdissect.pdf (Accessed 12 July 2010).

Moyle, P. B., and Cech, J. J., Jr. 1996. *Fishes: an introduction to ichthyology.* 3rd ed. Upper Saddle River, NJ: Prentice-Hall (590 pp.).

Ruppert, E. E., Fox, R. S., Barnes, R. D. 2003. *Invertebrate zoology: a functional evolutionary approach.* 7th ed. Belmont, CA: Brooks Cole Thomson (963 pp.).

Materials and Supplies

Prepared Microscope Slides

Branchiostoma (lancelet, or amphioxus) whole mount

Branchiostoma (lancelet, or amphioxus) cross section

Tunicate (Ascidian) tadpole larva whole mount

Dried Specimens

Sand dollar

Ganoid scales

Whole Preserved Specimens

Stalked crinoid, e.g., *Neocrinus* or *Endoxocrinus* (ethanol)

Feather star (ethanol)

Asterias (sea star) for dissection (Carosafe)

Variety of ophiuroids, e.g., *Ophioderma, Ophiocoma, Ophiothrix*

Variety of echinoids, e.g., *Lytechinus, Echinometra, Eucidaris,* sand dollar

Sea cucumber (ethanol)

Branchiostoma (lancelet, or amphioxus) (ethanol)

Sea squirt, e.g., *Molgula, Phallusia, Ascidia* (ethanol)

Myxine (hagfish) (ethanol)

Petromyzon (lamprey) (ethanol)

Chimaera (ethanol)

Shark, e.g., *Carcharhinus, Negaprion, Squalus* (ethanol)

Ray or skate, e.g., *Urobatis, Dasyatis, Raja* (ethanol)

Tuna or mackerel (Scombridae) (ethanol)

Toadfish (Batrachoididae) (ethanol)

Sea horse (Hippocampidae) (ethanol)

Perch for dissection (Carosafe)

Barracuda (Sphyraenidae) (ethanol)

Sardine or herring (Clupeidae) (ethanol)

Butterflyfish (Chaetodontidae) (ethanol)

Porcupinefish (Diodontidae) (ethanol)

Trunkfish (Ostraciidae) (ethanol)

Batfish (Ogcocephalidae) (ethanol)

Flatfish (e.g., Bothidae, Pleuronectidae) (ethanol)

Fish scales (ethanol)

Supplies

Ethanol

Equipment

Dissecting stereomicroscopes

Compound microscopes

Fine forceps

Probes

Dissecting trays

Scalpels

Scissors

Dissecting pins

Glass microscope slides

Glass microscope depression slides

Watch glasses or small petri dishes

Glass coverslips

Disposable droppers

Large, medium, and small glass bowls for specimen display

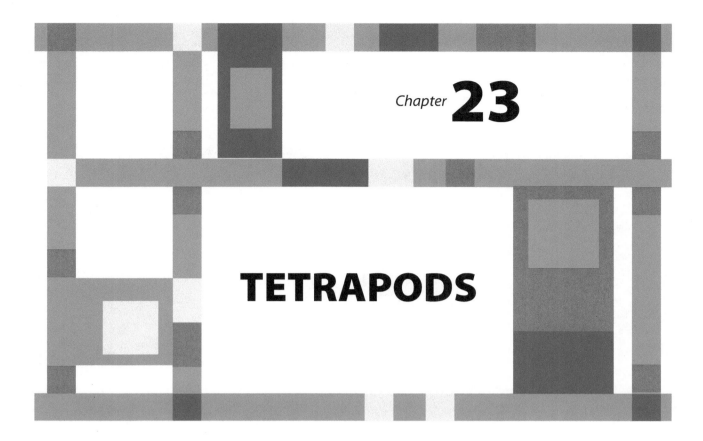

Chapter **23**

TETRAPODS

Introduction

In the previous laboratory exercise, you learned that the fishes constitute a **paraphyletic** group, one that includes a common ancestor but not all of its descendants. The homologous features that distinguish fishes are **plesiomorphies**—characteristics shared by the ancestors of the group, but not necessarily all descendants—i.e., gills, fins, and an aquatic lifestyle. We also distinguish them on the basis of a feature that they lack; they are vertebrates without four legs. By contrast, the **tetrapods**—vertebrates with four limbs—represent a **monophyletic** group that arose from a common ancestor (although some, such as snakes, caecilians, and legless lizards, have since lost their limbs) (Table 23-1).

Today, tetrapods are chiefly land-dwellers that breathe with lungs inherited from their aquatic ancestors, the **sarcopterygian** ("fleshy-finned") **fishes** (lobefins and lungfish). Although amphibians are still semiaquatic, most tetrapods have evolved features that permitted them to inhabit drier environments. Still, many tetrapods with fully terrestrial ancestors have independently returned to aquatic environments (e.g., sea turtles, crocodilians, ichthyosaurs, penguins, whales). In addition, powered flight has evolved independently three times: in birds, pterosaurs, and bats.

Classification and Diversity of Tetrapods

The earliest known tetrapods retained many fishlike attributes such as gills, a tail fin, and lateral line. These animals, such as *Acanthostega*, *Tiktaalik,* and *Ichthyostega*, from the Late Devonian period, were still aquatic. Their limbs were most likely used to crawl on the mud and among the vegetation of shallow ponds and streams.

Tetrapods live in a great diversity of habitats and exhibit a wide variety of feeding behaviors. Although an animal's physical form reflects its adaptation to the environment in which it lives, its specific features for habitat use and feeding develop as modifications of existing structures, not as the abrupt appearance of novel characteristics. Thus, related animals with different food habits or lifestyles possess **homologous** features modified for different functions, while unrelated animals with similar food habits or lifestyles often exhibit **convergent** (or **analogous**) features with different basic structures. You will examine the displays and specimens showing vertebrate divergence in (1) general morphology and (2) skeletal, limb, and tooth morphology.

TABLE 23-1 *Classification summary of groups discussed in this chapter.*

BILATERIA (continued from chap. 22)
 Deuterostomia (continued from chap. 22)
  CHORDATA (CONTINUED FROM CHAP. 22)
   Vertebrata (continued from chap. 22)
    GNATHOSTOMATA (continued from chap. 22)
     Osteichthyes (bony fishes) (continued from chap. 22)
      TETRAPODA
      Amphibia
       URODELA (SALAMANDERS)
       ANURA (FROGS, TOADS)
      Amniota
       SYNAPSIDA
        Mammalia
       REPTILIA
        Diapsida
         LEPIDOSAURIA (lizards, snakes)
         ARCHOSAURIA
          Crocodylia
          Pterosauria (flying reptiles)
          Dinosauria
           Aves (birds)
         CHELONIA (turtles)

Note that, although tetrapods arose as one lineage from among the bony fishes (Osteichthyes), the table repeats the size and font format beginning with Tetrapoda to avoid requiring unreadably small fonts for some of its subgroups. Also, although amniotes arose from one branch of ancient amphibians, they are ranked here with the same status as modern amphibians (see Figure 23-1).

The **cladogram** below (Figure 23-1) shows a simplified version of tetrapod phylogeny. A cladogram is a branching diagram that shows the sequence in which different characters appeared. Lobefin fishes branch off first, as they have not developed any of the characters discussed here. Amphibians branch off next because they only exhibit the first character—four limbs—the defining character of the tetrapods. The cladogram does not show all subgroups. The numbered names along the branches indicate the origin of some groups, e.g., mammals evolved from and are included within the Synapsida, characterized by a single postorbital **fenestra** (opening in the skull behind the eye). Mammals are the only branch of Synapsida shown. On the other hand, Diapsida (with two postorbital fenestrae) includes all branches above it (Lepidosauria, Squamata, Chelonia, Archosauria, Crocodilia, Pterosauria, Dinosauria, and birds).

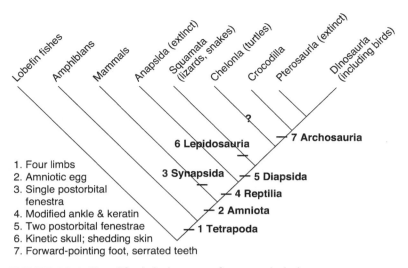

1. Four limbs
2. Amniotic egg
3. Single postorbital fenestra
4. Modified ankle & keratin
5. Two postorbital fenestrae
6. Kinetic skull; shedding skin
7. Forward-pointing foot, serrated teeth

FIGURE 23-1 Simplified cladogram of tetrapod phylogeny.

Amphibia

The earliest at least partly terrestrial tetrapods are known as amphibians. They diversified during the Late Paleozoic Era, particularly during the Carboniferous Period (Figure 23-2). Surviving amphibians retain more primitive features (plesiomorphies) than other tetrapods, including soft, unshelled, chiefly aquatic eggs lacking extra-embryonic membranes; aquatic, usually gilled immature stages; and thin, moist, glandular, naked skin, often modified for cutaneous respiration. Two major groups of amphibians survive: the Urodela (salamanders, newts, and mud puppies) and Anura (frogs and toads). A third, smaller group, the legless wormlike Gymnophiona (caecilians) is not discussed here.

Image courtesy of Charles G. Messing, 2011.

FIGURE 23-2 Amphibia: giant extinct Late Paleozoic *Eryops.*

■ Examine the available amphibian specimens.

• Determine how they most likely respire (e.g., do any still have gills?).

Movement on land presents very different problems from movement through the water. Adaptations to those problems brought about a major revolution in vertebrate locomotion. An animal in the water can push against the medium that surrounds it. Recall from the previous lab that fish swim via axial locomotion: undulatory movements of the trunk and tail. The paired fins of lobefin fishes were elongated, supported by a bony strut, and probably provided substantial grip against the substrate for wriggling through shallow, perhaps vegetation-choked, streams and ponds. Recall the functionally similar though structurally different (convergent/analogous) pelvic or pectoral fins of the bottom-walking batfish and frogfish.

The first tetrapod legs, which were slightly modified lobefin fins, appeared in animals that were still aquatic. They were **preadaptations**: structures developed for one purpose (crawling on a pond bottom) that happened to prove useful for another (crawling on land) when conditions became suitable. But, amphibians also inherited the undulatory movement of the axial skeleton from their aquatic ancestors.

Land provides a firmer substrate to push against, but air offers no support against gravity. Friction is also more of a problem. Dragging your body along the ground risks severe damage by scraping along, especially at higher speed. The transformation of the fins from steering and pushing devices to columns for support and suspension of the body involved extensive changes in the **appendicular skeleton**, the limb bones and associated pectoral and pelvic girdles. Slender fin rays had to give way to more solid supports that could be firmly planted as feet against the ground, and the connections between the appendicular and axial skeletons had to be modified and strengthened. In fishes, the **pelvic girdle** is a pair of ventral bony plates. Limbs pushing up against such a structure on land would force them inwards and compress the posterior internal organs. Development of a rigid connection between the pelvic girdle and the backbone (i.e., a pelvis) allowed the hind limb to support the weight of the posterior part of the body. This transmitted the force of the hind foot against the ground to the backbone without affecting the internal organs. By contrast, the fish **pectoral girdle** is joined firmly to the back of the skull. To absorb the shock generated as the front legs hit the ground, and to avoid transmitting this shock to the skull, the pectoral girdle became detached from the skull and, like the pelvic girdle, became articulated with the axial skeleton as a shoulder blade. This also produced a neck and mobile head. Other changes that increased limb support and strengthened the vertebral column came later as terrestrial tetrapods became more active.

Although we think of amphibians as laying aquatic eggs that hatch into larvae with gills, and then metamorphose into air-breathing adults with lungs, the group exhibits numerous variations. Some lay eggs in moist habitats out of water, and some frogs brood their larvae inside skin pouches, vocal sac, or even stomach. Adult amphibians may respire via lungs, pharynx, or skin. The mud puppy (*Necturus maculosus*) retains gills and remains aquatic as an adult. The Mexican axolotl (*Ambystoma mexicanum*) also retains gills as an adult, but may metamorphose into an air-breather under suitable conditions. Many plethodontid salamanders not only lay eggs on land and lack an aquatic larva; they also lack lungs and breathe through their mouths and skin.

URODELA (OR CAUDATA)

Among living amphibians, **salamanders**, **newts**, and **mud puppies** retain a more primitive structure, with similar hind and forelimbs, and limb girdles attached only weakly to a few vertebrae. Also, like the earliest amphibians, urodeles still exhibit a **sprawling posture** (Figure 23-3), with relatively weak limbs that extend sideways out from the body. The body still undulates, and the limbs chiefly transmit the force of the undulation to the ground. The gait is clumsy, slow, and waddling. It is also inefficient, because much of the muscular effort is exerted merely to keep the body off the ground rather than to propel it forward. The arrangement prohibits any substantial speed or development of great size.

Image © cristi 180884, 2011. Image used under license of Shutterstock, Inc.

FIGURE 23-3 Amphibia, Urodela: spotted salamander (*Ambystoma maculatum*).

■ Examine the mounted skeleton of the mud puppy (*Necturus maculosus*).

- What percentage of vertebrae (between the back of the skull and beginning of the tail) are associated with the attachment of the pelvic girdle and the pectoral (shoulder) girdle?

- Do the vertebrae show any differentiation into distinct sections? Compare your counts and features with those in the vertebral column of a cat or human.

- Is the mud puppy likely to be a fast mover? Why or why not?

ANURA

Frogs and **toads** (Figure 22-6) are highly modified and specialized amphibians that first appeared over a hundred million years after the first tetrapods. As with urodeles, they retain typical amphibian features: moist eggs lacking extra-embryonic membranes; aquatic gilled larvae, and in many cases the ability to breathe through the skin. Unlike other amphibians however, they lack tails as adults, and have shortened backbones and large elongated hind legs suitable for jumping. The term *toad* often refers to anurans with drier, warty skin that tend to live in drier habitats, but toads do not constitute a distinct monophyletic group.

- Examine the variety of frog specimens on display. Measure both body length (tip of snout to hind end) and hind leg length (base of leg to longest toe tip).
  - How do the proportions of body length to hind leg length vary among species?
- Examine the frog skeleton on display.
  - Compare the vertebral column, hind legs, and pelvis with those of the mud puppy. How do they differ?

Amniota

One evolutionary lineage of Late Paleozoic amphibians developed a series of adaptations that permitted a fully terrestrial existence, free from any aquatic phase of the life cycle. Numerous characteristics link these organisms together as a monophyletic group. Perhaps most important are a series of **extra-embryonic membranes** (Figure 23-4): the **amnion** surrounds, cushions, and protects the embryo (hence, the name of the group); the **allantois** stores embryonic wastes and serves in gas exchange, and the **chorion** surrounds the other membranes and serves in gas exchange. Other features include a stronger, more efficient jaw, more powerfully developed limbs for terrestrial locomotion and support, and limbs more firmly attached to pelvic and pectoral girdles. All amniotes have at least two sacral vertebrae attached to the pelvic girdle. Two other characteristics found in early amniotes as well as many living forms include shelled eggs and dry scaly skin that lacks glands. Of course, both of these features have become repeatedly modified. Some more advanced amniotes give birth to live young, while others, notably mammals, have soft, highly glandular skin.

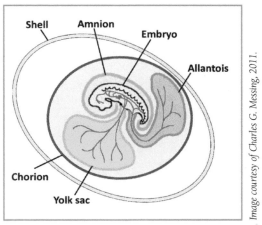

FIGURE 23-4 Amniota. Schematic diagram of amniote embryo.

Image courtesy of Charles G. Messing, 2011.

Some early amniotes (as well as a few more advanced but now extinct amphibians) developed a more efficient **semierect posture**, still seen in living lizards and crocodilians. The limbs are held closer to the body but still not directly underneath. Although more efficient, this gait is still wasteful; it dissipates muscular effort in lifting the body off the ground. The undulating backbone of a walking lizard also alternately compresses and expands each lung.

Later on, two different groups independently developed an **erect posture**, with the limbs fully under the body, supporting its entire weight and eliminating the need for constant muscular effort to raise the body against gravity. Limb movement became an entirely anterior-posterior swing, permitting a longer stride and greater speed. This posture arose among four-legged (quadrupedal) ancestors of mammals called therapsids, and among the two-legged (bipedal) immediate ancestors of dinosaurs. In both cases, these modifications opened up tremendous adaptive possibilities, and the two groups (the dinosaurs in the Mesozoic and the mammals in the Cenozoic) have dominated tetrapod communities for the last 225 million years.

- Compare hind limb orientation in the skeletons of the mud puppy, *Allosaurus*, cat, and human. View the latter three from the front.
  - Which illustrate the sprawling, semierect, and erect postures?

Amniotes quickly diverged into two major evolutionary lineages characterized in part by the number and location of openings in the skull (**fenestrae**, from the Latin for "window") in addition to the orbit (for the eyes) and the nasal openings. These openings, or archways, increased the surface area for muscle attachments, particularly muscles associated with operating the jaws. All of the early amniotes were predators (at least on insects). Stronger jaws and lighter-weight skulls permitted them to become larger and tackle larger prey.

SYNAPSIDA

The early members of this lineage are characterized by a single opening called the **temporal fenestra** (Figure 23-5) behind the orbit. The name synapsid means "with an archway." The earliest synapsids, called **pelycosaurs**, arose during the Late Carboniferous period but went extinct by the end of the Permian period. The most famous of these is the sailback "reptile" *Dimetrodon*, which is often incorrectly treated as a dinosaur, particularly in movies and children's toy sets.

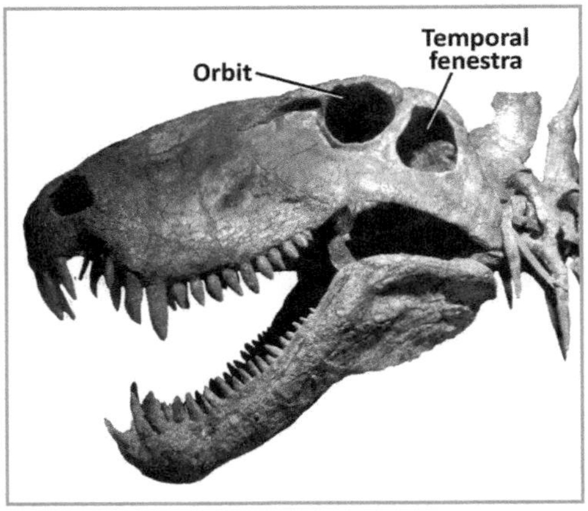

■ Examine the skull of the extinct Permian pelycosaur *Dimetrodon*.

    • Locate the single postorbital fenestra.

One group of pelycosaurs gave rise to a diverse group of Late Paleozoic and early Mesozoic animals called the **Therapsida**. Also called protomammals, or mammal-like reptiles, these animals were the dominant and most diverse group of tetrapods

Image courtesy of Charles G. Messing, 2011.

FIGURE 23-5 Amniota, Synapsida, Pelycosauria: extinct sailback "reptile," *Dimetrodon;* skull.

during the Late Permian and much of the Triassic period. Unlike reptiles, therapsids evolved teeth differentiated into incisors, canines, and molars, which permitted a great diversification of diets, including herbivory as well as carnivory. One lineage of therapsids gradually developed mammalian features, although it is not certain when many of the characteristics we associate with mammals—hair, warm-bloodedness, and a two-layered skin richly supplied with various glands, e.g., mammary, sweat, and scent glands—first evolved. Nerve openings in the snouts of some therapsids might have served whiskers (modified hairs), but similar openings are known in a few non–warm-blooded lizards.

Mammalia

Mammals (Figure 23-6) are distinguished from their therapsid ancestors by having three inner ear bones (incus, malleus, stapes) and the lower jaw, or mandible, composed of a single bone, the **dentary**. Amphibians, reptiles, and therapsids have a single inner ear bone, the stapes, and a lower jaw composed of multiple bones fused together. In one lineage of therapsids, the posterior lower jaw bones gradually became reduced and incorporated into the inner ear. Mammals also lost the temporal fenestra. Instead, the primary jaw-closing muscle, the **masseter**, anchors chiefly to the **zygomatic arch** (cheekbone). Like birds, mammals exhibit a distinctive kind of warm-bloodedness: **homeothermic endothermy** (a feature that arose independently in the two groups), in which a more or less constant elevated temperature (homeothermy) is derived from internal metabolic processes (endothermy). The most primitive mammals still lay eggs (oviparity) like early amniotes. As noted above, it is not

FIGURE 23-6 Amniota, Synapsida, Mammalia: macaques, *Macaca.*

clear just when the nonskeletal features that we associate with mammals—hair, warm-bloodedness, glandular skin—arose.

■ Examine the several mammal skulls on display.

    • Note the narrow curved cheekbones and the space available between the cheekbone and skull for the masseter muscle. Put your fingers on the rear part of your lower jaw and clench your teeth. You will feel your masseter muscle bulge.

Mammals are subdivided as follows. The **Monotremata**, which includes only the **duck-billed platypus** and echidna (spiny anteater), are oviparous (egg-layers) and have a **cloaca**: a single opening for feces, urine, and gametes. The male platypus is also the only poisonous mammal; the poison is delivered through spurs on its hind feet. All other mammals belong to the **Theria** and are characterized by eggs with little or no yolk, live birth, and molars with 3 cusps (tribosphenic molars). Within this clade, the **Metatheria**, or marsupials, are characterized by epipubic bones and marsupium (pouch); the offspring escape from the birth canal at early stage and continue their development attached to a nipple in the pouch. Famous examples include kangaroos, wallabies, koala, wombat, Tasmanian devil, and opossum. All other mammals are members of the **Eutheria**, the placental mammals. They have a longer gestation period, young born at a more advanced stage, and a **chorioallantoic placenta**. Members range from tiny shrews, rodents, and bats, through sloths, cats, apes, humans, and antelopes, to rhinos, elephants, walruses, and whales.

■ Examine the teeth of the placental raccoon and marsupial opossum.

- Under the dissecting stereomicroscope, compare the surfaces that come together when the jaws close. How do they differ?

As noted above, therapsids first evolved teeth differentiated for different functions: incisors for tearing, canines for piercing or puncturing, and molars for grinding. Tooth structure diversified and specialized even more among different groups of mammals. The **carnassial molar** of carnivores (e.g., cats, dogs, weasels, raccoons) is modified for shearing through flesh. The long gnawing incisors of rodents are large, self-sharpening, and exhibit continuous growth.

■ Compare the teeth of the specimens listed below. Describe them, and try to match them to the following diet types.

Bear (skull) _____

Beaver (skull) _____

Bottlenose dolphin (skull) _____

Cat (skeleton) _____

Horse (skull) _____

Steller's sea lion (skull) _____

Manatee (skull) _____

Opossum (skull) _____

Pygmy chimpanzee (skull) _____

[Extinct] Saber cat (skull) _____

Wild pig (mandible) _____

1. Generalized Herbivore—Flattened molars modified for grinding plant material.

2. Carnivore—Often have **carnassial** (bladelike) molars for slicing meat.

3. Gnawing herbivore—Large, self-sharpening incisors.

4. Ominivore—Generalized tooth pattern, may have both pronounced canine teeth for prey capture as well as a rounded molar pattern good for grinding.

5. Piscivore—**Homodont teeth** (numerous, all the same) used for catching/eating fish.

6. Rooting herbivore—Forward-projecting incisors and tusks for digging up roots.

■ The aardvark and giant armadillo are two placental mammals that specialize in eating ants and termites.

- Does the shape of their skulls reflect their diet? Why or why not?

- Do you think they are closely related within the mammals? Why or why not?

- Compare the skull of *Homo sapiens* with that of the male pygmy chimpanzee (*Pan paniscus*), one of our closest living relatives.

  - How do the proportions of braincase and jaw differ between the two?

  - Both chimps and humans have rather similar diets. What other functions might you attribute to the chimp's large canine teeth that we might not need?

REPTILIA (OR SAUROPSIDA)

Reptiles (Figure 23-7) include a tremendous diversity of body forms and lifestyles. Living species range from tiny burrowing snakes to enormous crocodiles, and extinct forms range even more widely, from giant sauropod dinosaurs—the largest terrestrial animals ever—to songbird-sized flying reptiles. Modern evolutionary analyses also include the birds here.

FIGURE 23-7 Amniota, Reptilia, Diapsida, Lepidosauria: lizard.

Image courtesy of Charles G. Messing, 2011.

The traditional concept of the reptiles, like that of fishes, represents a paraphyletic group. The distinguishing features—leathery eggs, ectothermic metabolism (cold-bloodedness) and dry scaly skin—are characteristic of their common ancestor and most members, but not all. Birds were separated as a distinct class from the Class Reptilia because of their numerous distinguishing features—feathers, wings, and warm-bloodedness. However, these are all characteristics unique to one lineage. One might just as easily, and incorrectly, separate the turtles and tortoises as a distinct class equivalent to the other reptiles on the basis of their shell and lack of teeth. Numerous features place the birds as a highly modified group within the reptiles, making this group **monophyletic**—composed of a common ancestor and all of its descendants.

The name Sauropsida is often used today because the original concept of Reptilia included animals such as *Dimetrodon* that are now placed in the Synapsida. However, many scientists treat the terms Sauropsida and Reptilia as basically equivalent.

Features that distinguish Reptilia from Synapsida are chiefly obscure but important characteristics of the ankle and skull. The integument produces structures (scales or feathers) that contain a hardened variation of the protein keratin, although this feature does not fossilize well and might be a primitive trait common to the earliest synapsids, as well.

The most primitive amniote species, called "stem reptiles" for their position at the base of the group's evolutionary tree, lacked any opening in the skull behind the eye. After the synapsids branched off, some early reptiles retained this feature, called the **anapsid** condition ("without an archway"). None survive, and we have no examples in lab. Until recently, turtles were thought to be derived directly from this primitive group. However, recent evidence from fossils suggests that the turtles belong to the next group, but lost the openings behind the orbit.

Diapsida ("two archways")

The great majority of living and fossil reptiles are diapsids. They have a pair of openings on each side of the skull behind the orbit (**postorbital**, or **temporal fenestrae**) (Figure 23-8), although some of their descendants have reduced the number to one or lost them completely. The early species all had long slender limbs, although, again, some descendants have much shorter limbs or have even lost them. Diapsids soon diverged into two major groups, the Lepidosauria and Archosauria. The group also includes the extinct marine reptiles known as ichthyosaurs ("fish lizards") and plesiosaurs—what everyone hopes the Loch Ness Monster turns out to be (but won't).

- Compare the skulls of the following diapsids: alligator, *Velociraptor*, *Archaeopteryx* (primitive bird) and *Pteranodon* (crested flying reptile).

  • Locate the two pairs of postorbital fenestrae.

- Birds are also descended from diapsid ancestors. Examine the mounted skeleton of a pigeon.

  • Can you locate any postorbital fenestrae? Can you offer any explanation? (HINT: consider the function of the postorbital fenestrae relative to how modern birds feed.)

LEPIDOSAURIA ("scaly lizards")

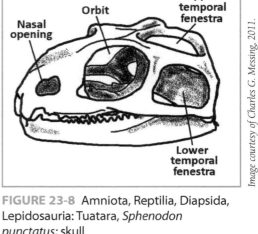

FIGURE 23-8 Amniota, Reptilia, Diapsida, Lepidosauria: Tuatara, *Sphenodon punctatus;* skull.

Image courtesy of Charles G. Messing, 2011.

Living members of this group include the tuatara (a lizardlike animal found in New Zealand that is the only survivor of a group that was more diverse during the Mesozoic) (Figure 23-8), true lizards, and snakes. True lizards (Figure 23-7) and snakes form a group called the **Squamata** with the following features. Squamates periodically shed their skin, with new skin and scales developing underneath. They have a **kinetic skull** with several bones hinged together, permitting considerable mobility. For example, in lizards, both upper and lower jaws close together on a food item, while, in snakes, upper and lower jaws can be detached from each other and the right and left sides can work independently, permitting large food items to be swallowed whole. Males have **hemipenes**—copulatory organs that are inserted one after the other.

- Examine the preserved specimens lizards and snakes.

  • Snakes are often thought of as being "all tail." Locate the anal opening of the ring-necked snake or water moccasin or other available specimens. What proportion of the body is trunk and what proportion is tail?

  • Examine a lizard and snake under the dissecting microscope. Make a drawing of their skin coverings. Do their scales overlap?

- When panicked, the basilisk lizard can get up and run for brief distances on its hind legs.

  • How has the anatomy of its limbs converged with dinosaurs such as *Allosaurus* (see the model skeleton of *Allosaurus*)?

- Water moccasins and rattlesnakes are pit vipers (Figure 23-9). Examine closely the head of one or more of these specimens (under a dissecting microscope, if necessary).

  • In addition to the nostril, do you observe any other openings at the front of the head? What purpose might this opening serve?

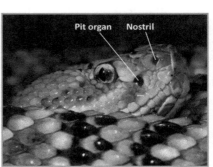

FIGURE 23-9 Amniota, Reptilia, Diapsida, Lepidosauria: timber rattlesnake, *Crotalus horridus;* close-up of head.

Image © voylodyon, 2011. Image used under license of Shutterstock, Inc.

ARCHOSAURIA

Archosaurs (Figure 23-10) were given their name ("ruling reptiles") from their dominance during the Mesozoic Era. Now that scientists place the birds here too, one might say that the group has continued a modicum of dominance into modern times: there are more than twice as many bird species as mammals and far more individuals. Archosaurs also include the Crocodylia, Dinosauria (to which birds belong), and Pterosauria (flying reptiles). Common features include a forward-pointing foot, an additional opening in the skull in front of the orbit (**antorbital fenestra**), another in the lower jaw (**mandibular fenestra**), and serrated teeth, although several groups have independently lost their teeth (e.g., ostrich dinosaurs, some pterosaurs, and modern birds).

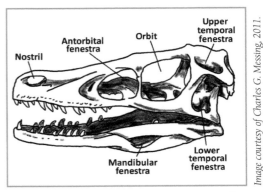

FIGURE 23-10 Amniota, Reptilia, Diapsida, Archosauria, Dinosauria: *Velociraptor mongoliensis;* skull.

Crocodylia

Crocodilians include the true crocodiles, alligators, and the narrow-snouted gharial. There are 23 species worldwide today, although extinct forms included long-legged runners and paddle-finned marine species. The nostrils sit at the tip of a long snout. Rows of armorlike bony **scutes** under the skin adhere to the backbone. The scales and skin are not shed, but grow with the animal. A secondary palate separates the nasal passage from the throat, so crocodilians can breathe through their noses while their mouth remains open underwater.

■ Note the two pairs of postorbital fenestrae in the skull of the alligator.

• This is a diagnostic character of which major group of reptiles?

Pterosauria

The extinct flying reptiles, one of the three groups of tetrapods, along with birds and bats, that independently evolved powered flight, dominated skies during the Mesozoic Era and became extinct with many other animals at the end of the Cretaceous period. Often called pterodactyls, named after the first species discovered, their wingspans ranged from that of a sparrow to that of a small plane. They had short bodies, reduced and fused hip bones, a large head and elongated jaw, and a hand with three short grasping fingers and an elongated fourth finger.

■ Examine the replica of the small fossil pterosaur (*Rhamphorhynchus*).

• Identify as many of the diagnostic features mentioned above as you can.

• What does the elongated fourth finger do?

■ Examine the skull of the advanced pterosaur, *Pteranodon*.

• Note the elongated crest at the back of the skull. What purpose might it have served?

Dinosauria

Dinosaurs (Figure 23-11) are, of course, the quintessential extinct animals, although the great weight of evidence points to birds having evolved from one group of carnivorous dinosaurs, the raptors. Those animals that we traditionally think of as dinosaurs, and that became extinct at the end of the Cretaceous period, are often called nonavian (nonbird) dino-saurs. Dinosaurs are characterized by having a forelimb significantly shorter than the hind limb, an S-shaped neck, and hind limbs with a vertical orientation that generated an erect posture. Mammals are the only other tetrapod group with an erect posture. Permanently lifting the body off the ground (unlike the sprawling amphibians or semierect crocodilians) permitted greater activity levels, faster speeds, and the development of larger sizes not allowed by the stresses of greater weight on limbs that stick out to the sides.

■ Examine the scale model of the Jurassic predatory dinosaur, *Allosaurus fragilis*. This predatory dinosaur was about 10 m long.

• Identify as many of the characteristics of dinosaurs as you can.

- To further reduce the weight of the skull, *Allosaurus fragilis*, *Tyrannosaurus rex,* and *Velociraptor mongoli-ensis* (Figure 23-10) have an additional skull opening, a small **maxillary fenestra** between the nostril and antorbital fenestra.

  - Locate the maxillary fenestra in the replica maxilla (upper jaw bone) of *T. rex.*

- *Velociraptor* was a small, highly mobile, predatory dinosaur (smaller than the ones in the film *Jurassic Park* and its sequels).

  - Compare the skull replica of *Velociraptor* with the image of the *Tyrannosaurus* skull at the beginning of this section. What might the obvious differences in relative bone mass between these two dinosaurs suggest about their feeding and diets?

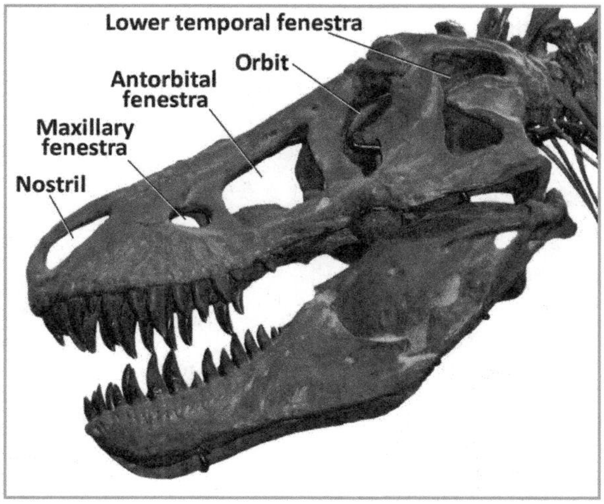

Image © Shutterstock, 2011. Image used under license of Shutterstock, Inc.

FIGURE 23-11 Amniota, Reptilia, Diapsida, Archosauria, Dinosauria: *Tyrannosaurus rex;* skull. Note the addition of the maxillary fenestra in front of the antorbital fenestra. The upper temporal fenestra is on top of the skull and is not visible in this view.

As with mammals, and unlike crocodilians and snakes, dinosaurs included both carnivorous and herbivorous species. Two herbivorous groups in particular, the horned ceratopsians and so-called duck-billed hadrosaurs, developed massive complex batteries of grinding molarlike teeth. The hadrosaur jaw and teeth offer an interesting example, like that of the bottlenose dolphin and alligator, of convergent evolution based on diet. Each side of each jaw bears up to six rows of as many as 60 teeth that develop at the bottom and top of the lower and upper jaw, respectively, and move up to the chewing surface as older teeth are worn down.

- Examine the replica lower half mandible of the hadrosaur *Edmontosaurus,* and compare it with the lower jaw of the horse skull (another grinding herbivore).

  - What important difference between the two can you find in the orientation of the grinding surface?

Aves (*"AH-vaze"*)

Birds (Figure 23-12) are a group of theropod dinosaurs (carnivorous dinosaurs with short forelimbs, e.g., *Allosaurus, Tyrannosaurus, Velociraptor*) characterized by feathers and the pelvic bones fused into a **synsacrum**. Birds also share with theropod dinosaurs an open hip socket, hollow-walled limb bones, and a specialized, hingelike ankle. Modern birds, unlike the traditional reptiles, are homeothermic endotherms. That is, they maintain a relatively constant body temperature by internal metabolic means. Just as limbs appeared in the earliest tetrapods before they left the water, so feathers appeared initially in small carnivorous dinosaurs likely as a means of insulation to reduce heat loss. The anatomy of such dinosaurs suggests an active lifestyle, which would have required some kind of endothermy to maintain high metabolic levels. Heat loss from small bodies with a high surface-to-volume ratio would have required some kind of insulation. Feathers also probably served in mating or territorial display behavior before being co-opted for flight.

FIGURE 23-12 Amniota, Reptilia, Diapsida, Archosauria, Dinosauria, Aves: brown pelican, *Pelecanus occidentalis.*

Image courtesy of Joshua Feingold, 2011

- Compare the skeleton of the pigeon with that of the model *Allosaurus* and the replica and skull of the earliest known bird, *Archaeopteryx*. (The fossil of *Archaeopteryx* that this replica was made from lacks imprints of long feathers on its wings and tail.)
  - Which of the three animals exhibit the following features:
    - Teeth
    - Forelimb claws
    - Long bony tail
    - Keeled sternum (breastbone)
    - Long wing and tail feathers (of course, not a skeletal feature)
  - Based on the distribution of these features, which of the three animals appear to be most closely related?
  - Why is the obvious answer probably not correct?
- Compare the skull of *Archaeopteryx* with that of *Velociraptor*.
  - How do the openings in their skulls compare?
- Modern birds have developed a suite of features that adapt them for efficient flight.
  - Locate the following features in the skeleton of the pigeon.
    1. Forearm bones fused as a carpometacarpus
    2. Reduced tail
    3. Enlarged orbits
    4. Keeled sternum.
    5. Synsacrum (fused pelvic bones)
- Modern birds have also developed a wide variety of beaks associated with different diets.
  - Compare the skulls and beaks of the pigeon, osprey, and pelican.

CHELONIA (OR TESTUDINES)

As noted earlier, turtles and tortoises lack any opening or archway in the skull behind the eye and were for a long time considered as survivors of the ancient anapsid lineage of early reptiles. Newer evidence suggests that they are actually diapsid reptiles that have lost the fenestrae. Because it is not yet certain whether they belong within or at least closer to either the Lepidosauria or Archosauria, we treat them separately here. Turtles and tortoises have the ribs and backbone fused to a rigid shell; jaws have horny sheaths and no teeth. All living species are oviparous, fertilization is internal, and males have a penis, which arises from the ventral wall of the cloaca.

- Examine the skeleton of the turtle.
  - What has become of the ribs?
- Compare the shapes of the carapaces in the more aquatic slider and the more terrestrial box tortoise.
  - What differences do you see? What might be the adaptive advantages of these two shapes?

Questions

1. How has gravity affected the evolution of the skeleton in terrestrial tetrapods? Consider both limbs and skulls.

2. Similar lifestyles of organisms that belong to very different groups offer interesting opportunities for examining convergent evolution. Compare and contrast the skulls of the bottlenose dolphin and alligator. Describe their teeth and suggest how their feeding habits might be similar or different.

3. Both dolphin and alligator live chiefly in the water. How does the placement of their nasal openings reflect their lifestyles? How does the position of the nasal openings in dolphins differ from that in other mammals?

Reference

Benton, M. J. 1997. *Vertebrate palaeontology*. 2nd ed. London, ENGL: Chapman & Hall (452 pp.).

Materials and Supplies

Skeletons and Replicas

Necturus (mud puppy) mounted skeleton

Frog mounted skeleton

Cat mounted skeleton

Allosaurus model skeleton

Homo sapiens (human) mounted skeleton

Dimetrodon skull replica

Raccoon skull replica

Opossum skull replica

Bear skull replica

Beaver skull replica

Bottlenose dolphin skull replica

Horse skull replica

Steller's sea lion skull replica

Manatee skull replica

Smilodon (saber cat) skull replica

Pygmy chimpanzee skull replica

Giant armadillo skull replica

Aardvark skull replica

Wild pig mandible

Alligator skull

Velociraptor skull replica

Archaeopteryx skull replica

Archaeopteryx fossil replica

Pteranodon skull replica

Rhamphorhynchus fossil replica

Pigeon mounted skeleton

Tyrannosaurus upper jaw (maxilla) replica

Edmontosaurus (duckbill dinosaur) half mandible replica

Osprey skull replica

Pelican skull replica

Macaw skull replica

Turtle mounted skeleton

Slider (turtle) dried specimen

Box tortoise shell

Whole Preserved Specimens

Variety of frog specimens, e.g., spadefoot toad, bullfrog, green frog, tree frog (ethanol)

Variety of salamander specimens (ethanol)

Necturus (mud puppy) (ethanol)

Variety of snake specimens, e.g., water moccasin, pygmy rattlesnake, ring-necked snake, garter snake (ethanol)

Variety of lizard specimens, e.g., basilisk, gecko, anole (ethanol)

Supplies

Ethanol

Equipment

Large forceps

Large, medium, and small glass bowls for specimen display

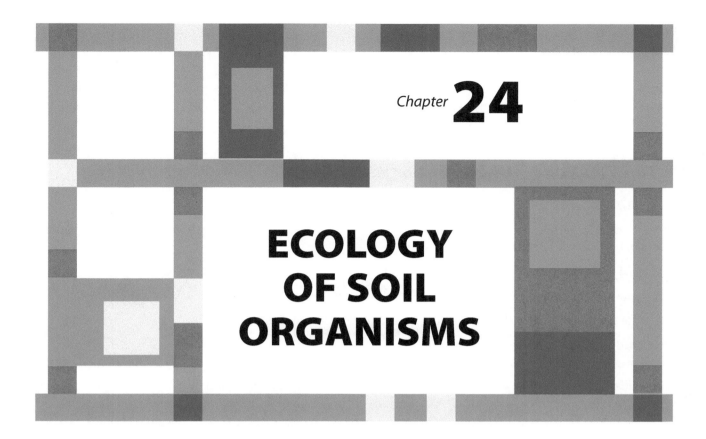

Chapter **24**

ECOLOGY OF SOIL ORGANISMS

Introduction

This lab will familiarize students with basic concepts of ecology and field techniques that allow ecologists to assess the environment.

Ecology (from the Greek *oikos* meaning "house or dwelling place" and *logos* "discourse in, or study of") is the study of the ways organisms interact with each other and with the physical and chemical environment. **Biotic** factors involve interactions among organisms, such as competition and predation. When an osprey catches a fish and eats it, that's a clear way in which two organisms interact. **Abiotic** factors concern environmental influences, such as temperature and rainfall. The increase in metabolic rate that a brown anole lizard experiences as it basks in the sun is an example of how the environmental factor of solar irradiance affects an organism. Ecology is a robust field, involving concepts of evolution, genetics, physiology, and behavior to better understand the distribution and abundance of organisms spanning a variety of spatial scales.

Two important "master factors" that determine organism distributions on land are temperature and rainfall. As examples, cacti exist in areas with very low rainfall (<5 cm y^{-1}) in temperate environments. You would also expect different types of soil organisms to live in soils with different moisture contents and temperatures. We can observe such differences over spatial scales ranging from hundreds to thousands of kilometers (biomes), to meters or fewer (microhabitats).

In general, **species richness** (the number of species in an area) and **species diversity** (a calculation that combines the numbers of species with their relative abundances) increase when temperature and moisture attain "optimum" levels. For example, if temperatures are too high or low, organisms become stressed and typically fewer species can tolerate the extremes. In terrestrial environments, water is usually a limiting factor, but you can have too much of it. As you may have experienced, summer weather in south Florida often includes tropical downpours, which can saturate the soil and create problems for some soil organisms, such as reduced levels of oxygen. Many soil organisms are detritivores, relying on decaying organic material as their source of energy. Because they are also ectotherms, they require a balance among moisture, temperature, oxygen content, and organic content to operate at their most efficient metabolic levels.

Because it is impractical to find and observe these types of interactions with large organisms such as birds or lizards during one lab period, we will use the organisms in smaller scale local soil communities to demonstrate these concepts. We will be investigating differences among local habitats in the area around the Mesozoic Garden east of the Parker Building.

Methods

1. Habitat Survey

We will measure temperature, and estimate qualitative differences in moisture content and organic composition among three different local habitats:

1. leaf litter next to the gazebo in the Medicinal Garden adjacent to the Mesozoic Garden,
2. sandy soil under the trees just south of the Mesozoic Garden east of the concrete sidewalk, and
3. the lawn just west of the gazebo southeast of the Mesozoic Garden.

Small, red flags mark these three locations.

Your laboratory section will be divided into working groups of three to several students each. Walk to the study area (flashlights are available for night labs) and record the differences among the three collection locations as follows:

1. Measure the soil temperature with a lab thermometer carefully inserted ~3 to 4 cm into the ground. **(INSERT THE THERMOMETER GENTLY TO AVOID BREAKING IT.)**
2. Rank soil moisture by inserting your finger into the ground, then lifting it up and having it act as a simple "wet bulb" thermometer. The greater the moisture content of the soil, the cooler your finger will feel when raised.
3. Examine the soil *in situ* and a sample of each soil type under the dissecting microscope to assist with the comparisons of organic content. The inorganic component of local soil (which is not "natural" but has been emplaced during construction of the university) is chiefly silica sand. The organic component consists of the decomposition products of local vegetation.

Between 48 and 72 hours before your laboratory, a soil sample from each of the three habitats was dug up and placed in a Berlese funnel. This simple apparatus consists of a large funnel with a screen inside the base (to prevent soil from falling through) and a collecting tube, jar, or beaker containing preservative (in this case, 50% ethanol) attached to the bottom. Light and heat from an incandescent light source placed above each funnel drive soil organisms downward to escape desiccation, and they eventually fall into the collecting container. Specimens from each container are poured into a culture dish (two dishes if too many specimens are collected) for identification and quantification.

2. Species Richness

Distinguish the number of different kinds of organisms (richness) in your assigned culture dish(es). This type of measurement is often referred to as alpha (α) diversity. Use the available artificial keys, the appendix of this handout, online resources, and the assistance of the professor and laboratory assistant to identify each taxon of organisms to the lowest possible taxonomic level, which may only be phylum or order (e.g., Nematoda, Isopoda, Diptera). Identification to the species or genus level is typically not possible in this exercise. When you encounter more than one taxon within a group, use convenient and simple characters to distinguish the different taxa, e.g., Diptera species 1 (round wings); Diptera species 2 (red eyes). Figure 24-1 includes examples of organisms found in previous years.

Each group of students will separate the organisms in the assigned culture dish(es) into distinguishable taxa and count the numbers of organisms in each taxon.

FIGURE 24-1 Examples of local soil organisms. A. Diplopoda, millipede. B. Crustacea, Amphipoda. C. Crustacea, Isopoda; arrow indicates ventral brood pouch. D. Hexapoda, Diptera, fly larva. E. Hexapoda, Diptera, fly; arrow indicates haltere. F. Hexapoda, Dermaptera, earwig; arrow indicates terminal forceps-like cerci. G. Hexapoda, Hymenoptera, ants. H-J. Cheliceriformes, Arachnida, Acarina, mites.

3. Species Diversity

It is important to understand not only the number of different kinds of organisms (richness), but their relative abundances. This type of measurement is often referred to as beta (β) diversity. As an example, consider two hypothetical communities, each composed of 10,000 individuals belonging to 10 species. In one community, organism numbers are evenly divided, i.e., there are 1,000 of each species. In the other, their abundances are highly unequal, e.g., 9,950 of species 1, 40 of species 2, 3 individuals of species 3, and 1 individual of each of species 4 through 10. As an ecologist studying these communities, you cannot count every individual. You must try to take representative samples; say, you can only trap 100 individuals from each community. Your samples are very likely to include different proportions of different species. Ecologists use a measure called a diversity index to reflect such differences. The index is a relative number used in comparing two or more communities or populations. The index value increases both with the number of different species in the sample, and as the numbers of each species are more evenly distributed. In comparisons between communities having the same species richness, diversity is highest in the one supporting populations of each species in equal numbers. When species richness is the same in two communities, diversity is lower in the one dominated by larger numbers of fewer species (i.e., your sample of 100 is more likely to collect fewer species) and higher in the one with more evenly distributed numbers of each species (i.e., your sample of 100 is likelier to include more species).

Although several different diversity indices are available, the Shannon Index (also called the Shannon-Wiener Index) (H') is perhaps the most commonly used to describe this parameter of biodiversity. The formula for calculating the Shannon Index is:

$$H' = -\sum_{i=1}^{S}(p_i \ln p_i)$$

Where:

S is the total number of species (species richness)

p_i is the relative abundance of each species. This is calculated as the proportion of the number of individuals in a given species (n_i) to the total number of individuals for all species (N), or n_i/N

An Excel-based calculator will be used to do the calculations. Your professor will process your data and you will input the diversity indices in the chart in the Results section.

Results

1. Habitat Survey

Fill in the following table with your temperature measurements (°C) and qualitative estimates of moisture and organic content using a scale of Least / Middle / Most.

	Lawn	Sand	Leaf litter
Temperature			
Water			
Organic			

2. Species Richness

Compile your data on the following sheets. It is important for each group to work carefully because it is easy to overlook some of the organisms. Some samples have fewer organisms than others, so be patient while the groups with many organisms finish. Do not leave early; you'll need the data from the other groups.

Sample Location: **Lawn**

	Taxon	*Number of Individuals*
1.		
2.		
3.		
4.		
5.		
6.		
7.		
8.		
9.		

Sample Location: **Sand**

	Taxon	*Number of Individuals*
1.		
2.		
3.		
4.		
5.		
6.		
7.		
8.		
9.		

Sample Location: **Leaf Litter**

	Taxon	*Number of Individuals*
1.		
2.		
3.		
4.		
5.		
6.		
7.		
8.		
9.		

Complete the following chart summarizing the results of your observations:

	Lawn	Sand	Leaf litter
Number of Taxa (Richness)			
Number of Individuals			

3. Species Diversity

Insert the diversity index values provided by your professor as well as the richness values from the previous table.

	Lawn	Sand	Leaf litter
S-W Diversity Index			
Richness			

Discussion Questions

1. Based on your habitat survey results, where do you expect to find the highest number of species? Briefly explain why.

2. Where did we find the highest species richness? Explain why you think this occurred.

3. Where did we find the highest species diversity? Is each community ranked in the same order for species diversity and species richness? Explain why or why not.

Appendix

List of organism taxon names used in previous lab sections. Most soil organisms are arthropods, nematodes, or annelids.

ARTHROPODA: ARACHNIDA
    Acarina (large mite)
    Acarina (small mite)
    Acarina (turtle mite)
    Araneae (spider)

ARTHROPODA: CRUSTACEA
    Amphipoda
    Isopoda (pill bug)

ARTHROPODA: HEXAPODA
    Protura
    Collembola (springtail)
    Hymenoptera (ant)
    Coleoptera (beetle)
    Dermaptera (earwig)
    Diptera (fly)
    Hemiptera (large sucking insect)
    Hemiptera (small sucking insect)

ARTHROPODA: MYRIAPODA
    Chilopoda (centipede)
    Symphyla

NEMATODA
    Nematoda (roundworm)

ANNELIDA
    Oligochaeta

Materials and Supplies

Equipment

Berlese Funnels

Ring stands

Colored laboratory tape

Collecting tubes

Incandescent lamps (clip-on or gooseneck)

Medium glass specimen bowls

Small glass specimen dishes

Thermometers

Fine forceps

Droppers

Dissecting microscopes

Squeeze bottles

Supplies

50% ethanol

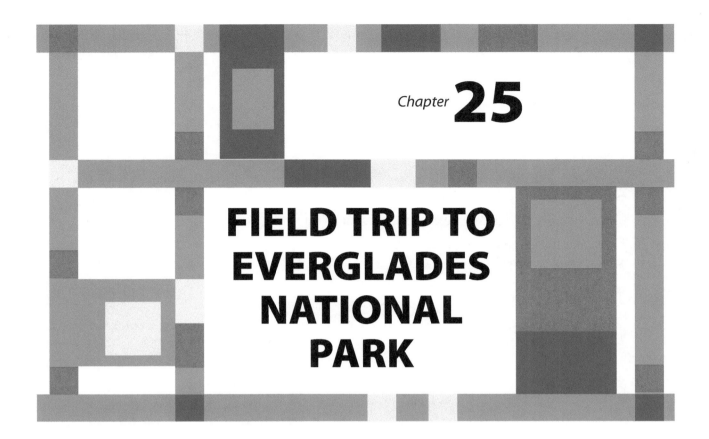

Chapter **25**

FIELD TRIP TO EVERGLADES NATIONAL PARK

Introduction

The primary goal of the Everglades National Park field trip is to acquaint you with this unique South Florida environment and to help develop your observational abilities. Even if you have been to the Everglades before, this is an opportunity to connect concepts learned in class with field observations and experiences.

The Everglades is a large watershed; from its source in Lake Okeechobee, it runs south to Florida Bay, a distance of approximately 160 km (100 mi). This "river of grass" flows south through the center of the state as a wide swath of slow-moving shallow water generally no more than 1m deep. Some sections known as "sloughs" are slightly deeper and faster moving.

Everglades National Park is the only subtropical preserve in North America. It contains a diversity of both temperate and tropical plant communities, including sawgrass marshes, hardwood hammocks, pinelands, and cypress and mangrove swamps, as well as marine and estuarine environments. The park is known for its rich bird life, particularly large wading birds such as the roseate spoonbill, the wood stork, the great blue heron and a variety of egrets. It is likely that you will see alligators. Crocodiles are also found in the park, but not at the sites we visit, as they live in brackish water.

Everglades National Park has been designated a World Heritage Site, an International Biosphere Reserve and a Wetland of International Importance. Your professors and laboratory assistants will point out as much wildlife and points of interest as possible.

The Everglades originally encompassed an area of nearly 28,000 km^2 (11,000 mi^2). Approximately half of the original ecosystem has been lost to agriculture and urban development.

This field trip will visit three habitats:

- **Sawgrass Marsh**—The Anhinga Trail extends along and over this habitat, which typifies much of the Everglades and is part of Taylor Slough, one of the main drainage pathways of the Everglades. However, the deep pond and canal adjacent to the buildings and walkway of the Anhinga Trail are manmade.

- **Tropical Hardwood Hammock**—The Gumbo-Limbo Trail is a short walk through this habitat. Hammocks are elevated areas also known as tree islands, which support more terrestrial vegetation that are intolerant of chronically flooded soil. Note the solution holes in the bedrock and different types of vegetation that occur here as compared to the plants along the Anhinga Trail.

- **Pineland**—This habitat type is among the driest in the Everglades and is dominated by Florida Slash Pine with an understory of Saw Palmetto. This is a fire-maintained community, and you should look for evidence of recent controlled burns. Part of the Pine Island Trail gives a good view of pineland, and it also goes through another tropical hammock.

- Three additional habitats that you may see from the van during your visit include cypress hammocks (freshwater) and mangrove (brackish water) swamps and coastal prairies.

More information about Everglades National Park is available at:

http://www.everglades.national-park.com/info.htm
http://www.nps.gov/ever/

Field Trip Itinerary

07:45 – **Meet at the circular driveway on the east side of the University Center next to the bronze Mako shark statue.** You will meet the professor who is leading the trip and your classmates, and then you will board the provided NSU vehicles.

08:00 (sharp) – Vehicles depart for Everglades National Park, Main entrance (Homestead). If you are late, you will miss the trip. Don't be late!

09:30 – Vehicles arrive at Ernest Coe Visitor Center. This center is accessible before entering the Park and paying the entrance fee. If you are driving yourself to the Park, please be on time. There will be a brief bathroom break and orientation. We plan to visit three sites (Anhinga Trail, Gumbo Limbo Trail and Pine Island Trail), but the exact itinerary is subject to change.

09:45 – Depart for the Royal Palm area.

10:00 – Begin walking tour of Anhinga & Gumbo Limbo Trails, both located at Royal Palm.

~12:30 – Lunch in the Park (likely Long Pine Key).

13:15 – Begin walking tour of Pine Island Trail.

15:30 – Vehicles depart for NSU.

17:00 – Arrive at NSU

Equipment: Please bring clothing and supplies to make your life pleasant for an outing in the Everglades that involves walking and observing animals and plants. Wear comfortable shoes; bring sun protection (sunscreen, hat, and long sleeve shirts or layers). You may also want to bring insect repellant. If you have a camera or binoculars, bring them too.

Weather: The trip runs rain or shine! We recommend that you show up for the field trip so that you are aware of last-minute decisions. If there is severe weather (thunderstorms or hurricanes), the trip will be rescheduled, but note that the weather in the Everglades is often very different than what you observe on main campus. Check the weather forecast; bring a raincoat and/or umbrella if rain is forecast.

Food: Bring lunch and drinks with you. Vending machines are available at the Park Entrance only, and there is a poor selection. Water is available at the Ernest Coe Visitor Center and the Royal Palm area, but it has a particular taste that some students do not like.

Field Report Guidelines

Your field report will be approximately four pages long, including the title page and references (follow guidelines for research papers in the syllabus). Be sure to include the following elements:

1. Title Page. Include the title (Everglades National Park Field Trip Report), your name, the course number and section, your professor's name and the name of the professor who led your trip (if different).

2. List of Animals and Plants Observed. Include the following:

   a. The date and time of your observations. A time range is fine for the entire visit to each site. There is no need to give a specific time for each observation.

   b. The Latitude and Longitude of each site. These will be announced during the trip or will be given to you in class. We plan to visit three sites—Anhinga Trail, Gumbo Limbo Trail and Long Pine Key—but the exact itinerary is subject to change.

   c. A list of at least 10 animal species (5 vertebrates and 5 invertebrates) **from Anhinga and Gumbo-Limbo Trails,** and a second list of at least 10 animal species (5 vertebrates and 5 invertebrates) from **Long Pine Key.** This means that you will have 20 total animals in your report. If you observe some of the same animals at both sites, you may use them in both lists.

   d. A list of at least five plant species **from each site** (Anhinga Trail, Gumbo-Limbo Trail, Long Pine Key). This means you will have 15 total plants in your report. It is expected that you will list different plant species at each of these sites, so that's a total of 15 different species (no duplication).

   *** Only list organisms that you have personally observed! ***

3. A succinct, one-page written essay on **one** of the organisms from your list outlining its status (e.g., threatened) and population size, distribution and its role in the Everglades ecosystem, along with one interesting observation that you made (behavior if an animal and type of interactions with animals if a plant). The observation should last a minimum of five minutes. This can be done at any of the sites we visit. You must personally observe the organism and behavior/interaction.

4. At least three references supporting your text about your essay organism. Don't forget to cite your references in the text.

Because there are multiple field trip dates to choose from, you are expected to go on one of the organized trips. A waiver for an independent trip will only be granted under exceptional circumstances and with prior approval by your professor. Because students may not accompany their own instructor on the field trip, trip leaders will share the numbers of taxa observed on their particular trip.

Field Report Grading Rubric—The following items will be evaluated in your report, and points will be reduced if they are not included.

General Information and Organism Lists

> Latitude and longitude of each site.
>
> Date and time of the visits to each site.
>
> 5 vertebrates, 5 invertebrates from Anhinga Trail (including Gumbo-Limbo Trail, if needed)*
>
> 5 plants from the Anhinga Trail*
>
> 5 plants from the Gumbo Limbo Trail*
>
> 5 vertebrates, 5 invertebrates and 5 plants from the Pine Island Trail*
>
> Use correctly formatted scientific names (genera are capitalized and italicized, and species are lower case and italicized, e.g., *Homo sapiens*).

[*Trip leaders will share information about their trips in case fewer than expected species are observed in any habitat on any particular trip.]

Essay

> Organism status (e.g., threatened or protected status, geographic range, population size)

> Ecological role in the Everglades

> Details of a 5-minute observation of the organism's behavior (if an animal), or interaction with an animal (if a plant)

Driving Directions (in case you drive yourself)

Destination: Ernest Coe Visitor Center, Main Entrance, Everglades National Park, Homestead, Florida

NSU will provide vehicles for transportation, and we encourage their use. If you choose to travel on your own, plan to leave the Davie area by 08:00 (vehicle departure time). We expect the drive to take about 1/2 hour from NSU. You need to be at the Ernest Coe Visitor Center by 09:30. We encourage students to ride in the NSU vehicles as it is more efficient (smaller carbon footprint) and engenders camaraderie; plus it is free! Tolls and gas cost about $35 for a private vehicle to make the trip.

Directions:

- From the Davie area, go South on the Florida Turnpike to its end at US 1 at Homestead / Florida City.

- Nearly immediately, turn right at the traffic light at 344th Street / East Palm Drive and head west.

- Turn left at the stop sign at Tower Road and head south. You will see the *Robert Is Here* fruit stand on the SW corner of this intersection.

- Turn right at the stop sign at Ingraham Highway / State Highway 9336. You will see the Florida Department of Corrections facility on the SE corner of this intersection. We do not recommend visiting there.

- Continue on Ingraham Highway / State Highway 9336 as it curves around to the Ernest Coe Visitor Center at the main entrance of Everglades National Park.

NOTE: Previous trips visited a different location in Everglades National Park: Shark Valley on Tamiami Trail (US 41). **DO NOT** go to Shark Valley—you will be in the wrong place.